EQUATOR
TEAU
Belem
Amazon R.
São Francisco R.
MATO GROSSO
BRAZILIAN HIGHLANDS
Rio de Janeiro
TROPIC OF CAPRICORN
Titicaca
La Paz
GRAN CHACO
Iguaçu Falls
DESERT
LOS ANDES
Buenos Aires
Montevideo
Río de la Plata
Mt. Aconcagua
PAMPAS
PATAGONIA
FALKLAND ISLANDS
SOUTH GEORGIA
SOUTH SANDWICH ISLANDS
TIERRA DEL FUEGO
Kenneth Thompson

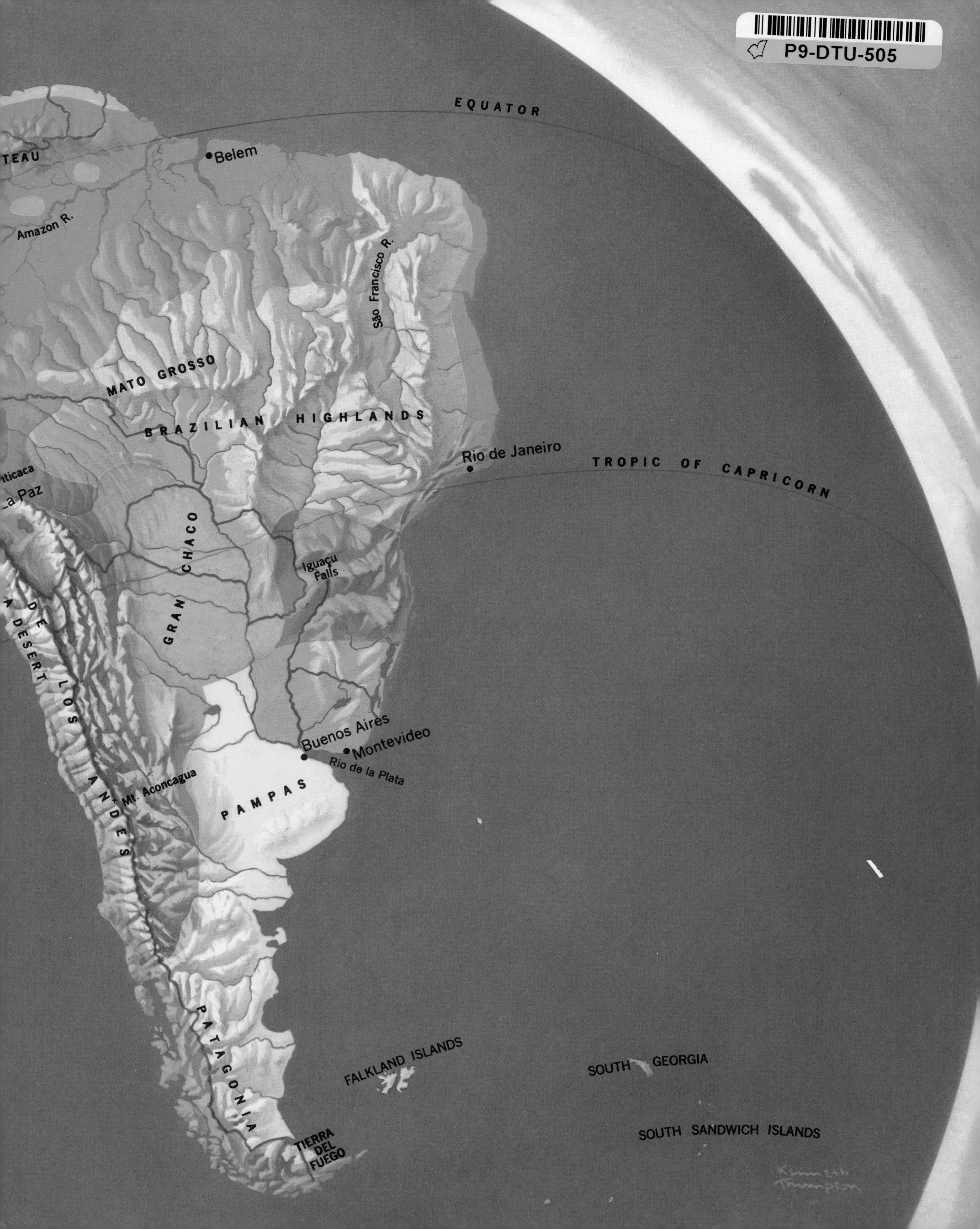

SOUTH AMERICA
AND CENTRAL AMERICA

Photographs by

Rolf Blomberg

Weldon King

E. Aubert de la Rüe

Tad Nichols

Robert Lawrence Pastner

Carl Rettenmeyer

Edward S. Ross

Paul Schauenberg

Harald Schultz

Paul Schwartz

Karl Weidmann

and others

Maps drawn by Kenneth Thompson

SOUTH

Jean Dorst

A Chanticleer Press Edition

The Continents We Live On

AMERICA
AND CENTRAL AMERICA

A NATURAL HISTORY

Random House · New York

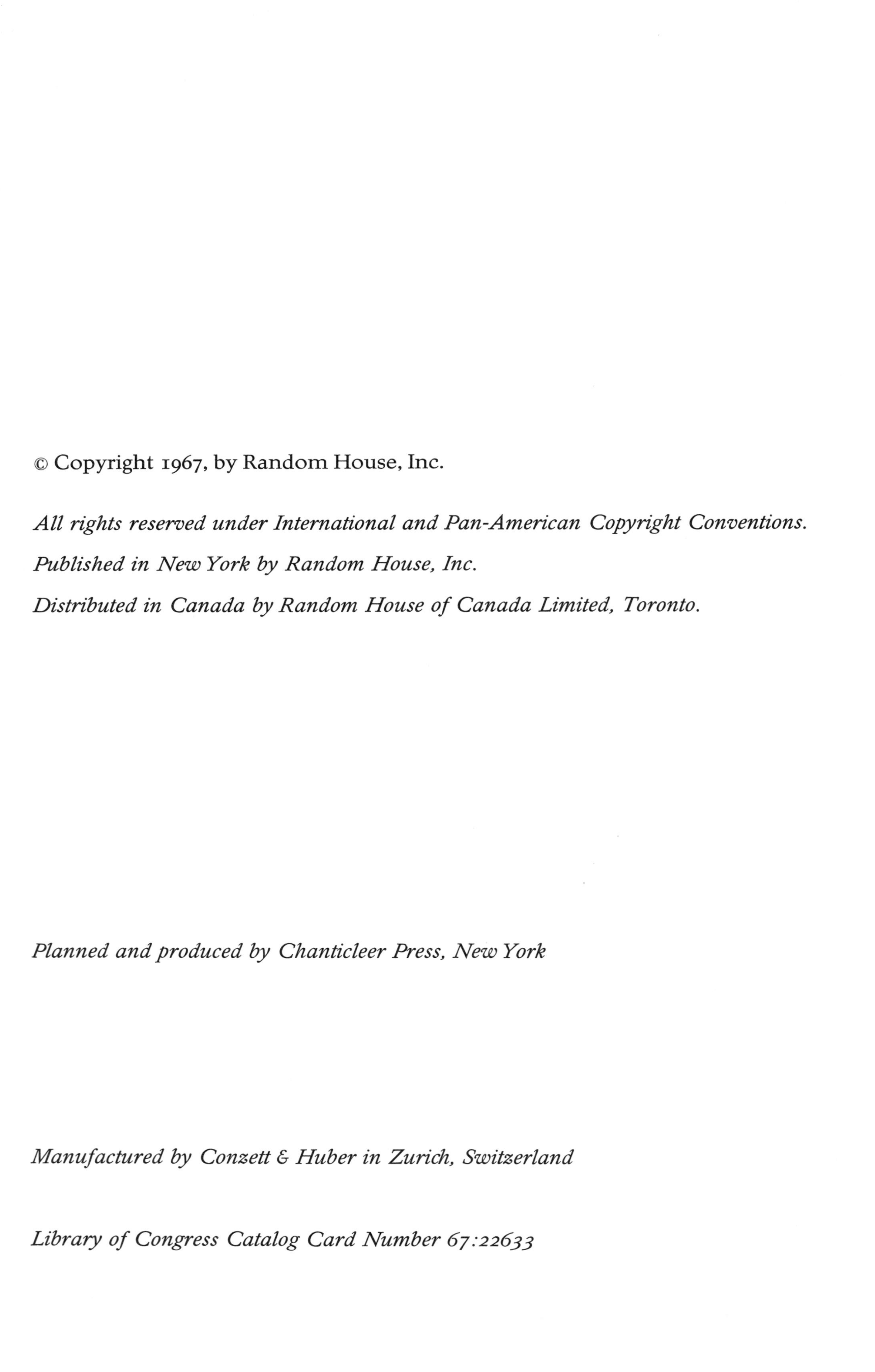

Published in New York by Random House, Inc.

Distributed in Canada by Random House of Canada Limited, Toronto.

Planned and produced by Chanticleer Press, New York

Manufactured by Conzett & Huber in Zurich, Switzerland

Library of Congress Catalog Card Number 67:22633

Contents

Foreword

For two centuries after Columbus landed in the West Indies and later in northern South America, Spanish explorers came to South America only to find gold. They expected to discover it in fabled El Dorado, a land they believed lay somewhere in the heart of the continent. All of them recorded observations on their journeys; by weeding out fantastic inventions and exaggerated native tales from these records, we can learn many fascinating things about the landscapes, plants and animals that they encountered.

The era of scientific expeditions began in the eighteenth century, when the most able naturalists of the time visited South America, returning with a wealth of scientific observations. Among them was the Frenchman de la Condamine (1701–1774), who went to Ecuador to investigate problems of astronomy but gathered much information concerning natural history. At the close of the century the German von Humboldt traveled throughout the "equinoctial regions" accompanied by a Frenchman Aimé Goujaud, called Bonpland, and brought back a mass of scientific documents and specimens. On the famous voyages of the *Beagle* in 1832 and 1836, Charles Darwin gathered the vital data, particularly in Patagonia and the Galapagos, that he used to formulate his theories of evolution.

These men are only a few of the many who have been lured and inspired by South America. At present, research centers set up by South American governments are doing important research in natural history and there is a constant flow of expeditions from Europe and North America. Much has been learned and there is a good deal of information at our disposal. There are, however, many gaps to be filled, especially in regions that are inaccessible or enveloped in dense forest. Such gaps are partly due to the unimaginable immensity and diversity of this continent.

It is this diversity that I have tried to convey in this book, if only by giving a general impression of each ecological region. In each region I describe in broad outline the topography and climate and then go on to the characteristic features of the natural habitat. Rather than attempt a catalog of many animals, I have concentrated on a few, trying to make clear their way of life and their adaptation to the environment. Mammals and birds have been given prominence at the expense of invertebrates, chiefly because they have been more easily observed and most often studied.

The scientific (Latin) name of a species has, in general, been given only the first time a plant or an animal is mentioned. For the convenience of the reader, however, such a name has sometimes been repeated in a later chapter.

I have drawn this book not only from the wealth of literature on the subject but the knowledge I gleaned during various scientific missions to South America in which I crossed the cordilleras of Ecuador and Peru, the forests of the Amazon basin, the plateaus of Brazil and the islands of the Antilles.

This book could never have been accomplished without the aid of many friends and colleagues. It would be impossible to pay tribute to all those who helped me during my travels in South America, including not only learned scientists but humble Indians of the mountains and jungle. I would, however, like to express my particular gratitude to Dr. Hernando de Macedo of Lima; together we spent long months on the High Andean plateaus. I was also fortunate to have benefited from the Reverend Father Robert Pinchon's vast knowledge of the natural wonders and inhabitants of the Antilles.

Many specialists were of great assistance with the manuscript, several being kind enough to read and criticize entire chapters, notably E. Aubert de la Rüe, Bertrand Flornoy, L. Harrison Matthews, F. Carlos Lehmann, Mlle. Alice Lourteig, Hernando de Macedo, Roger Perry and Robert Pinchon.

To help cross the language barrier into English, Mrs. Herma Briffault and Miss Susan Grafman made an excellent translation. Milton Rugoff edited and reworked the text without ever distorting the content, bringing to the task insight and long experience. His collaboration and that of Miss Grafman made it possible for me to bring this book to fruition.

To Kenneth Thompson goes credit for the vivid and attractive maps, and to Ulrich Ruchti for fusing text and photographs into a handsome design. Miss Odile Jachiet spent endless hours typing and retyping the manuscript. Lastly, I am delighted to thank my wife for her help; this book is dedicated to her. To all of these go my deepest thanks.

JEAN DORST

The Most Diverse Continent

In January 1961, I was camping on the banks of the tiny Rio Checayani at an altitude of more than fourteen thousand feet in the Andes of southern Peru. My tent was at the edge of one of the rare wooded areas of the highlands, but wherever I looked and as far as I could see were vast undulating plains, completely bare or covered with hardy vegetation, and broken only by black cliffs. All day long I had been closely observing the few birds that still inhabit these bleak heights. Alone except for two devoted but uncommunicative Indians, I pictured to myself what a tiny speck I occupied on the map of this immense continent.

After this austere sojourn on the heights of the Andes, I went down to Lima, amid the deserts bordering the Pacific, and from there left—by plane, alas—for Brazil, soaring over the Andes and the low plateaus that form the heart of South America. I visited the forests of eastern Brazil, went up the coast toward Salvador and then toward the arid northeast, before making a brief tour of the lower Amazon, starting at Belem. Stopovers in the Caribbean allowed me to visit Trinidad, Martinique and Puerto Rico.

Although it was my fourth journey to South America, I left each place regretting not being able to stay longer: the riches of nature can only be discovered slowly by the biologist. Places seemed to pass before my eyes like the dissolving scenes in a film. But the immense distances I traveled in so short a time did serve to impress upon me the unrivaled and incredible variety of nature on this continent.

South America is a landmass 4,500 miles long and, at its widest point, about five degrees south of the Equator, three thousand miles wide. It is about seven million square miles in area, two thirds of which are plains no more than one thousand feet above sea level. Yet its backbone is a colossal mountain range.

It is attached to North America by a kind of continental bridge, Central America, and in the Caribbean it thrusts out a chain of islands that, taken together, have a mass almost equivalent to a continent. But this has not always been the case. South America was entirely separated from the rest of the world several times in the course of its geological history, and certain living creatures always found it hard to make the passage over the water. In fact, next to Australia, South America is the most isolated continent in the world.

South America is, without a doubt, the most diversified of all the great continents, in sharp contrast, for example, to Africa, which forms a consistent whole in spite of the great variety of its natural habitats. This is the result of many very different factors. To begin with, this is the only continental mass that extends so far toward the Antarctic. Geographical factors also favor its diversification. The continent has two major mountain ranges of unequal mass. The Andes mountain system extends down almost the entire continent from north to south, but is crowded to the west, bordering the Pacific, thus throwing the whole topography of the continent out of balance. A drop of rain that falls only one hundred miles east of the Pacific will flow toward the Atlantic, 2,500 miles away. The Andean range attains altitudes exceeding twenty thousand feet over an area of more than 3,500 miles; it forms a wall with few passes less than twelve thousand feet above sea level in the median sector.

On the eastern side of the continent, bordering the Atlantic, are the Brazilian Highlands, much less elevated, and sloping gently toward the west. Between the two are the interior plains at an altitude of one thousand feet or less, traversing Brazil and descending toward Argentina.

The geological history of South America is a long one and still little known. The most ancient parts are made up of an old Archean shield extending over the Guianas and Brazil, formed of crystalline rocks, separated by a threshold through which the Amazon now flows. According to one quite plausible theory, most of South America was part of a continent, called Gondwana by the theorists, which encompassed South Africa, Australia, New Zealand and the Antarctic. Certain characteristic plant fossils, notably the *Glossopteris,* support this theory.

Later on, in the Cretacean period, the Andes appeared with an incredibly complex structure. Resting on an Archean base, they have continued to fold and uplift to the present—an extremely long period. After erosion had worn down a part of the central range, a new uplifting brought these eroded highlands to an altitude averaging twelve thousand feet, which explains the character of the high plateaus of Peru, Bolivia and northern Chile. Vulcanism has strongly marked the Andean range at every epoch in its history. The central plains of South America are formed of sediments eroded and carried down from the Andes from the Tertiary to the Quaternary periods.

Climate also contributes to the diversity of the environment. Temperature, humidity, and rainfall vary widely. The western coast of South America is very humid in the Colombian and southern Chilean sectors, but very arid in Peru and northern Chile. The Guianas, the Amazon basin, and the Atlantic slopes of Brazil are generously watered, while the interior of the Brazilian plateaus, northeast Brazil and the eastern districts of Patagonia are much drier. Rainfall also varies greatly, some regions having rain throughout the year, others only during a short period. Temperatures are greatly modified by altitude, and especially by the Andes, which have served in a unique way to bring vast cold areas to an equatorial region. This infinitely varied physical environment is fully reflected in the vegetation. Rain forest occupies the most humid sections, among them the immense Amazon basin, which covers an area 2,200 miles long by 1,200 miles wide, thus forming the most extensive forest in the world. Rain forest also covers the Guianas, southern and eastern Venezuela, and a part of the eastern slopes of Colombia, Ecuador, Peru, and Bolivia; it is found again on the Atlantic coast of Brazil, on the Pacific coast of Colombia and the northern part of Ecuador. These forests are of rare luxuriance, burdened with epiphytes and abounding in plants with the most extraordinary forms.

Dense forests occur in central Chile, on the slopes exposed to the great western winds. They are a temperate-zone type of forest, with the Antarctic beech predominating, but they are nonetheless of a luxuriance usually found only in tropical rain forests. They resemble the most humid districts of the State of Washington and British Columbia.

Other parts of South America are covered with tropical deciduous forests resulting from a pronounced dry season that interrupts the growth of vegetation. Such is a part of the Orinoco Valley, the Chaco and northeastern Brazil, where the caatinga is made up chiefly of the drought-resistant plants known as xerophytes. Other portions are covered with savannas, grassy expanses more or less mingled with trees, ranging from the open forests of the Mato Grosso to the *llanos* (level plains) of Venezuela and the grasslands of the pampas, which are entirely without trees in the natural state.

There are also true deserts, among which the harshest is the one at the foot of the Andes on the Pacific coast from Peru to northern Chile.

We must also note the many different altitude zones on the Andean slopes. Each community of plants occupies a definite tier, extending all along the cordilleras from Colombia to Bolivia, modified only by local conditions. Thus the habitats range from the tropical rain forests of the low regions to the dry *puna,* the bleak regions of the high Andes of Peru and the humid *paramos* or moors of Colombia, bristling with strange plants.

A map of South America's vegetation is thus a mosaic in which the most diverse habitats are often adjacent, where temperate, torrid, and polar zones are found almost side by side, and where the tundra on high mountains is not far from the great equatorial forest.

The native animal life, which has no direct resemblance to that of the rest of the world, is equally rich and diversified. In many of the groups one can still observe the profound influence of the geological history of this continent and the evidence that it was time and again separated from North America. In the Cretacean and Eocene, a land bridge between the two Americas allowed the passage from north to south of the ancestors of some of the present-day marsupials, sloths, armadillos, anteaters and primates. When the land bridge vanished for a time, a unique mammalian fauna developed. The communication was reestablished in the Late Miocene, allowing a new invasion of animals. These rivals partly eliminated the native fauna, but some, particularly the marsupials, have managed to persist into our day. South America and Australia are the last refuges of the marsupials, except for a

An extreme in South American landscapes: Lake Pehoe high in the Cordillera de Payne of Chile, surrounded by mountains worn down by erosion and glaciers. (Emil Muench)

few species that migrated from South America into Central or even North America. It is worth noting that South America has not been colonized by certain mammals: the small number of ungulates is particularly striking, especially as compared with Africa or Asia.

In what zoogeographers call the Neotropical region, South America is, moreover, characterized by a large number of indigenous groups that have diversified into a remarkable variety of species. One can almost observe the process of differentiation of species. To enumerate all the animal families is of course impossible. The birds are so numerous that South America has been called the "bird continent." They comprise at least a fourth of all known species. Among the sixty-seven families represented, half are native to this continent. Although it is the only continent where songbirds are in the minority, they are so numerous that some families, such as the Furnariidae, or ovenbirds, number no less than five hundred species. And among these birds are many strange ones without counterparts elsewhere in the world.

The same is true of the mammals. Although certain groups are absent or poorly represented, others are amazingly diversified. The rodents have had an explosive evolution here. The monkeys also exhibit a remarkable evolution, none of the forms showing any relation to their counterparts in the Old World. Again, the same is true of the bats. The Phyllostomatidae, a group of strange species, are native to tropical America.

So numerous are other invertebrates and insects that the mind is staggered. And there is a sufficient variety of natural environments to satisfy the most stringent requirements. On one and the same continent the penguin and albatross can live in the midst of snow and ice, while the parrot, toucan and hummingbird can enjoy the warmth and humidity of tropical forests. No other continent can boast such a profusion of animal or vegetable life.

It is this exuberance that I have tried to reflect in this book. Following the guidelines of biogeographers and ecologists, I have divided South America into a number of regions. Some of them are fairly arbitrary and can be justified only on geographical grounds, as, for example, the area from eastern Bolivia to the plains of Uruguay. However, such a division allows us to see how one environment gradually modulates or merges into another.

I have dwelt longest on the most interesting regions: the Amazon Valley, the Andes and Patagonia. Similarly, among the animals, I have dwelt especially on the vertebrates. I have certainly omitted a great deal. I need hardly add that to cover comprehensively a continent as varied as South America would require a whole library.

I have also been struck by how limited our knowledge of the wildlife of South America is. There are vast areas in the heart of the continent where no scientific investigations have been made. And our biological information concerning most of the zoological groups, including the birds, which have been studied more closely than the other groups, is rudimentary. I am afraid a book such as this must reflect some of that ignorance.

This marvelous flora and fauna are now in grave danger. The destruction of nature began a long time ago in some sections of South America. On the Brazilian coast the forests were given the axe from the very beginning of the colonial period. Moreover, as a result of unrestricted hunting, many species of animals have become virtually extinct. Such is the fate of the chinchilla of the High Andes, ruthlessly hunted for its precious fur, and the fur seal of the Juan Fernandez Islands, likewise killed for its pelt. The islands have suffered most of all. In the Galapagos, generations of pirates and privateers have exterminated the giant turtle, once the glory of an archipelago known for a unique archaic fauna.

Of course vast expanses still remain untouched on this gigantic continent. The exploitation of the Amazon Valley, the largest rain forest in the world, is still very limited, and immense expanses of the interior of Brazil, Paraguay and northern Argentina are very close to their primitive state.

But now an exploitation of natural resources has begun in every South American country. The Brazilians are ruthlessly clearing the araucaria forests and are planning to do the same in the Amazon Valley. The eastern slopes and the low plains of the Andean lands are everywhere being turned over to the bulldozer and the saw. Mining constantly requires new clearings, highways and settlements.

It is of course understandable that the nations of South America should want to put to use their natural resources. But it is intolerable that they should do this without concern for the natural environment, that primeval nature which is their most precious heritage. Already there are signs of an accelerated erosion of ground imprudently laid bare—an irretrievable loss of fertile soil.

Most South America governments are now aware of the need to preserve the natural environment. National parks and reserves are scattered through their territories, preserving many interesting sites. But this is not enough, when we consider the speeding up and the mechanization of agriculture and industry, and the population explosion so apparent throughout Latin America. These measures of preservation must be reinforced, must be made more functional, and natural resources must be utilized according to a controlled and rational plan. This will not only preserve the land but protect the flora and fauna on it. Yet compared with Europe, long ago despoiled; with North America, so industrialized; with overpopulated Asia; or with Africa and Australia, where the fauna has so desperately suffered, South America still represents a paradise for the lover of the natural world.

Another South American extreme: a humid jungle in which tall trees thrust out of a dense tangle of shrubs, lianas and creepers. (Karl Weidmann)

Land Bridge Between Two Continents

Central America

1

In reconstructing a picture of the earth in prehistoric times, geologists and paleontologists have visualized entire animal populations crossing from continent to continent on natural bridges of earth. Most such bridges eventually sank into the sea, but they allow biogeographers to explain why the animal and plant populations of continents now separated by immense oceans show certain affinities. Central America still constitutes just such a bridge between two gigantic landmasses: North America and South America.

The geographic limits of the Central American world are remarkably distinct. They are marked on the northwest by the Isthmus of Tehuantepec, and, 1,840 miles to the southeast, by a swampy depression through which the Atrato River flows toward the Gulf of Darien—a lowland that actually separates South America from the northern section of the New World. Between these two boundaries, Central America presents a strange outline—narrow necks of land alternating with broad masses. The northernmost part, the Isthmus of Tehuantepec, is only forty-eight miles wide, but south of it, Central America stretches five hundred miles wide at Yucatan, and then narrows to three hundred miles at Honduras, and only thirty-one miles at the Isthmus of Panama.

VOLCANIC HISTORY

Central America has a very complex geological structure, as might be imagined from the many reshapings it has undergone and the volcanic action still continuing. No less than one hundred large volcanos and 150 small ones mark it, all emerging from a substructure covered with thick beds of lava and cinders.

Structurally the land is made up of two different parts. The high regions of the northwest represent the western segment of the Great Antilles and consist of ranges and parallel depressions running from east to west. These very ancient mountains rise to high crests furrowed by canyons and ravines. The sierras of Chuacus and of the Minas of central Guatemala and those of the Grita and the Espíritu Santo of Honduras are old ranges on which many more recent formations have been imposed. Some are of a sedimentary nature, such as the limestone Sierra of Cuchumatanes in central Guatemala, a continuation of the Mesa Central of Chiapas, Mexico. This mountain, attaining a height of some twelve thousand feet, forms a wall forty miles long overlooking on the south the Rio Negro Valley.

Most of these mountains are still volcanic. The original outlines have been buried under the lava and ash that poured from the craters and spread over an area of 525 miles by 125 miles in Guatemala, Honduras and Nicaragua. These plateaus are dominated by volcanic cones oriented in a northwest-southeast direction. Tajumulco (13,812 feet), the highest peak in Central America, is extinct. But Santiaguito-Santa María (12,362 feet) has been spewing mud, smoke, and water mixed with sulphurous gases since the beginning of this century; the outpouring, estimated at 5,450 million cubic meters, is spread over a vast area. The German geographer, Karl Sapper, who studied the area, observes that the whole countryside looks as though there has been a heavy snowfall. Through their outpourings three volcanos, Atitlan, Toliman, and San Pedro, have created a lake at an altitude of 5,300 feet.

This picturesque body of water is as interesting to the naturalist as to the tourist because it forms a natural sanctuary for a grebe strictly indigenous to the region, the Lake Atitlan giant grebe *(Podilymbus gigas)*. This bird, related to the pied-billed grebes found in small populations across South America, has evolved in a sort of natural test tube, isolated from other stocks that could have influenced it genetically. Thus it is distinctly different from all other grebes. The populations of the Lake Atitlan grebe were doubtless never very numerous because of the relative shallowness of the lake and the small extent of the reedbeds, the only place where this aquatic bird can nest. Because the Indians hunt them there are probably no more than fifty pairs of these birds left. Thus a remarkable natural experiment that clarifies some of the aspects of evolution is in danger of disappearing because of man.

The chain of volcanic cones extends to El Salvador and includes Acatenango (12,992 feet) and the nearly perfect cone of Izalco (6,183 feet), called the "lighthouse of the Pacific" because it is visible from far out at sea when it is active.

Volcanic activity began in this region after a fracture of the earth's crust along the Pacific coast. As a result, the history of all the cities is marked by seismic catastrophes. The capitals of Guatemala demonstrate this. Antigua, the ancient capital, founded in 1547 on an imposing site dominated by Fuego and Acatenango, was for a long time the true metropolis of Central America. It boasted 150,000 inhabitants and was brimming with riches when an earthquake completely destroyed it on July 27, 1773. It never rose from its ruins and a new capital, Guatemala City, was built at an altitude of 4,800 feet on a plateau that was easily accessible and reputedly calm. This reputation was unjustified for a series of shocks completely devastated the city between September 25, 1917, and January 24, 1918.

To the south of this part of Central America extends a

Smoking craters and a fresh lava flow in Nicaragua illustrate the volcanic activity constantly present in Central America. (George Bell)

Central America is a land bridge linking the two great landmasses of North America and South America. Volcanic activity accounts for the complex geological structure of the area.

second range, simpler in structure and distinct from the first. It appears on maps in the form of an S and includes most of Panama and Costa Rica. It is actually a continuation of the most western volcanic chain of Nicaragua.

This part of Central America forms an isthmus that is not more than forty miles wide at the point where the Panama Canal was dug. It is a bridge consisting essentially of an axis of volcanic mountains that drops from 6,100 feet in Darien to about 300 feet in Panama—thus permitting the Panama Canal to be cut through it—then rises again to 9,272 feet in the mountains of Tabasara. In Costa Rica, this axis becomes a much compacted mountainous mass with such volcanic cones as Poas, Barba, Irazú, and Turrialba—all between nine thousand and eleven thousand feet. This complex chain extends northeastward to Nicaragua via a series of coastal volcanos. Between the coastal chain and the oldest plateau of Central America lies a depression where the waters have gathered in two large lakes, Lake Managua and the larger Lake Nicaragua.

These mountain chains constitute the main body of Central America and are flanked only by narrow coastal plains, at most twenty-five miles wide on the Pacific slope and hardly more on the Atlantic side. To the northeast, and continuing into Yucatan, extend vast low plains formed of limestone. There the alternate advance and retreat of the seas has created a terraced terrain with gentle undulations, where volcanic action is unknown.

Thus Central America consists of a chain of volcanos stretching some seven hundred miles and constituting an integral part of the "ring of fire" that encircles the Pacific.

Intermittently a bridge between two vast continental masses, Central America has permitted the migration of both terrestrial and marine plants and animals. Among the mammals, the marsupials and primates came south from North America in the Cretaceous and Eocene epochs, while other groups of more recent mammals followed during the Pliocene and Pleistocene epochs. The animal life of South America reveals traces of this double invasion. Other animals have moved in the opposite direction, going from subtropical regions toward the north; the number of them, especially birds, found in the fauna of Mexico and the United States attests to the significance of Central America as a bridge for migration.

Reptiles, too, testify to this origin from two different areas; that is what makes the group so remarkably diverse. Also found here is a huge freshwater turtle *(Dermatemys mawi),* sole representative of a species once distributed throughout Europe, Asia and North America, showing that Central America has also served as a haven for so-called "living fossils."

On the other hand, in the periods during which the earth was torn apart and allowed the Atlantic and the Pacific oceans to meet, exchanges of marine animals took place. The similarities in plant and animal life on both sides of the Isthmus of Panama are evidence of the extent of this mixture. Caribbean currents that now wash against the coast swept on west into the eastern Pacific. They doubtless reached at least to the Galapagos, judging by the distribution of certain organisms.

Central America is thus truly a crossroads for all the plant and animal life of the Western Hemisphere.

PASSAGEWAYS ACROSS CENTRAL AMERICA

After the discovery of America, the Spanish conquerors began to seek a waterway across Central America. But once Balboa reached the Pacific Ocean in 1513 there was a growing realization that such a passageway did not exist. The north-south mountain barrier in Central America was not, however, continuous; there were gaps in it through which men could easily pass. The Isthmus of Panama was one of these and, despite the unhealthy climate, cities were built along a land route that allowed men and goods from the Pacific coast to cross to the Atlantic.

It needed no more than this to encourage man to split Central America with a canal. At least thirty routes were proposed: the most interesting were the one through the Isthmus of Tehuantepec, where Lake Nicaragua flowed into the Atlantic by way of a navigable river, and the one over the Isthmus of Panama. The Panamanian route finally won out because of the very low pass of the Culebra Cut and the narrowness of the isthmus at that point. The canal was begun in 1879 by a French company headed by Ferdinand de Lesseps, but it failed, mainly because it did not use sluice locks. Such locks were especially necessary because the tides at Cristobal, on the Atlantic, measured little more than three feet, while at Balboa, on the Pacific, they reached almost twenty-three feet. The United States resumed the project, using locks, and opened the canal in 1914.

Irazú, an 11,260-foot volcano in Costa Rica, is part of a chain of volcanic mountains extending the entire length of Central America. (Kurt Severin)

THE ATLANTIC AND PACIFIC REGIONS

There is a sharp contrast between the two slopes of the chains of mountains running the length of Central America. On the Pacific side the slopes are steep and show signs of fracture and of sinking below the waters of the Pacific; on the Atlantic coast they are gentler. The two slopes are just as dissimilar in climate. Both have a rainy season from May to October, with a maximum rainfall in June and September. But on the Caribbean slope, trade winds, laden with moisture all year round, scatter considerable rain even during the so-called dry season. Then, relieved of their watery load, these winds sweep down the western peaks and add to the dryness of the Pacific slope. Precipitation, then, is far more copious on the east coast than on the west, and is distributed almost throughout the year, whereas in the west the dry season is very pronounced. There is an annual rainfall of at least 127 inches at Colon, on the Atlantic, while there is only 69 inches at Balboa, on the Pacific—two places scarcely forty miles apart.

The vegetation reflects these profound differences in climate. The traveler on a Pacific-bound steamer crossing through the Panama Canal notices that after the vessel passes the dividing line at Gaillard Cut, the surrounding vegetation is stunted, in sharp contrast to the luxuriance of the forests on the Caribbean slopes. Contrasts as distinct as these are also seen further north in Central America.

Altogether, plant life in Central America is diversified and extremely lush. The richness of the soil resulting from the decomposition of volcanic rocks, together with the wide range of temperatures and precipitation, creates a great variety of environments and an elaborate differentiation in species and plant associations. Furthermore, the flowering elements come both from the north and the south. It is therefore not surprising that Guatemala has no less than eight thousand species of vascular plants. The neighboring countries, especially Panama, are equally lush.

The lower regions of the Caribbean slopes up to a height of 2,500 or 3,000 feet are covered with a dense tropical rain forest similar to those in South America. The luxuriance of this forest is enhanced by the great number of palms, tree ferns, lianas and epiphytes, all of which reflect the humidity of the environment. The Pacific slope up to an altitude of three thousand feet is, on the other hand, covered by a tropical deciduous rain forest that, depending on local conditions, is sometimes of a scrubby nature and sometimes intersected by treeless grasslands. The vegetation here droops during the dry season, but awakens at the first rains. At certain points, especially in Guatemala, where a more humid zone extends from an altitude of 2,000 feet to 4,000 feet, the vegetation takes on the appearance of a true rain forest, with tree ferns particularly numerous and well differentiated. But other drier districts are covered with a mixture of cactus and acacia. Pines *(Pinus caribaea)* occupy wide areas, notably in the region of Petén in Guatemala.

The higher zones, above 3,000 feet, and sometimes only above 5,000 feet, shelter an entirely different vegetation, much of it arborescent. This upland forest is made up of oaks *(Quercus), Ilex, Prunus,* and *Alnus,* as well as numerous Lauraceae, Euphorbiaceae and Melostomaceae. At many points a cloud forest rich in tree ferns, orchids, begonias, bromeliads and aroids extends from 4,500 feet to 7,000 feet. Elsewhere, at altitudes from 5,000 feet to 12,000 feet, stretch magnificent coniferous forests, pure or mixed stands with pines, including *Pinus oocarpa, strobiliformis, Ayacahuite,* and *Montezumae.* Species of juniper *(Juniperus)* as well as conifers of the genera *Cupressus, Abies* and *Taxodium* cover extensive areas, especially in the Sierra of Cuchumatenes. After this comes the alpine level, which consists of patches above ten thousand feet, peaks of volcanos or the highest plateaus of ancient ranges. These alpine meadows, made up of expanses of low herbaceous plants and shrubs, include a strong element from the north; the proportion of endemic plants is also high.

Central America is thus a dreamland for the botanist, the gamut of habitats ranging from humid tropical rain forest to alpine meadow resembling those of the high mountains of North America.

Right: Lake Atitlan is widely known for its location in a vast, 1,000-foot-deep crater high in the volcanic mountains of Guatemala. It is the home of the giant grebe (Podilymbus gigas). *(D. Forbert: Image International) Below: A golden frog* (Atelopus varius), *from El Valle, Panama, hunts for insects and other small prey. (John Kaufmann)*

BIRD WITH AN UMBRELLA

The birdlife of Central America consists mostly of obviously tropical elements related to those of the neighboring parts of South America. It is much too rich and variegated to describe in detail; but among its more curious figures is a black bird the size of a large jay called the "umbrella bird" *(Cephalopterus ornatus)* because in the male the feathers curve into a huge crest in the front of its head. The male of this member of the family of cotingas also has a long feather-covered pendant dangling from its breast. The species inhabits the low and middle slopes of the Andes from the Brazilian Mato Grosso to Colombia, Venezuela and Central America.

The umbrella bird seems to be very rare, and even naturalists who have lived in Costa Rica for years have seen them only once or twice. In a hidden ravine with steep and timbered sides, Charles Cordier, the American ornithologist and collector, finally discovered one of the places where these birds still live. The birds greet the dawn by hooting from the tops of the highest branches, where they spend the night safe from wildcats, skunks and other carnivores. Cordier located them through their resonant sounds—like those one makes by blowing across the mouth of a bottle. To produce this call, the bird inflates a bright scarlet air sac on its throat to the size of a large tomato; the fleshy pendant is similarly distended. The hooting sound is produced as the sac is inflated; next, the bird jerks its head back, thrusts it forward, and expels the air in its sac with a whistling sound like that emitted by a snarling cat. These vocal effects seem to occur during the mating dances, when several males gather in a tree to indulge in displays intended to attract females.

WINTER QUARTERS FOR NORTHERN TRAVELERS

European birds that are sensitive to cold seek refuge in tropical Africa, but they must surmount many obstacles to reach their winter quarters. They must cross the vast Mediterranean or make a long detour through Asia Minor or across the Strait of Gibraltar. Then they face the Sahara, an immense expanse so lacking in food or water that many birds must cross it without stopping. Only beyond these sands can the birds find the warmth and sustenance of the tropics.

The birds of the New World do not face such great dangers. The deserts of the southwestern United States and Mexico and the waters of the Gulf of Mexico certainly present serious obstacles to the annual migration of birds from the United States and Canada. The least venturesome among the migrants can, however, avoid these hazards by going the long way around. It is thus really not remarkable that the principal wintering zone of North American migratory birds extends from Mexico to Panama.

The ornithologist Ludlow Griscom counted 161 Nearctic species wintering in Guatemala, in addition to thirty transients and five accidentals among a bird population totaling 736 species. In El Salvador, Donald R. Dickey and Adriaan J. Van Rossem have recorded 138 transients or winter visitors, against 308 nesting species. The numerical importance of this high proportion of winter residents coming from North America is even more striking. Nowhere else can one see such a congregation of "tourists" coming to live in the tropics for half the year. On one farm on the plains of Guatemala, the last Wilson's warbler was seen on May 22 and the first one

Right above: A two-toed sloth (Choloepus hoffmanni) *from Costa Rica, its recurved claws showing its adaptation to life in trees. Right: Another primitive mammal, Allen's opossum, of Panama, owes its survival to the great humid forests. Far right: The white-faced monkey* (Cebus capucinus), *a small, light-footed creature with the handlike tail that characterizes monkeys of the Central and South American forests. (All by Carl Rettenmeyer) Below: The spectacled caiman, which owes its name to a bony ridge joining the eye sockets, usually lives in slow-moving muddy rivers. (Lorus and Margery Milne)*

returned the following September 3, the species thus being absent from this area for only about three months a year.

Wood warblers make up an important section of these migratory birds. In species as well as individuals they represent the largest group of birds in Central America. Some of them are concentrated in a limited area: for example, the chestnut-sided warbler, which is widely distributed across the United States and Canada, winters only from the southern part of Nicaragua to the center of Panama. Certain warblers, such as the yellow warbler, chestnut-sided warbler, American redstart, common yellowthroat and ovenbird, prefer a hot and humid climate at low and middle altitudes. Others, like Townsend's warbler, Audubon's warbler, and the hermit warbler, prefer high altitudes and a more rugged climate. Many flycatchers, swallows, thrushes, tanagers, finches and orioles also congregate in Central America in bad weather.

This extraordinary concentration of birds can be explained by the abundance of food, but it is also due to simple geographic factors. As we have seen, Central America roughly forms a large triangle with its southern tip in Panama. Following converging paths, the mass of migratory birds thus congregates during the winter at this narrow southern point. It is not surprising that they swarm to these rich winter quarters, but by doing so they constitute serious competition for the resident birds; this lasts until the migrants depart during the period from March to May. The resident birds wait until the migratory birds have disappeared before they begin to nest. thus saving their young from having to reckon with the voracity of the winter visitors.

BARRO COLORADO—NATURALISTS' PARADISE

An unexpected landscape unrolls before the eyes of a passenger on a liner sailing toward the Atlantic through the Panama Canal. Having gone through the locks that separate east from west, the vessel penetrates the large lake at Gatun and sails into a maze of islands and creeks where every bit of land is covered with dense vegetation. After passing through the famous Culebra Cut, where the canal narrows between two hills and where dredges are incessantly removing landslides that have fallen into the bed, the ship passes a large island covered by thick forest, with a few white buildings standing in a small clearing. This is how I first saw Barro Colorado, the biologist's paradise whose name appears in so many works on zoology, botany and natural history.

Barro Colorado was not always an island. When Captain Luis de Castillo, commander of the Spanish forces, camped there in 1670, it was still hardly more than a promontory overlooking the Chagres River. (It was Castillo, incidentally, who named it after the red clays that formed it.) It became an island when the construction of the Panama Canal flooded the valley of the Chagres River and caused its waters to rise some eighty feet and cover 165 square miles, transforming the summits of hills into islands. Barro Colorado, nearly midway between the Atlantic and the Pacific and the largest of these islands, is less than three miles wide and rises to a height of 452 feet above the waters of Gatun Lake. Covered by forest except for some small clearings, it is particularly interesting because it shelters plant and animal communities in perfect balance. Since the flood waters rose very slowly, the concentration of animals on the islands is no greater than on the mainland.

The howler monkey with its prehensile tail is a good example of the adaptation of South American monkeys to their life in trees. (John Kaufmann)

This helmeted iguana (Corythophanes) *uses the crest above its neck to frighten its enemies by making itself seem larger. (Nicholas Smythe)*

Barro Colorado is truly representative of the forest environment of Central America. The plant kingdom is represented by more than a thousand species, some of which are trees more than 130 feet tall. More than 250 species of birds have been identified there. All the large mammals that one might expect to see in this entire region—pumas, ocelots, tapirs, collared peccaries, white-lipped peccaries, monkeys, sloths, tamanduas, tayras, agoutis, and even jaguars—are present. The island thus forms a balanced biological unit, representative of the wooded regions of Panama.

These circumstances gave rise to the idea of converting the island into a natural laboratory where biologists might study

The white-tailed deer (Odocoileus virginianus) *has spread into a variety of habitats, including the dense forests of Central America. (Lorus and Margery Milne)*

the animals of their speciality under ideal conditions. This was carried out in 1923 under the aegis of the Smithsonian Institution of Washington. Thanks to some enthusiastic American naturalists, a biological station was established in a small clearing overlooking the canal and within view of passing ships. Some of the buildings are laboratories or workrooms, while others provide comfortable lodgings in a healthful climate where malaria and other local diseases are unknown. Barro Colorado is not a natural park, nor a recreation area for the public. It is primarily an open-air laboratory where nature is preserved in its virginal state and access is restricted to scientists. The nonspecialist may find many opportunities to observe nature in surrounding areas that still remain untamed in many respects.

That the station should be perfectly integrated with the environment was understood from the start. I remember seeing wild peccaries coming for the remains of a meal left for them by the occupants of the laboratory. Birds abound in the neighborhood and many of them perch on the electric wires and posts. As for the coatis, these appealing carnivores come to poke about in the houses as familiarly as though they owned them.

Well-marked paths have been laid out all over the island, forming a network perhaps twenty miles long. As we set out on one of these paths, we come almost at once on a colony of oropendolas *(Ostinops wagleri)* established in a big tree. There they have hung enormous nests resembling elongated pouches, and they bring the tree to life with their incessant movements. They remind us, too, that the great naturalist Frank M. Chapman conducted his long study of them from a comfortable armchair with the aid of 24-power binoculars mounted on a tripod—which illustrates perfectly how convenient it is to do research on Barro Colorado.

As we push into the forest, the coatis are so numerous that we soon take no notice of them. Some howler monkeys *(Alouatta)* survey us from the treetops showing no trace of uneasiness except for a swaying of their bodies.

In a bush, a manakin with deep black plumage and a startlingly red head begins its mating dance, uttering bizarre buzzing, whirring and snapping noises, and hopping about as if it were doing a jig. A little farther away there is a Gould's manakin, a bit larger, with black head, back and wings, orange nape and throat and an olive-green belly. It is also on parade, making its wings vibrate over its back. In the thickets, antbirds whistle as they dig among the dead leaves, their tiny, upturned tails giving them the look of miniature roosters. Lifting our gaze we observe the dazzling colors of many tanagers, motmots with flattened tails, parrots and toucans and, perched on a branch, absolutely motionless, a clumsy-looking puff-bird. Flowering trees—guayacans with golden blossoms, mauve jacarandas, robles with shell-pink flowers—attract flycatchers and ever-moving hummingbirds.

We pass the trails of big cats but we haven't yet caught sight of one by day. Perhaps we shall set a photographic trap for them near a watering-place, using bait and a string stretched across a track, the apparatus set to take a flashbulb exposure during the night. We then go down toward the shore along a damp ravine where we may have a fleeting encounter with a tapir. There we see iguanas in great numbers perched on trees and dropping—not too nimbly—into the water with a big splash. There are more than forty miles of shores on Barro Colorado, which has greatly multiplied the habitats of these huge reptiles.

We return to the laboratory and put our notes in order before night falls. Seated on the terrace with binoculars at hand—and a cooling drink not too far away—we watch the many birds coming out of the forest to take advantage of the last glimmer of day. At dusk begins the formidable concert of the howlers, practically at our feet, and along the waters of the canal pass great liners and heavy freighters, flying the flags of every nation. Nowhere else has civilization been more happily merged with untamed nature than at Barro Colorado. This island remains a "dream castle" for biologists who want to work in one of the most inaccessible environments in the world: the tropical forest.

THE MISCHIEVOUS COATI

The coati is a type peculiar to the Procyonidae (a family of which the most familiar are raccoons), with a pointed and elongated muzzle, short legs and a long tail that is always held erect. About the size of a large cat, the coati is covered with a thick, soft coat of a warm brown touched with white at the shoulders and on the muzzle, and with alternating brown and black rings on its tail. These animals are widely distributed over tropical America from Central America to northern Argentina, but practically all that is known of them was learned at Barro Colorado, where they have become the emblem and the mascot. They were even featured on the postage stamp commemorating the twenty-fifth anniversary of the station in 1948.

This carnivore with a lively intelligence and mischievous eye is entirely diurnal in its activity. It is found throughout the forest in little troops, as solitary individuals, or sometimes in pairs. According to recent observations, the females and young males form bands of from four to twenty members. Arriving at adulthood after about two years, the male is expelled from the band and leads a solitary existence, subject to the hostility of members of the group when he approaches them. He rejoins them only during the mating season. At that time, each male then attaches himself to a band of females. Each of these groups occupies a domain of 85 to 110 acres, at the center of which is a core area where the band spends 80 per cent of its time. It ventures beyond the borders of its territory only during the season when fruit is abundant there. In this way the distribution of the coati population is regulated, but it has some leeway to roam.

The coati, a raccoon-like little animal, has strikingly mask-like markings across its face. It uses its long nose to find the vegetation it prefers. (Jean Dorst)

An animal active throughout the day, except during the hottest hours, the coati spends most of its time looking for morsels in the humus and under the leaves of the forest, depending heavily on its acute sense of smell. An omnivorous diet allows it to take a great variety of foods, but it shows a preference for fruit and insects, caterpillars and spiders, and for large tropical mollusks. The coati has a special way of treating its prey, rolling it along the ground with its forepaws before devouring it. It does this particularly with strong-smelling spiders or certain caterpillars covered with spiny hairs, obviously trying to remove anything that may irritate its mouth or digestive membranes. This behavior reminds one of the raccoons, cousins of the coatis, who also rub their prey before ingesting it.

Although terrestrial, coatis are such excellent climbers that certain authors have exaggeratedly called them arboreal. They rush up and down the tree trunks headfirst at top speed. The tail serves as a balance, and since it is largely prehensile, it acts as a brake when the animal dashes down the trunk. Coatis are the clowns of the tropical forest and constitute one of its major attractions.

Tropical Islands in Deep Seas

The West Indies

2

Those who think of the West Indies merely as islands scattered in the Caribbean Sea will be surprised to learn that they are the peaks of a submerged range of mountains. A glance at a map will reveal, moreover, that they form an arc from Florida to Venezuela, encircling the Gulf of Mexico and the Caribbean. Medieval writings refer to lands located somewhere in mid-ocean to the west of Europe, and crude maps based on the tales of early navigators labeled their uncertain outlines Antilia and treated them as though they were part of a continent. After Columbus' second voyage, when the lands were found to be a chain of islands, subsequent maps used the plural form Antilles, as the West Indies are still known.

This partially submerged range includes some of the steepest slopes in the world. The highest peak, Pico Duarte, on the

Right: Coconut palms, seen here on Montafan Beach, Tobago, occupy a considerable area of the Antilles. (Emil Muench)
Below: The tody, here shown near Montego Bay, Jamaica, is a member of a colorful, wren-sized family found exclusively in the West Indies. (B. Brower Hall)

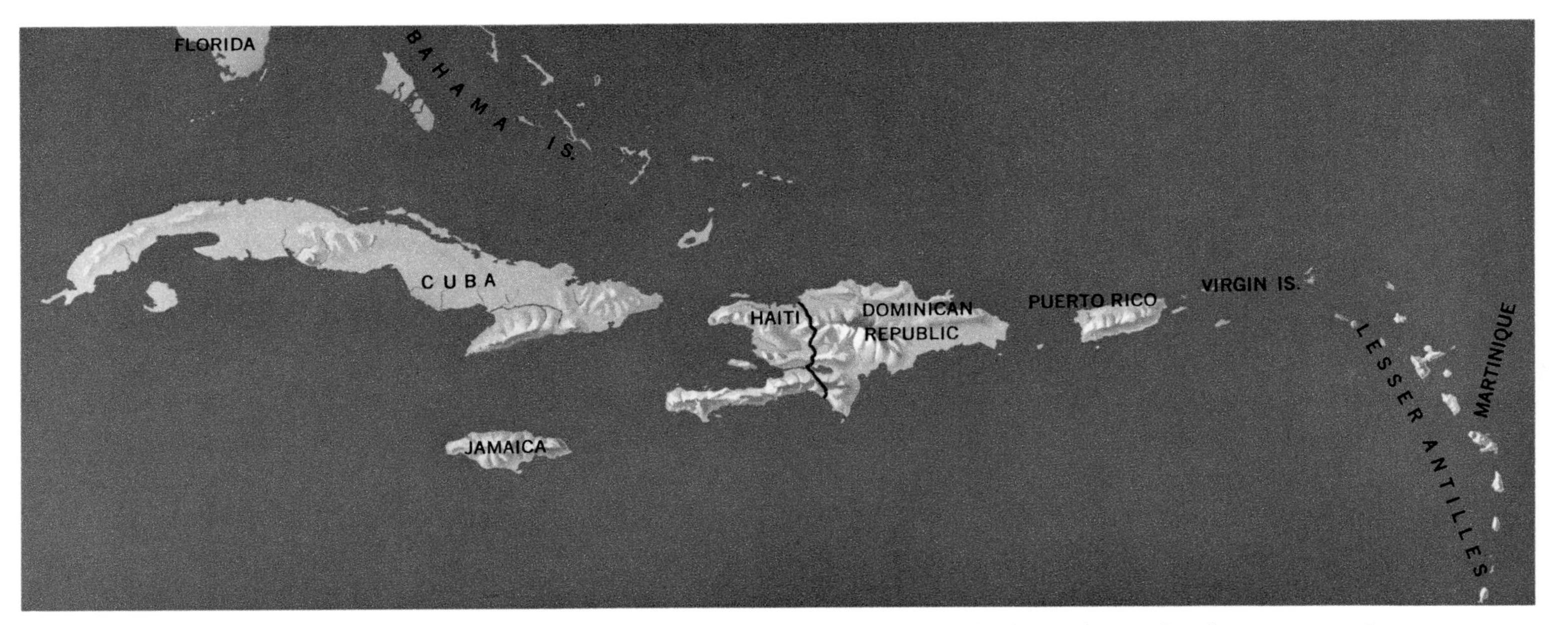

The West Indies, the peaks of submerged mountains, form a chain of islands from Florida to Venezuela.

island of Hispaniola, is 10,477 feet above sea level, but to this must be added an immense drop into one of the deepest of the world's seas. The average depth of the Caribbean is 8,685 feet; the average depth of the Gulf of Mexico is 4,961 feet; and soundings made in 1954 showed that one of the deepest ocean trenches in the western world, 24,498 feet or well over four miles, lies just north of Puerto Rico. The Antilles are therefore amazingly high projections on the surface of the globe. It has been said that if the waters were to subside in this region, the most imposing of all mountain ranges would emerge.

The necklace of islands of every size and shape that forms the archipelago comprises a total land surface of about 100,000 square miles, or slightly less than half the area of France. The islands fall into three groups: the Bahamas, the Greater Antilles (Cuba, Jamaica, Hispaniola and Puerto Rico), and the Lesser Antilles (all the remainder except Trinidad, which is considered a part of South America, being separated from the continent by only a very narrow body of water). The Lesser Antilles are further divided into the Windward Islands (St. Lucia and the islands south of it) and the Leeward Islands (those to the north of St. Lucia). The Greater Antilles show no recent signs of volcanic activity, while the Lesser Antilles are really a chain of still active volcanos. And although the two groups have much in common in physical characteristics and in flora and fauna, they show distinct differences.

Except for the Bahamas, the West Indies all lie in the Torrid Zone, and are still regarded as tropical Edens, as they were by the first explorers and missionaries. The seventeenth-century French missionary, Father Jean Baptiste Labat, a Dominican friar stationed in Guadeloupe, wrote of the island of Grenada: "In itself it was all that man could desire. To live there was to live in Paradise." Tourists today say the same of much of the West Indies.

VOLCANOS AT WORK

Geologically these islands are remarkably uniform. They are made up in part of crystalline schists (of pre-Cretaceous age) and volcanic rock, and partly of sandstone and limestone, most probably Cretaceous, overlaid in Cuba, Jamaica, and Haiti with chalk and radiolarian earths. These rocks appeared in the course of many geological upheavals, and since the region is still volcanically tempestuous, more activity may be expected. In the Greater Antilles there are deposits indicating that in the early Oligocene period (about thirty-five million years ago) the land subsided, but toward the middle of the Oligocene there was another tremendous upheaval, during which the islands may have been united with one another and with Florida. On the other hand, no deep sea deposits have been found in the Lesser Antilles, and this accounts for some of the differences in the fauna and flora.

The inner zone of the arc formed by the Lesser Antilles is one of continuous volcanic activity equalled nowhere else in the world except in the Aleutian Islands, Japan, and a part of the Sunda archipelago.

In 1961 I visited St. Pierre, a port of Martinique that has suffered time and again from disastrous eruptions of nearby Mont Pelée. I was fortunate enough to be able to make some interesting botanical and ornithological excursions with Father Robert Pinchon, an authority and an inexhaustible source of information on the natural history of the Antilles. After a day spent wandering about the mountainsides gathering specimens, we usually settled down in the evening on a café terrace for one of the rum punches for which the island is famous.

We talked of what we had observed during the day, and especially of such sights as an *Erythrina* bush in flower, with the four species of native hummingbirds on it. I recalled that Father Labat, who came to the Antilles toward the end of the seventeenth century, described these tiny creatures and called them the most beautiful birds in the world.

We also talked of our activities of the preceding day when we had sought out the Audubon's shearwater *(Puffinus l'herminieri)* on the coasts. These singular-looking birds had established a colony in the nearby little island of Hardy in Baie des Anglais to which five hundred pairs returned at nesting time every year. I say *in* the island because the birds lay their eggs in subterranean galleries or niches carved in the

The Mont Pelée range in Martinique has a reputation for prolonged and disastrous eruptions. (Emil Javorsky)

rocks by the sea. The rocks are as riddled by these holes as a Swiss cheese. It is possible for a man to visit these galleries but they are so cramped that he must do so on hands and knees and at some points he can barely wriggle through.

From the terrace we had a splendid view of Mont Pelée—the "flaming mountain," as the native Caribs described it to the earliest explorers. There it was, a peaceful-looking peak, 4,200 feet high, with not even a wisp of smoke curling up from its vaguely cone-shaped top. Not extinct, Father Pinchon assured me, merely dormant—a sleeping monster that might at any time wake, spout fire, and bring destruction as it had so many times in the past. In pre-Columbian times a particularly violent eruption blasted the top off the mountain, scattering blocks of pumice stone over the northern part of the island and burying entire communities. Of that buried civilization there remain only primitive pottery and carved stones.

After that holocaust, Mont Pelée entered a period of inactivity that apparently lasted many hundreds of years. Some people thought it was extinct. The wooded sides of the mountain were a favorite place for Sunday picnics, and the more athletic young men climbed to the top and peered unafraid into the wide, elliptical crater. Then, on April 25, 1902, a column of black smoke, ash and cinders rose hundreds of feet into the tropical sky. The next day a nearby village, Le Prêcheur, was covered with a fine layer of ash. Three days afterward, some daring mountain climbers went to the top of the volcano and came back with the report that the crater was filled with seething hot mud, and that a cone of cinders was building up in the cauldron. On May 3 and 4, a major eruption destroyed some sugar plantations to the north, killing more than one hundred people. On May 5, there was a tremendous explosion and the crater overflowed, carrying enormous masses of lava and mud down the volcano's sides and killing twenty-five people. A steady rain of ashes fell on St. Pierre, seven detonations were heard in the night, fire spouted upward, and the sides of the crater collapsed.

On the morning of May 8, a terrible quake shook the entire island, while a black cloud of ash streaked with fire, poured down the sides of the volcano and spread over the town of St. Pierre, burying it completely, and taking the lives of all of its 28,000 inhabitants. Fire swept the port, destroying most of the ships anchored there. The final eruption lasted five days, and took from 30,000 to 40,000 lives. "When the wind cleared the smoke away," wrote Alfred Lacroix, one of the greatest of French mineralogists, "the few survivors clinging to floating spars or on anchored ships could see nothing left of the town but burning ruins. And in the nearby countryside, houses and vegetation had disappeared beneath a shroud of gray ashes." In the buried town there were only two survivors; one of them happened to be imprisoned in a thick-walled jail. "Rarely if ever has a natural catastrophe taken so many human lives," declared Lacroix. About twenty square miles of plantations were ravaged in the first two days of the eruptions. Mild eruptions continued sporadically until October 30. Then the flames issuing from the volcano died down, leaving for a time a giant finger of hardened lava about one thousand feet high, pointing upward from the crater. After ten months it collapsed. Such formations present a danger in this kind of volcano, known as pelean: the lava can block up vents, holding back grases and liquids and thus increasing the internal pressure that may eventually cause another explosion.

Mont Pelée became active again in September, 1929, but this period of activity, although it lasted until 1932, caused only moderate damage, the flaming clouds being fortunately blown toward deserted regions. Since then, Mont Pelée has been quiet, and is, for the time being, listed as dormant.

Guadeloupe, the largest of the French West Indies, has also had volcanic eruptions in modern times. The portion of the island called "Basse Terre"—it is hardly true lowland—is crossed by a mountain range that has peaks almost five thousand feet high, culminates in a dome of peaks about four thousand feet high, and has, like Mont Pelée, slopes so steep that only very skilled mountain climbers can scale them. Its flattened summit is a volcano with a great number of vents, one of which, called the Grande Fente, is covered with a rich deposit of sulphur. This volcano, the Grande Soufrière, erupted in 1797, causing much damage, and again in February, 1943, when a tremendous earthquake lasting almost two minutes destroyed all the plantations on the island and took two thousand lives. There were no less than 324 other quakes in the next fourteen months. Since then, volcanic activity has been manifested chiefly in fumaroles and thermal springs.

It is evident that the volcanic activity that originally formed the West Indies is not ended, and that, unfortunately for its inhabitants, this submerged mountain range has not yet assumed its definitive form. Danger still stalks, then, among islands considered among the most beautiful in the world.

A DELIGHTFUL CLIMATE—DESPITE THE HURRICANES

The climate of the West Indies, which lie between 10° Lat. N. and 28° Lat. N., is ideal. The temperature varies at different altitudes but on the lower levels it is generally around 80° F. Even in the coolest months, January and February, the thermometer rarely drops below 70° F.

While the temperature is fairly constant, rainfall varies greatly from island to island, depending upon location, topography, and whether or not the mountain slopes are exposed to the northeasterly trade winds that bring the rain. The low islands on the outer rim of the island chain, especially the Bahamas, have no marked elevations to retain the humidity of the sea breezes. In the Lesser Antilles the part played by land elevations is particularly evident. Dominica, one of the Leeward Islands, has an annual rainfall of eighty-six inches, because of its lofty and jagged mountains, while Martinique, which is also mountainous, has 85 inches and St. Lucia 79 inches. But the low, flat island of Barbados gets only 57 inches. In the southern Caribbean, the Windward Islands, swept by the trade winds, are very dry; Curaçao is an instance of this aridity.

The seasons are not too marked. In the Lesser Antilles the months of March and April are generally the driest, whereas September and November are the most humid. There are roughly four seasons in the islands: dry and cool from December to March; dry and warm from April to June; humid and hot from July to September; humid and cool from October to December. But great variations from this norm may be observed from island to island and in various localities on each island. For instance, the period of maximum rainfall on the island of Dominica coincides with the period of minimum rainfall in Martinique, and vice versa; the rain on Martinique comes with the south wind, while Dominica receives its rain from the north wind that prevails at another period of the year.

Periodically, the Caribbean area is swept by devastating winds. In September or October, when the hot weather has built up an accumulation of heat and the great rainfalls occur, whirlwinds form and the hurricanes roar over the archipelago in a vast parabola, usually moving from the Lesser Antilles north of Barbados to Florida and up the Atlantic coast of the United States. The word hurricane itself originated here: it comes from a Carib word meaning evil spirit. The phenomenon is always heralded by an ominous calm, then a sudden fall in barometric pressure, followed by the appearance of opaque clouds and showers. Cyclones or hurricanes are accompanied by violent circular winds with a velocity above 125 miles an hour. As the "dead center" or "eye" of a hurricane passes over a point there is a moment of great calm, while all around is whirlwind and devastation. The cyclone months are usually August, September and October, 88 per cent of the cyclones occurring at that time. The fact that 135 have struck in thirty-five years testifies to their regularity. With improvements in meteorology, the occurrence and path of hurricanes are being predicted with reasonable accuracy, but so far no means of preventing or diverting them has been found. Besides sugar, coffee, rum, and tobacco, the West Indies may be said to export disaster.

Besides destroying crops and sinking ships, the cyclones and great east winds that cross the Atlantic from southern Europe

Tropical forests have suffered severely from the spread of agriculture. A few have been saved, among these El Yunque Rain Forest in Puerto Rico, the last refuge of various parrots. (Emil Javorsky)

and northwest Africa play an important role in carrying birds and insects away from their native localities. American ornithologists have several times recorded the arrival of exhausted Caribbean birds on the Gulf coast, and some species native to this part of the United States have been blown north by the winds. It is probable that the winds in this area of the Atlantic and the Caribbean have accidentally blown certain species of birds from the Old World to the New. In the autumn of 1959 a significant number of European common herons *(Ardea cinerea)* were blown from the west of France to the Antilles. One of a number of birds banded in the Loire Valley has been captured on Trinidad, and another on Montserrat in the Leeward Islands. This doubtless also explains the appearance in America of cattle egrets *(Bubulcus ibis)*, an Old World species so called because they are often found feeding in the vicinity of cattle. When a colony of these water birds was first recorded in Venezuela, about 1950, it caused a great dispute among ornithologists. Some maintained that the birds had escaped from a zoo, while others contended that they had been carried from Europe by very strong winds and cyclones. The latter were right, as was proved not long ago by the capture in Trinidad of a related species, a white egret that had been banded in the Guadalquivir marshes of Spain. Besides establishing colonies in Venezuela, the cattle egrets soon migrated north and south, so that today they are found everywhere in the New World from Canada to Argentina.

PLANT LIFE OF THE ANTILLES

Since the time of the first explorers these islands have been justly praised for the beauty and diversity of the vegetation. The richness of the soil, so much of it volcanic, and the quantity of rain and the length of the rainy season—except on a few isles—fully explain this exuberant growth. Each island retains a certain individuality in its flora. Yet, as a whole, the West Indies have a number of features in common. The larger islands, such as Cuba and Jamaica, and the highest, such as Dominica, Martinique and Guadeloupe, present a complete sampling of the different types of vegetation in the archipelago.

One of the most common and basic forms of vegetation is the mangrove. On the low-lying and marshy shores of most of the islands, one finds the red mangrove *(Rhizophora mangle)* and the black mangrove *(Avicennia nitida)*, both common on the American coasts. Mangrove formations often occupy considerable areas; they comprise 8 per cent of the total surface of the Grande Terre of Guadeloupe. Along the freshwater streams and rivers a forest of the dragon gum tree *(Pterocarpus officinalis)* flourishes, including trees one hundred feet or more in height. This kind of forest is found especially on Dominica and Trinidad.

The arid regions, especially in the lowlands, are covered with varieties of xerophytic plants—that is, adapted to a poorly watered environment—such as the succulents. Where the annual rainfall hovers between twenty-two and fifty-five inches, the forest is composed of prickly shrubs and trees such as the acacias, mingled with countless cacti. The landscapes of Curaçao and other dry islands, such as St. Martin, owe their

The Pitons in St. Lucia, West Indies, present the characteristic outline of volcanic mountains. (Lorus and Margery Milne)

The jagged leaves of philodendrons stand out in the dense undergrowth. (Emil Javorsky)

special character to this type of vegetation. The soil of Curaçao is in part of coral origin and is notable for its abundance of cereus cactus, with its long columnar stems. There are also the thick fronds of the maguey *(Agave veta)*, from which both pulque, a beerlike beverage, and tequila, a strong distilled liquor, are derived. In the regions of greater humidity, where the annual rainfall is about sixty-five inches, the prickly plants give way to forests of deciduous trees that have small hairy leaves and often milky, sticky sap. Among the plants that flourish on sandy soil is the famous manchineel tree *(Hippomane mancinella)* of the euphorbias, called in the French West Indies the poison tree or tree of death. This tree, which reaches a height of from fifteen to twenty feet and resembles a tall pear tree, is covered with thick and crenelated leaves and bears fruit resembling ribbed apples. It secretes an acrid, milky sap, so virulent that it was used to poison the tips of arrows. Legends of the fearful powers of this tree abound: even to stand in its shade is fatal, the very vapors given off by it being deadly. Meyerbeer in his opera *L'Africaine* uses this fable and makes it all the more inaccurate since his drama takes place in Africa, whereas the manchineel tree is native to tropical America and in particular to the Antilles. Father Jean Baptiste Dutertre in his excellent history of the Antilles, published in 1667, declares that "even the raindrops that touch the leaves of this tree absorb the poisonous qualities, so that it is very dangerous to pass under it during a rain."

Elsewhere, many-branched trees with small, shiny, tough leaves are found in association that cannot but remind us of the Mediterranean *macchia* or *maquis*.

Gradually, as one passes into the more humid regions, the forests become denser and greener and are composed at least in part of varieties of evergreens differing according to the soil. On calcareous or clay soil, the *Simaruba* (called the paradise tree) and the *Cedrela* (timber trees related to the mahogany) seem to predominate, mingled with the torchwood *(Fagara caribaea)* and spiny palm trees, such as the *Aiphanes minima*. On volcanic soil flourish such trees as the *angelin-savonette* of the French West Indies, *Andira,* called the "cabbage tree" and the *Lonchocarpus* along with various Leguminosae and members of the pepper- or spice-bearing family (Piperaceae).

Higher still, at altitudes between one thousand and three thousand feet, the vegetation becomes rain forest of the type found in most of the West Indies. This kind of growth covers vast expanses of Martinique, Guadeloupe, Dominica, St. Kitts, St. Lucia and St. Vincent; it is absent on the smaller and lower-lying islands such as Barbados and Curaçao, but is present in the Greater Antilles, especially in Cuba and Puerto Rico, where trees with great trunks rise to heights of from 100 to 125 feet. Entangled with lianas and covered with mosses and lichens they recall the rain forests of the South American continent.

Between three thousand and five thousand feet up, the trees are smaller because of the violent winds, the colder temperatures and an annual rainfall of between 220 and 360 inches. These low, many-branched and bushy trees form the "elfin woodlands" of English foresters. The foothills and slopes are constantly swept by rains and are covered with mountain mangrove *(Clusia)*.

By comparison with the Greater Antilles, the flora of the Lesser Antilles makes a poor showing. There are perhaps slightly more than 4,500 of the flowering plants *(Phanerogamia)* and about five hundred of the ferns *(Pterydophytia)* while in Cuba alone there are eight thousand species of vascular plants. The wealth of flora native to each of the islands naturally depends upon its climate and size. Thus, St. Martin and St. Barthélemy can count no more than about five hundred species, while Guadeloupe possesses 2,015 vascular plants and Martinique 1,798. The number of local species is less than one might expect. Botanists estimate that of 1,700 species examined in the French West Indies, only 165, or slightly less than 10 per cent, were endemic, and these were for the most part native to high altitude forests. No doubt this is a result of the transitional location of the Lesser Antilles between South America and the Greater Antilles, their recent geological development, and the many volcanic catastrophes.

Palms thriving on the humid banks of a forest stream in the Caribbean National Forest of Puerto Rico. (Emil Javorsky)

As a whole, then, all the West Indies, even the smallest of them, contribute to a strange and interesting assemblage. Unfortunately, as we shall see, these islands have suffered since their settlement by man, and especially the white man.

A RICH VARIETY

Amidst many similarities in geological structure and climate, these islands present some remarkable differences, resulting from both natural causes and the impact of man. Colonized by many European peoples and by the Negroes brought there as slaves, the islands have been much altered by man's land use.

Among the natural causes of diversity, the elevation of the land is a prime factor. Cuba, with its 44,218 square miles, is a small continent in itself, with a wide range in climate and habitats. On the other hand, the tiny island of Montserrat in the Leeward group and other small, low-lying, flat islands that look on the map like mere chips in the Bahamas have almost uniform conditions. Variations in the soil and rainfall also have a great effect upon the topography of the islands, especially on the extent of erosion.

All these differences in soil, altitude, and humidity provide a great range in habitats, from rain forests, oak and evergreen stands, and savannas to thickets of dwarf oaks and xerophytic plants mingled with cactus.

The fauna reflects this diversity but is, of course, considerably poorer than that of the neighboring continents. Many animals have been unable to swim from the continental landmasses to the islands or from island to island. This is especially true of the vertebrates and particularly of the mammals; but even the birds are far less diversified than on the continents. Thus, the proportion of fauna that is indigenous is large and many species are found only on a single island. In these fragmentary populations, nature has evolved a series of species as if in a test tube—another reason why these islands are of exceptional interest to biologists. We have space here to describe only a few aspects of the fauna and flora of a few of the islands. Indeed, the charm of the Antilles is that each has a character of its own.

THE FLAMINGOS OF THE BAHAMAS

A level island under a blazing sky . . . an unpleasant terrain, which is difficult to cross since it is neither solid nor liquid. Such is the island of Inagua, one of the most remote of the twenty-nine islands of the Bahamas. But if one wants a view of the red flamingos that abound here, one must cross this treacherous ground and enter salt marshes. These are linked to the sea at high tide, and one risks an encounter with the ferocious barracudas that sometimes gather here. The mud is thick and sticky, and it is mixed with coral fragments as sharp as razors. The waters here are five times as saline as the sea. When the tide recedes, the marshes dry out, leaving hard crusts of salt that glitter in the sun and crumble beneath one's feet. As one goes farther into the marsh the mud becomes a black liquid in which the salt crystals scratch the ankles cruelly. Often the water is reddened by myriads of microscopic flagellates.

Suddenly in the distance, seen through air quivering with heat, appears a long, bright red band like some strange décor: these are the flamingos *(Phoenicopterus ruber)* of the Caribbean. One of the most vividly colored birds in its family, its plumage ranges from pink to scarlet and even extends to the long, thin legs while the oddly downcurving beak is bright yellow and black. This species is the most insular of all flamingos, and the Bahamas and the Greater Antilles have always been the center of its distribution. But it also forms colonies at certain points on the mainland such as the coasts of Yucatan and the Guianas, not to mention an outpost on the Galapagos Islands. Thirty-two nesting colonies are known, with half of them in the Bahamas, and half of these on the small island of Andros.

Apparently this flamingo, which attains a height of close to five feet, has never been as numerous as others of its family. Strangely enough, no explorer in the past ever mentioned colonies anywhere as sizeable as those in India, and on certain lakes of Africa's Rift Valley. The small surface of the islands where the flamingo forms colonies, along with the losses due to cyclones may account for this. But, it is estimated that in former times there were at least 95,000 of these birds in twelve major and seventeen minor colonies. Today there are no more than 21,500 in two major and three minor colonies. Egg collecting, senseless hunting, planes flying low over the colonies—this flamingo is one of the most timid of all birds—and the exploitation by man of the habitats, especially for salt extraction, have destroyed from 70 to 80 per cent of these birds in three centuries.

How strange it is, Charles Darwin exclaimed, that any creature should be able to live in salt marshes. The fact is that flamingos are the only vertebrates that have managed to flourish in this restricted habitat. Indeed, flamingos look for salt above anything, which explains why this bird is found not only on coastal lagoons of the Caribbean but also on isolated lakes thirteen thousand feet up in the Andes. Far from being devoid of life, salt marshes are inhabited by countless lower organisms that are completely adapted to this strange environment. According to some observers, the flamingo feeds exclusively on mud formed largely of organic material synthesized by bacteria and algae. But this is only partly true; their food also includes worms, mollusks and crustaceans, and it is this nutriment that gives the bird its bright red or pink coloring.

I watched a band of flamingos feeding in a shallow lagoon bordered with halophilous plants, those thick, round-leaved plants that have adapted to salt water. Bending their goose-shaped bodies on their stiltlike legs, and moving slowly in regular circles, the birds swing their downcurving beaks backward through the shallow water, sifting food out of the ooze. At regular intervals the flamingos reverse their direction and repeat the operation. With a bill that acts like a filter, a tongue with hooked edges directed toward the throat, and a throat that works like a pump, these birds are an outstanding example of adaptation to an unusual environment.

Like all flamingos, those of the Caribbean build a cone-shaped nest of mud sometimes a foot high, in which the female lays a single egg. At the end of a month, a large and almost formless chick is hatched, quite hideous and giving no indication that it will become a graceful adult. All the chicks of the same age are assembled in a kind of nursery, where the parent birds can easily watch over them. As soon as the young are able to fly, the colonies break up and disperse. At

Orchids are able to grow on a tree in Jamaica because of the moisture in the air. (J. Allan Cash)

that time the migrating flamingos can be seen streaking across the Caribbean skies. Regularly they appear on the Florida coast and in small numbers even as far north as North Carolina and more rarely along the Gulf coast. They also visit the low coasts of Colombia and the Guianas, where they once nested.

At the next nesting season they will all return to the protection of their remote breeding ground. Perhaps they retire there because of a natural timidity; on the other hand, it might be that this very isolation has been the cause of their wary and timorous nature. Measures must be taken to protect this bird if it is to remain the most beautiful ornament of this entire region.

CUBA

South of Florida lies the island of Cuba, northernmost of the Greater Antilles, comprising half of the land area of the West Indies. It is not volcanic in origin but represents the most northerly part of South America, from which it was separated ages ago. It is made up chiefly of gentle slopes and rolling land. However, the eastern portion is very mountainous, the Sierra Maestra running for 150 miles from Cape Cruz to Guantanamo Bay, the southern bluffs plunging almost directly into the sea. This rock wall is practically two thousand feet high all the way, culminating in the 6,578-foot Pico Turquino. Chains of islets, coral reefs and keys fringe the northern and southern coasts of the island. There are some excellent natural harbors, the city of Havana being situated on one of the best. In the western province of Pinar del Rio, a long uneven spur, the sierras of Rosario and of Los Organos, covered with thickets and pine forests, alternate with fertile valleys. The landscape here is varied and often magnificent. Elsewhere, the island is rolling countryside with rounded limestone hills and mountains that sometimes have steep flanks full of sinkholes and caves. About halfway along the southern coast is a chain

An anolis lizard makes a threatening display. (Lorus and Margery Milne)

of reefs and offshore islets called "the gardens of the queen," emerging from a sea as clear and polished as a looking glass.

With its tropical heat modified by sea breezes, Cuba's average temperatures scarcely vary, ranging from 70° to 81° F. The hottest months are July and August, and of course the highest temperatures are registered in the low valleys and at sea level. Rainfall governs the seasons; as in Mexico, the rainy season is from May to November, the dry season from November to April. The average annual rainfall is fifty-four inches, but at Pinar del Rio it sometimes reaches sixty-five inches.

There is a rich flora, thanks to the tropical climate and the island's geological origin as part of the South American continent. Thus it is estimated that close to six thousand species of plants of Mexico, Central and South America, and tropical Florida are to be found on the island. There are many palm trees, more than thirty species; the "bull thatch" palm *(Sabal florida)* flourishes here, and the royal palm *(Roystonea regia)* attains a height of more than one hundred feet.

The coconut palm is abundant and is cultivated in plantations. In the lowlands, fields of sugar cane furnish the main export crop, with tobacco coming second. Pineapples and bananas are grown and enormous quantities are exported. Coffee trees grow in the shade of the wide-leafed banana trees. Citrus fruits are indigenous but have not been greatly exploited.

A dense tropical forest covers the hills of Oriente province, and pine trees on some of the mountainsides attain great size: the *Pinus cubensis* and *P. occidentalis* sometimes have trunks four feet in diameter and reach a height of 150 feet.

With such a variety of habitats and profusion of species one would expect to find a rich fauna, but Cuba has been isolated from the mainland too long, and, except for insects (17,000 species have been counted), the zoologist is apt to be disappointed. As everywhere in the West Indies, the bird population has suffered from indiscriminate slaughter by man, and some species have become extinct. Of the 297 species found there, 70 are indigenous. There are only 31 species of mammals, of which 29 species are bats. Reptiles are numerous and the turtles are remarkable. Crocodiles and caimans inhabit the southern swamps.

JAMAICA, ISLAND OF SPRINGS

"Xaymaca," meaning "island of springs" is what the Arawak aborigines called the island of Jamaica. The Arawaks were exterminated before the middle of the seventeenth century, but the name, slightly changed, remains, and the springs still gush from the hillsides and mountains of one of the most beautiful islands of the Antilles. With an area of 4,413 square miles, and with a mountainous backbone, Jamaica is about 50 miles wide and 146 miles long. Mainly composed of Tertiary plateaus of white sandstone, ranging from about one thousand to three thousand feet high, culminating in Blue Mountain Peak at 7,402 feet, the many rivers and streams and the bountiful rainfall (averaging seventy-four to seventy-seven inches annually) have carved out deep ravines and canyons, at the bottom of which lie quiet pools. The mountainsides are perforated with caves into which some of the rivers flow, emerging elsewhere after their underground passage. As might be expected in a limestone region, there are many sinkholes and "cockpits" with steep sides. In a northern climate this weirdly eroded landscape would be forbidding, but here, beneath a tropical sky, where a luxuriant vegetation flourishes, the effect is enchantingly fairylike.

The rainfall is almost constant throughout the year, slackening off only slightly in February and March. The central and northeastern areas get more than one hundred inches annually, and the John Crow Mountains have almost three hundred inches. The southern part of the island is sheltered from the wet winds, and some districts there have less than thirty inches of rain annually. Temperature in the lowlands is almost constant; at Kingston the average is between 80° and 86° F. In the highlands the average temperatures are delightfully cool; at Hill Gardens in the Blue Mountains the average is about 45° F.

The vegetation of course reflects these climatic variations. There are more than three thousand species of flowering plants, of which two hundred are orchids. Mosses and ferns are likewise abundant, being represented by 530 species. The drier southern slopes have a poorer vegetation while the central plateau region, very much altered by man, still retains some primitive vegetation in the form of woodlands.

A large part of Jamaica has been under cultivation for many years, producing mainly sugar cane but also bananas and coffee. But it is noteworthy that just about all the species grown have been introduced and practically none is native to Jamaican soil.

Good pasturage for horses and cattle occurs in the interior of the central plateaus and on the southern plains. These districts are reminiscent of Normandy and certain parts of southern England. The central plateau, once covered by ancient forests, has suffered greatly at the hands of man, but the remaining woodlands, mostly second growth, still provide much useful timber—mahogany, rosewood, various hardwoods for building purposes, and several dyewoods. Palm trees are plentiful, and there are coconut plantations. Various fruit trees common to the Caribbean region, such as the mango, the guava, and the breadfruit, are found here.

I am especially attracted by the wooded mountain regions, not only for their luxuriant vegetation but for the abundance of hummingbirds. Perhaps I feel this way because it was there that I first saw this fascinating bird in the wild state. I had written my doctoral thesis on the anatomy of the Trochilidae and had studied hummingbird skins and specimens at the Sorbonne and at the Museum in Paris. But I had never seen a live hummingbird until I made a stopover at Kingston, Jamaica, in 1954.

I well remember my first trip up the Blue Mountains by car, the road winding higher and higher above deep ravines, entirely surrounded by dense growths of palm trees, bamboos, tree ferns, lianas. In the midst of this rich mantle of green a streak of iridescent color flashed before my eyes—by chance one of the most spectacular hummingbirds in the Antilles, the long-tailed doctor bird *(Trochilus polytmus)*. The male is clearly identified by the two long tail feathers that trail behind it in flight and create a peculiar sound. Its dazzling green plumage contrasts with a black cap and red beak. The species is indigenous to Jamaica and very common there. Obligingly, the bird lingered nearby, probing the flowers of a climbing plant, so that I had time to observe it carefully.

The St. Lucia parrot (Amazona versicolor), *limited to the mountain forests of the West Indian island of St. Lucia, is becoming rare. (Lorus and Margery Milne)*

I soon had an opportunity to watch another bird of a family native to the Greater Antilles: the tody. The Todidae are distantly related to the motmots and the kingfishers. The tody is only four inches long, with a long flattened beak, bright green back and shoulders, red breast, and yellowish white belly. Other species are found in Cuba, Hispaniola and Puerto Rico, where they line up on telegraph wires like swifts, on the lookout for the insects that are their main food. In flight they make a kind of whirring sound, apparently a result of the fluttering of their tapered primaries. Like the kingfishers, the todies construct burrows in banks of roads or rivers, and there lay their eggs. Since mammals—except for bats—are almost entirely lacking, these friendly birds are among the most interesting wildlife in Jamaica.

PUERTO RICO

A commonwealth of the United States since 1952, Puerto Rico is the smallest of the Greater Antilles, but still one of the larger islands in the Caribbean. Oriented east-west, it is 113 miles long and 40 miles wide. A chain of mountains rises out of the sea in the west, attaining a height of 4,389 feet at Cerro de Punta, and extends toward the east, dividing into the Sierra of Luquillo and the Sierra of Cayey. On each side of these sierras stretch coastal plains, especially toward the north. Seventy per cent of the island is mountainous.

Because of the warm but agreeable climate, with almost continuously clear skies and an annual rainfall averaging 74.4 inches (occurring mainly from May to November), a rich vegetation might be expected on this island. But the population there is very dense and the land is cultivated intensively, even on the steep mountain slopes, so that plantations have superseded wild and primitive growths. There remain vestiges of tropical forest in the highlands, but even these are not, properly speaking, primeval forests. In the lower portions to the north of the sierras, the damp climate encourages a similar forest growth with, however, a somewhat different type of flowering, but even these forests have now been replaced by plantations, mainly of sugar.

As a result of man's inroads, Puerto Rico is poor in fauna. Bats, dolphins and manatees are the only indigenous mammals. Even birds are scarce, only 190 species being represented, of which eighty-nine nest here and only thirty-six are indigenous. The number of birds has decreased markedly in recent years. Thus, the Puerto Rican parrot *(Amazona vittata vittata)*, which used to be very numerous in all parts of the island, is now scarce. Fortunately a bird sanctuary in the Luquillo National Forest in the northeast part of the island may yet save this parrot from the fate of related parrots in Guadeloupe, Martinique and the Culebra Islands—all now extinct. Many other species of birds are also threatened with extinction as a result of bird hunters and the destruction of natural habitats. The United States government is studying projects for other forest reserves and sanctuaries, such as those established on the Virgin Islands of the United States.

The Jamaican brown owl (Pseudoscops grammicus), *a native of Jamaica, nests in holes in tree trunks. (Lorus and Margery Milne)*

Game fish are still plentiful and provide an attraction for tourists. Among these are the yellowfin tuna, white marlin, sailfish, kingfish and wahoo.

The tourist should not leave Puerto Rico without visiting one of the island's curiosities: the famous *Bahia Fosforescente* or "Bay of Fire," situated near Parguera, at the extreme western end of the southern coast. At night, the wake of a boat, the stroke of a swimmer, or even the movement of the waves creates a luminescent path in the water. The passage of a school of fish near the surface makes a series of fiery trails. Moving over it has been compared to passing over a cache of exploding Roman candles. Elsewhere this phenomenon of phosphorescence, called bioluminescence, is usually sporadic or seasonal, but in this bay it is constant and may be observed every night. It is caused by myriads of flagellate microorganisms, the *Pyrodinium*, each one no more than 1/500th of an inch in diameter. These organisms abound in waters rich in vitamin B-12, synthesized by bacteria. But it is still a mystery how and why at night each of these protozoa transforms itself, at the least excitation, into a living neon tube.

TRINIDAD

Trinidad, with an area of 1,864 square miles, is the largest of the Caribbean islands south of the Greater Antilles. In geology and zoogeography, it has, however, very few of the characteristics of the archipelago; it is far more closely related to the mainland of South America, and in particular to Venezuela, from which it is separated by the two very narrow mouths of the Gulf of Paria, which is at most only eighty-eight feet deep. Certainly its fauna and flora bear a much closer resemblance to those of Venezuela than of the West Indies. The resemblance is particularly marked in the mammals, most of which are totally absent on the Caribbean islands but are present on the mainland.

The geology of Trinidad reveals even closer ties with Venezuela, especially in the island's northern hills, which show every sign of being a prolongation of the Venezuelan coastal ranges. The southern slopes of these mountains are gentle, but the northern slopes are abrupt, plunging directly into the sea. Waterfalls are numerous, with Maracas Falls, 312 feet high, to the northeast of Port-of-Spain, the best-known and perhaps the most beautiful. Apart from the ranges of hills in the center and in the south, the rest of the island is level or undulating. On the plains, volcanic oil and pitch well up; the famous Pitch Lake, near La Brea thirty-eight miles southeast of Port-of-Spain, has a circumference of two miles. Always liquid and bubbling at its center, it produces a seemingly inexhaustible supply of asphalt, one company extracting no less than 140,000 tons of this valuable product annually.

The slopes of volcanic Saba Island, between St. Kitts and the Virgin Islands, plunge so steeply into the sea that scarcely any vegetation has colonized them. (W. van de Poll: Bavaria Verlag)

Petroleum was discovered near Aripero in 1867, and oil now constitutes 75 per cent of the exports of Trinidad, making it the third-largest producer of oil in the British Commonwealth.

A plentiful rainfall from May to January, ranging from 50 to 110 inches according to the locality, combined with a great variety of soils and an average temperature of 80° F, has fostered a great variety of vegetation, again recalling Venezuela. The more humid mountainsides are covered with a dense evergreen forest, which gives way in lower and sandy regions to semi-monsoon forest with a great variety of species, some of them deciduous. The trees include valuable timber, rubber, and dye-woods, and many varieties of palms. On the plantations, cocoa, sugar cane, coconuts, and coffee are cultivated.

The wooded northern mountain range is of surpassing scenic beauty and of the greatest interest to the naturalist. These mountains so captivated the great American biologist, William Beebe, that he established an observation station there that has become perhaps the most famous biological center for studies of the tropical world. Sponsored by the New York Zoological Society, it is located at Simla, near the town of Arima, at an altitude of eight hundred feet—a district that closely resembles the Rancho Grande of Venezuela in its forest growths. As a result, Trinidad is associated with some of the most valuable tropical studies ever made, not only of mammals, especially bats, but of batrachians, mollusks, crustaceans, arachnids, and insects, among which the moths and butterflies are the most colorful. Twenty-five years ago, five hundred species of butterflies and about one thousand moths were known; the studies made on the island of Trinidad have added a great number of hitherto unknown species. Among the vertebrates of this region are 16 species of frogs and toads, 15 of lizards, 27 of serpents, and 70 of mammals, among which are an armadillo *(Dasypus novemcinctus)*, a deer *(Mazama rufa)*, a peccary *(Dicotyles tajacu)*, a tamandua or ant bear *(Tamandua longicaudata)*, and a silky anteater *(Cyclopes didactylus)*, not to mention rodents, bats, marsupials, and the ocelot *(Leopardus pardalis)*.

Birds are even more abundantly represented. Among the 347 species counted in Trinidad, 230 are land birds, and no less than 164 of these, representing 70 per cent of all land species, have been found at or near Simla. Tinamous, birds of prey, cuckoos, parakeets, hummingbirds (sixteen species of these alone), ant birds, flycatchers, thrushes, honeycreepers, warblers during the winter, and tanagers, are all found in great numbers, along with finches and trogons.

Among the most interesting birds of Trinidad are the manakins, related to the cotingas, which are also found throughout the Amazon region and tropical America. The manakins are small birds, with elongated throat feathers. The heads of the males are a gaudy red, yellow or bright blue, their backs and sides blackish green, while the females are a dull olive-green. Like many primitive passerines they emit strident whistles, but what astonishes visitors is the metallic rattle of their stiff feathers when they fly. They are usually found in dense undergrowth, where they hunt their insect prey.

The nuptial display of this polygamous bird is elaborate. The males choose an opening in the forest surrounded by low branching bushes, where each commands a parade ground. After clearing the area they indulge in a series of aerial acrobatics accompanied by various calls and a great fluttering of their bright plumage. Each movement of the dance has been labelled: there is the snap-jump, the rolled snap, the grunt-jump, the slide-down-the-pole, and the fanning, all of them calculated to attract the females. The *bailadores,* as the natives call the birds, perform the dances all day long but with greatest intensity at dawn and toward midday. Occasionally the females join the males in an aerial *pas de deux.* Once paired off, the females must build the nests and hatch and care for the young.

All birds indulge in some kind of "nuptial parade," but perhaps no other bird, except the cock-of-the-rock, performs dances as complicated as these. Students of animal behavior have been fascinated by the way the males here show a social instinct in choosing a common display area and at the same time illustrate a territorial instinct, with each male ready to defend with beak and claw his own patch of ground. The dances constitute a sexual stimulus leading to copulation, and are an integral stage in the reproduction of the species.

Only thirty miles to the northeast of Trinidad is the small island of Tobago, with an area of 114 square miles, a volcanic mountain mass which rises to a height of eighteen hundred feet, and is covered with dense forests. Naturalists come here mainly to study the birds of paradise, which were introduced from New Guinea many years ago and have become completely acclimatized.

BURIAL GROUND OF EXTINCT ANIMALS

Few parts of the world have suffered more from the depredations of the white man than the West Indies. The limited size of each island creates a situation wherein a local decimation of species cannot be counterbalanced by an influx of the species from adjacent areas. The massive deforestation of many of the islands has had most serious consequences, bird species disappearing in direct proportion to such deforestation. On the island of Hispaniola, where there are still 5.8 acres of forest per inhabitant, no species has disappeared; while in the Lesser Antilles, where there is only one acre of forest per inhabitant, from two to four bird species have disappeared on each island.

In addition to the depredations of man there are those of the various animals that have been introduced by man. The spread of rats throughout the world has had its usual effect here. Then, in 1870, the mongoose was introduced from Asia into Jamaica to combat snakes, especially the rat-tailed viper or fer-de-lance *(Bothrops lanceolatus* and related species). This viper, which can give birth to as many as seventy-one young at a time, swarms everywhere in the Lesser Antilles, especially Martinique. Its venom can cause an agonizing death. The mongoose has not succeeded in exterminating this dangerous serpent and has itself become something of a pest. There had been no predators in the West Indies and the introduction of this carnivore upset a delicate balance of nature.

There are remarkably few mammals here; the sea separating the islands from the continental landmass presents an insuperable obstacle to most of them. However, there are some very specialized types, among them, the solenodons, insectivorous mammals the size of a domestic cat. Two species of solenodons are known in the West Indies, one a native of Hispaniola *(S. paradoxus),* the other of Cuba *(S. cubanus).* Solenodons have long pointed snouts, and a stiff fur that is blackish-brown in color, with the undersides somewhat lighter. Discovered in Cuba and mentioned by the Spanish chronicler Oviedo in 1535, this animal was not scientifically described until almost the middle of the nineteenth century. After the introduction of the mongoose and the transformation of the habitats where solenodons were common, they vanished for a time and were considered extinct. Then, on Hispaniola in 1907 and on Cuba in 1909 they were found again. Although their number is now greatly reduced, a small population continues to live in the midst of rocky forests. They are virtually living fossils and should be preserved as examples of a fauna that has disappeared elsewhere.

Among the rodents, the agoutis *(Dasyprocta albida),* which were described by voyagers of the seventeenth century—especially Father Dutertre, who told of their edibility and how they were hunted by specially trained dogs—have mostly disappeared. They survive only in the most wooded islands, provided the mongoose is not also present in great numbers. The same applies to various rodents with more or less spiny pelts, all known as *hutias,* several species of which are found in some of the Greater and Lesser Antilles, and, in small numbers, on the islands of Jamaica and Cuba. But for the most part, the hutias vanished in ancient times, leaving behind only skeletons in caves, which seems to indicate that the aborigines fed on them.

The birds of the West Indies have suffered grave, and in some cases irreparable damage, at the hands of man. For instance, the most spectacular member of the parrot family, the ara of Cuba *(Ara tricolor),* with its red and yellow plumage, was last observed in swampy southern parts of the island in 1885; other related species have apparently disappeared before being scientifically described. The beautiful aratinga of Guadeloupe and several Amazon parrots have also been exterminated.

As for the species that have become distinctly rare, the list is long. For instance, the *gorge-blanche (Ramphocinclus brachyurus),* a mocker native to Martinique and once very numerous, was thought to be extinct as a result of deforestation and the ravages of the mongoose; but is was seen again not long ago in the wooded district of the Caravelle Peninsula, a narrow cape on the eastern shores of the island. But its numbers certainly do not exceed a few dozen, and these will disappear if that woodland is destroyed.

The West Indies show us clearly how precariously island fauna exists, and how, with the alterations made by man in the natural environment and through the introduction of alien species, many animals seem destined to disappear.

The saffron finches (Sicalis flaveola), *introduced into Jamaica from South America, have evolved into a much more vividly colored race than those on the mainland. (B. Brower Hall)*

Grassy Plains Under the Sierras

Venezuela

3

Like most South American countries, Venezuela does not comprise a distinct biological unit. It is, instead, a land of contrasts, for it takes in several of the natural regions of this vast continent. It is the northernmost Andean country in the chain of the Cordilleras, yet part of it reaches into the Guiana plateau. Above all, it is the land of the great plains of the Orinoco basin, the so-called *llanos*. They are distinct from everything that surrounds them, for they are hemmed in by the chain of mountains bordering the Caribbean and by the Orinoco set against the Guiana Highlands. Savannas and forests are here found side by side and often merge. Venezuela thus forms a crossroads where geographical features of the Andean, Amazonian, and Guianan regions meet.

THE CARIBBEAN COAST: THE SIERRA NEVADA DE MÉRIDA

A branch of the eastern range of the Andes curves toward the northeast and east, crossing more than 750 miles of northern Venezuela bordering the Caribbean and terminating at the Paria Peninsula facing the Island of Trinidad. It is this mountain range that gives splendor to the coast of Venezuela. Although this Caribbean mountain chain is a structural unit, it divides into three sections isolated by cross-valleys. Their altitude gradually decreases from the west to the east: the Sierra Nevada de Mérida reaches more than sixteen thousand feet, with peaks that are perpetually snow-covered, while the central Venezuelan chains are less than ten thousand feet, and the Cumaná Andes barely attain seven thousand feet.

The vegetation that flourishes on the higher reaches of these mountains resembles that of the most elevated levels of Colombia and Ecuador. At an altitude of about ten thousand feet, the climate is temperate: potatoes and wheat are cultivated. Above this level trees become increasingly rare and stunted. This is the *paramos* region, where the vegetation is mostly herbaceous, with thick roots and tough leaves, the latter often arranged in rosettes at the base of the plant. Many have brilliantly colored flowers and these, during the period of blooming, make some districts resemble magnificent alpine meadows. A number of species of *Hypericum* and *Geranium, Potentilla heterosepala,* and several gentians and lupines are a few of the plants that give the landscape its subalpine or alpine character. Also found here are frailejons *(Espeletia)* comparable to those of Ecuador, and some bushy plants, especially Ericaceae, on rocky mountainsides sheltered from the wind and warmed by sunlight.

The fauna of these elevated regions is poor, but has some quite interesting elements. Some are of northern origin, for example a shrew *(Cryptotis thomasi),* a representative of Insectivora that has penetrated the northern portion of South America in comparatively recent times. Other examples of animal life in these elevated regions came originally from the south. For instance, certain ovenbirds such as the dusky cinclodes *(Cinclodes fuscus),* are found along the entire length of the Andes, from Patagonia northward. The cold lands of Venezuela thus form a strange meeting place for animals hailing from diametrically opposite directions.

The Andes of central Venezuela, or the Andes of Caracas, include the coastal range and a second interior range of less elevation. These ranges are separated by a longitudinal depression where waters accumulate without an outlet to the sea, forming the Lake of Valencia. The coastal range, attaining an elevation of 8,047 feet at the Silla de Caracas and 8,428 feet at the peak of Naiguatá, dominates the northern shoreline.

The city of Caracas, it should be noted, is not situated in the central depression or on the coast. It occupies a narrow ravine, an opening in the very heart of the cristalline massif at an altitude of 2,600 feet. The road that connects it with the port city of Guaira gives the traveler an idea of how indented the mountainous coastline is, for it crosses many deep ravines spanned by graceful bridges.

To the east of Cape Codera, the coastal mountain range is broken by a huge gap that allows the waters of the llanos to flow directly toward the ocean by way of the Unare and Aragua de Barcelona rivers. Beyond the gap the coastal range is known as the Cumaná mountain mass, and extends onto the Paria Peninsula. To the west it borders an indented seacoast strewn with rocky islands. To the east, it dominates a low plain which forms the coast of the Gulf of Paria and is drained by slow watercourses into which the tide rises. Since damp winds blow from the east, this part of the coast is, as could be expected, well watered and contains dense forests similar to those of the Paria Peninsula. Many of these forests are flooded when the Orinoco is in spate. The difference between the high and low watermark is sometimes seventy feet, and at flood time the volume of fresh water poured into the sea is such that the surface of the sea is fresh water for twenty miles along the coast. The western part is drier and appears to herald the arid plain of Barcelona, which is protected from the wet winds by the mountains.

The 16,422-foot summit of Pico Bolívar, one of the highest peaks of the Cordillera de Mérida, is crowned with a rich alpine prairie. (Karl Weidmann)

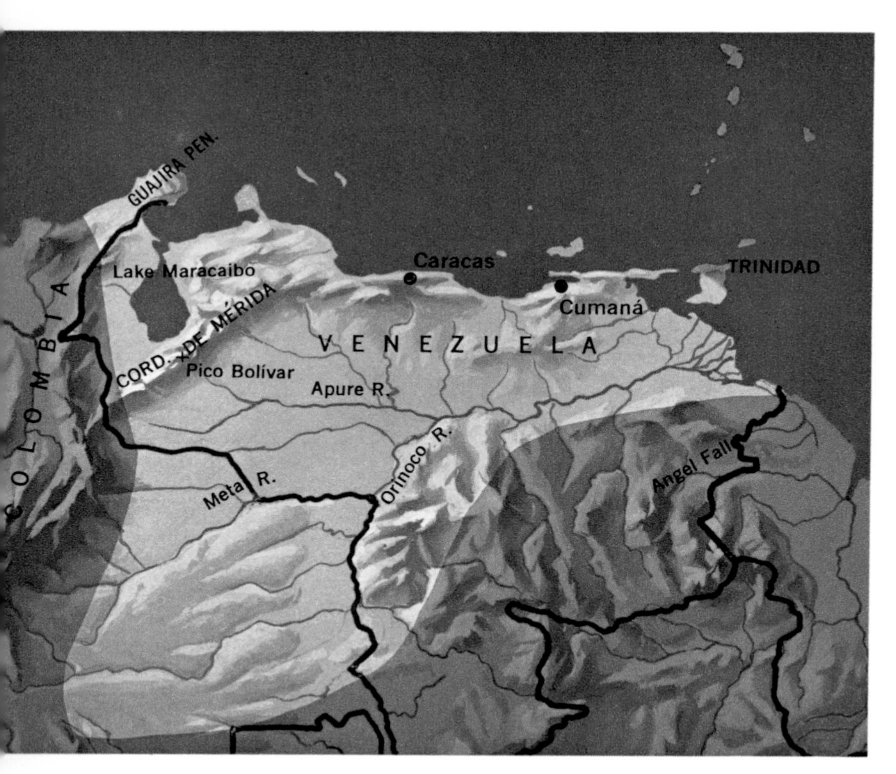

Venezuela consists of the Orinoco River Valley hemmed in by the mountain chains of the Caribbean coast and the Guiana plateau to the south.

FORESTS OF THE TEMPERATE ZONE

Like most naturalists, I have always been fond of paradoxes in nature. That is why I took advantage of a stay in Venezuela to see the temperate levels of the Caribbean range—a cold region in a tropical zone.

Leaving the beautiful town of Caracas, enclosed in its mountainous valley as if in a jewel case, the route tends toward the northwest, climbing slopes that are all too often spoiled by man. Beyond Colonia Tovar, at about 5,500 feet the road goes through a series of hairpin turns on deforested slopes scattered with clumps of tall and elegant palm trees. Then one comes upon a subtropical or temperate forest of amazing beauty, especially on the verge of the ravines that cut into the mountain; here birds, notably hoccos and tinamous, abound. The trees form a dark vault, supported on powerful trunks covered with lianas and epiphytes. Aroideae *(Monstera, Philodendron)* with glossy and indented leaves, orchids, palms and tree ferns form an almost impenetrable ground cover. The clearings are encumbered with bamboo *(Chusquea)*. Such plants create an unusual effect—that of tropical flora in a delightfully cool atmosphere.

Animal life is less flourishing here than in the lower and hotter regions. There are fewer species and less variety, but they are no less interesting. The mountain masses which comprise the Caribbean range have allowed a much greater diversification of species—particularly in the case of birds—than in the plains.

Particularly distinctive are the hummingbirds, which often occur in very restricted locations. Consider the case of *Hylonympha macrocerca*, the *Colibri Tijereta* of the Venezuelans. which was until recent times known only by some sixty skins shipped from Trinidad. In the course of the last century enormous collections of birds were made in America for the market in feathers, established in London and Paris to supply the fashion industry. Salvador, Bogota and Port-of-Spain were the principal centers in America for this commerce, which at one time involved hundreds of thousands of skins. It was in these shipments that ornithologists discovered this species of hummingbird, which for some time remained a mystery. Certain it was that the species did not inhabit Trinidad; but that was not at all surprising, since the collectors hunted well beyond the island, notably on the continent in the lower Orinoco, Trinidad being only a central commercial depot. Not until 1947 did Ramon Urbano, a collector for the American ornithologist William H. Phelps, discover the true habitat of this rare hummingbird—strictly localized in the subtropical forests of the Paria Peninsula.

THE RANCHO GRANDE RESERVE

In the early thirties of this century, when a road was opened across the Caracas Andes from Maracay to the coast, there was reason to fear the disappearance of the practically uninhabited forest solitudes of this vast district. Happily, the Venezuelan authorities soon realized the interest in this region and classed it as an integral natural reserve, widely known by the name of Rancho Grande although its official name is the Henri Pittier National Park. Nothing can give one a better idea of the Caracas Andes than a visit to this reserve, which occupies about 220,000 acres on the two slopes of the Cordilleras, from the steep coasts of the Caribbean to the alluvial plains of Lake Valencia. It includes a lower tropical zone characterized by primeval forests, a subtropical zone, and the temperate zone of the summits.

Since these mountains are no more than approximately eight thousand feet high, and are nearly always surrounded with clouds and mist, the humid atmosphere encourages an exuberant vegetation to proliferate to the very summit of their peaks.

Rainfall is heavy, the wet season varying according to the slopes. In summer—roughly from April to December—the southern slopes are heavily drenched by the rains coming from the plains of the Orinoco. In winter, on the contrary, this slope is dry, while the rains coming from the Atlantic lash the northern slope. But in fact the humidity is high throughout the year. The mean annual rainfall is thirty-six inches in the vicinity of Lake Valencia, but it is sixty-seven inches on the central crest of the range, and to this must be added the condensation of fog. The mean temperatures remain constant throughout the year, varying only with the altitude: 82° F on the Caribbean coast, 79° F on the plains surrounding Lake Valencia.

As one climbs from Maracay, one leaves the oppressive heat of the plains, which are mainly under cultivation, and passes into a humid forest bathed in a dense, damp fog. Still climbing, one reaches, at an altitude of 3,600 feet, a ridge which is continually swept by showers and wind. Here vegetation and

Only the female of the blue-breasted hummingbird (Sternoclyta cyaneipectus) *builds the nest and feeds its young. (Paul Schwartz: Photo Researchers)*

animal life teem. The ridge crossed, one confronts slopes entirely covered with dense forests, choked with liana and parasitic plants, frothing off to infinity. The sea is visible on a clear day. These are cloud forests where the predominant tree species is often the *niño* or *cucharon (Gyranthera caribensis),* associated with species of the genera *Tovomita, Virola, Nectandra, Pseudolmedia, Quararibea* and *Airtella.* Ferns are likewise very numerous.

This forest shelters a remarkable wealth of fauna, although here as in all tropical forests the numerical density of animal life is low. Birds, best known of all the inhabitants of Rancho Grande, include 515 species according to the present count, among them tinamous, hoccos, the *Penelope,* and parrots of all kinds, notably the red-cheeked parakeet *(Pyrrhura haematotis)* found only in the subtropical zone of the Caracas Andes. Among the innumerable hummingbirds, thirty species have been counted in the reserve. The passerines are particularly diversified, and among those found here are the ant birds, cotingas, tangaras and manakins. There are no less than fifty-eight species of tyrant flycatchers.

All other groups of animal life abound, particularly the insects. The Coleoptera are brilliantly represented by giant beetles such as the *Dynastes* or Hercules beetle and the enormous long-horned beetle. Butterflies, very numerous, engage in veritable migrations from one slope to the other, and many more will surely be discovered as our studies of the region continue.

Descending toward the Atlantic, one reaches the coastal district, markedly drier and covered with a xerophytic vegetation. Cacti are numerous, especially various species of *Cereus* and *Opuntia.* A biological station adjoins the reserve, thus happily coordinating the preservation of nature and the detailed study of animal life in a dense tropical forest environment.

THE GUACHARO, BIRD OF DARKNESS

Among the birds of Venezuela one of the most remarkable is the guacharo, or oilbird *(Steatornis caripensis),* which resembles other nocturnal or crepuscular raptors such as the night hawk and whippoorwill, but has characteristics so peculiar that scientists have placed it by itself in a special family, the Steatornithidae. About the size of a crow, its plumage is rusty brown mottled with white, its beak is strong and hooked, and it lays its pure white eggs in a rock fissure of the dark cave where it spends the daylight hours. Humboldt and Bonpland discovered it in a cave in Caripe near Cumaná in the state of Sucre, and it has since been observed in Peru, Colombia and Ecuador.

The native Indians regard this bird as diabolical and hunt it out in the dark caves with great fear. Their fear is increased by the clamor set up by the parent birds when the Indians enter with long poles to knock down and massacre the plump nestlings. The guacharo's food is mainly pulpy fruits, which build up an inordinate amount of fat; hence the common name. The Indians render this into a clear odorless oil, the

This Sahara-like landscape is typical of the northeastern coast of Venezuela. (Karl Weidmann)

process being carried out in kettles hung over a fire at the cave entrances.

Until recent years it remained a puzzle how the parent birds could fly without colliding against the rocky walls in the pitch-dark caverns. The American biologist, D. R. Griffin, has offered a solution to this puzzle. His experiments were carried out in the very cave where Humboldt discovered the bird more than 150 years ago. Griffin found the nests of the guacharos at a distance of seven hundred yards from the entrance, where total darkness reigned.

In the midst of a deafening clamor from the parent birds, he could distinguish several kinds of calls. Some were sharp and brief and were repeated rapidly and regularly by the guacharos when leaving the cavern at twilight and returning in the darkness of night. He measured their frequency at between six thousand and ten thousand vibrations per second. Supersonic frequencies were never demonstrated, contrary to what had been shown in the studies of bats. The duration of the calls is about one thousandth of a second, these being separated by intervals of from 1.7 to 4.4 thousandths of a second. The calls are said to be still audible at a distance of 250 yards.

We can therefore accept Griffin's conclusion that the high sound-frequencies emitted by the guacharo create successive airwaves that serve to guide the bird in the darkness, these sound vibrations echoing back from obstacles encountered on the line of flight, enabling the bird to judge its distance from these obstacles.

To verify this, Griffin captured several adult guacharos and carefully plugged the ears with absorbent cotton and a plastic glaze. When the birds were set loose, they were incapable of finding their way in the darkness and collided with obstacles and with the walls of the testing room. After the plugs were removed, the birds recovered all their navigational ability. The guacharo therefore finds its way by sonar echoes, as does the bat; however, unlike the bat, it does not resort to ultrasonic calls but employs shrill notes that are within our range of hearing.

The manatee, a kind of living fossil, has a globular head terminating in disklike lips that enable it to graze on aquatic plants. (John Hoke)

THE LAKE OF MARACAIBO

In northwestern Venezuela between the Sierra de Mérida and the Peripa range, an extension of the eastern Andes of Colombia, there is a vast triangular depression, an alluvial plain dotted with lakes that are formed by the many watercourses pouring down from the mountains. At the very foot of the mountains are found rocks, gravel and sometimes very fine sand. In the center of this depression is the large freshwater lake of Maracaibo. It is 133 miles long, 72 miles wide, and 30 feet deep inside the sandbar that almost obstructs the narrow strait through which it empties into the Gulf of Venezuela. Vessels of quite large size can enter the lake through this strait at high tide.

The dense forests of the mountain slopes that surround the alluvial plain, especially the eastern slopes, where the annual rainfall is eighty-six inches, give way lower down to deciduous forests, then to expanses of xerophytic growth. Here, cactus and thorn bushes predominate, for the northern end of the basin receives less rain than any other place along the Caribbean coast of South America.

The region of the Lake of Maracaibo was one of the most poverty stricken in Venezuela until the early years of this century, when the shores were found to be rich in petroleum. The basin is more or less outlined by geological faults; the surface deposit of Quaternary alluvium and gravel washed down by the Andean mountain torrents has folded Tertiary beds underlying it, a condition particularly favorable to such oil deposits. The first wells were sunk in 1917 and the output soon attained gigantic proportions: by 1963 the production of crude petroleum in Venezuela was more than a million barrels a year. The eastern shores of the lake are particularly productive, and the plains are studded thickly with thousands of wells.

Petroleum has since been discovered in other parts of Venezuela, chiefly in the eastern lowlands, between the Orinoco River and the Caribbean range, and in the approaches to the delta where a lake of asphalt, Bermudez Lake, sometimes called Lago Asfalto, exists about twenty-five miles up from the Gulf of Paria on the San Juan River. However, the region surrounding the Lake of Maracaibo is still of prime importance, accounting for two thirds of the total production in Venezuela and remaining the oil center of Latin America. Petroleum has long dominated the Venezuelan economy, and at present Venezuela is third in world production, but surpasses all other nations in the exportation of petroleum, shipping out 95 per cent of its product.

A scene near the sources of the Orinoco River. (Karl Weidmann)

THE ORINOCO RIVER AND THE LLANOS

Between the coastal ranges of the Venezuelan Andes in the north, the Andes of Colombia toward the west and the Guiana massif in the south there extends a vast basin, that of the Orinoco and its affluents. It is the third-largest river system in South America, occupying about 360,000 square miles, and comprising four fifths of Venezuelan territory and a fourth of Colombia.

For a long time it was thought that this river led to the famous El Dorado sought by so many Spanish explorers in the sixteenth century. This country, with its legendary cities of Manoa and Omagua, was supposedly situated somewhere within the confines of the high valleys draining into the Orinoco and the Amazon. It was to find El Dorado that Gonzalo Pizarro crossed the Andes from Quito in 1539 and Francisco Orellana descended the Napo and the Amazon in 1541–1542. Sir Walter Raleigh was also looking for it when he went up the Orinoco in 1595. Of course, all these men were pursuing a myth.

The Orinoco, 1,281 miles long, has its source in the Parima Mountains, near the Brazilian frontier, at an altitude of 3,523 feet, not very far from the Rio Negro. At first it flows west and then north. It plunges down a series of steep rapids, and issues forth into the depression bounded on the north by the Andean ranges. Swollen by large tributaries such as the Meta, it becomes a powerful river winding slowly east.

The vast and almost perfectly flat plains drained by the Orinoco are relatively low in altitude. They are comprised of alluvia brought down by the Andean mountain torrents which soon become transformed into deep and tranquil rivers. Where the clay forms an impermeable layer, the plains become vast

marshes, especially between the periodically flooded Meta and Apure rivers. Approaching the ocean north of Barrancas, the river divides into a series of arms forming the Amacuro Delta (about five thousand square miles in size). Between its two main branches the delta confronts the island of Trinidad.

The climate of the Orinoco basin is divided into two distinct seasons: the rainy season, April to October, and the dry season, from November to March. The rainy season causes annual floods which at Ciudad Bolívar attain a height of from fifty to sixty feet, with the maximum occurring in July and August.

The Venezuelan llanos terminate in the south at the edge of the Guiana plateau, the first sector of which is called *Gran Sabana* (Great Plain) because of the high, flat-topped mesas that constitute it. This region, which is still very wild (although it forms one half of the Venezuela surface it has only 3 per cent of the total population), is a series of plateaus four thousand to five thousand feet in altitude and is carved by rivers into a chain of steep canyons. It is at the brink of one of these mesas of close to eight thousand feet in altitude and 160 miles distant from Ciudad Bolívar that the highest cascade in the world was discovered in 1935: Angel Falls. It is located on the Carrao River, an upper affluent of the Caroni. It is 3,281 feet high and measures five hundred feet in width at its base. The name was bestowed upon it in honor of James Angel, the American explorer who discovered it, and who was killed in 1956 when his plane crashed in this region. Many other falls almost as spectacular are to be found on the edge of the Gran Sabana.

The base of the Guiana plateau, at its southern end, is in the Orinoco basin, and has become important since 1947 when one of the greatest ore finds of our time revealed a hill capped with iron, the Cerro Bolívar. This, with another and smaller iron deposit at El Pao, fifty miles to the east, assures a fabulous wealth to the country, much more real than the fabled El Dorado. The total reserve of ore containing 65 per cent of iron, is, it has been estimated, 2,000,000,000 tons.

Since the plains of the Orinoco are alluvial they are scarcely favorable to the growth of trees, but these llanos are covered with great stretches of grasses—a type of growth consonant with the extreme droughts of part of the year. However, they are nothing like the prairies in the Mississippi Valley or the pampas of Argentina. In certain localities, it is true, there are plains covered with grasses as far as the eye can see. But forests and savannas also exist along the river. The trees are almost always deciduous and of medium size; the most characteristic palm trees are the *palmas redondas (Copernicia tectorum)*, and the *moriches (Mauritia flexuosa)* which grow in the forest galleries along the riverside.

Left: The great blue heron (Ardea herodias) *is one of the most common water birds in tropical America. (Rolf Blomberg: Full Hand)*

Right above: In the llanos, rich in swamps and ponds, water birds, such as herons, egrets and ibises, nest in great flocks. Right: The subdued coloring of the tiger heron (Tigrisoma lineatum) *helps it hide among the branches from which it watches for its prey. (Both by Karl Weidmann) Far right: The tody flycatcher* (Todirostrum) *hunts its prey in the densest foliage and feeds its young mainly caterpillars. (Paul Schwartz: Photo Researchers)*

Guiana palms cluster in a grassy savanna. (Janis A. Roze)

Elsewhere the llanos are covered with more or less dry grasses that constitute the most characteristic feature of the Orinoco basin. Some of these, the *sabanas de esteros* or marsh savannas are submerged during the rains. Others have a xerophilous aspect that is very little altered by the rains.

The llanos constitute an important center of stock breeding and they support large herds of cattle and mules which, despite vicissitudes, have provided the wealth of this part of Venezuela. Here as elsewhere in the world, shepherds and cowhands and their herds have contributed to the extension of the grasslands and the retreat of the forest regions. In the districts where stock raising has declined, the forests tend to return.

THE MANATEE

The vast Orinoco and its tributaries are inhabited by innumerable fish, most of them belonging to the same groups as those of the Amazon. Like the Amazon, this is also the domain of the inia *(Inia geoffroyensis)*, a freshwater cetacean we will discuss later. A still stranger inhabitant of these waters is the manatee *(Manatus inunguis)*, vaguely resembling the Cetacea in their torpedo-like bodies without a trace of posterior limbs and their flippers (residual forelimbs). The Sirenia, however, are easily distinguished from the Cetacea by many anatomical differences in the teeth, and by the paddle-like form of the tail. The enormous head is provided with an extraordinary upper lip, flattened, very mobile, and rounded like a horseshoe, and is joined to the body by a very short neck. The skin is dark gray, very thick, and quite hairless, except on the lips, which have numerous bristles, probably sensorial. The length of the manatee is usually from eight to ten feet.

Needless to say, these strange fish-like mammals have given rise to countless legends. Among them is the legend of the mermaid: seen at a distance when floating upright in the water, they have a half-human aspect. At any rate, when the pirogues are beached for the night and the campfire lit on the shores of the great river, sailors have always entertained their listeners with tales of these fabulous creatures.

This species inhabits rivers exclusively and is replaced along the coasts and in the estuaries from North Carolina south to the northeast portion of South America by a related species, *Manatus manatus*.

Manatees swim slowly and sleep quietly for long hours. They assemble in small families or in bands of from ten to fifty individuals. Exclusively herbivorous, they feed chiefly during the night on aquatic plants, and this alone would distinguish them clearly from the carnivorous cetaceans. Sometimes, to reach their pasturage at the bottom or sides of rivers, they hold themselves almost vertical in the water, and the sound their prehensile lips and molars make when chewing can be heard for a distance of several hundred feet.

The female gives birth once a year to her young, which accompanies her for at least a year and often much longer. Manatees are hunted by the Indians for their flesh and their oily blubber although some of the aborigines regard them superstitiously as taboo. They are caught either by harpoon or with the aid of nets stretched in the calm and narrow shallows of the river where they come to sleep or feed. They rate low in intelligence; their eyesight is weak (although their sense of hearing is rather sharp), and they constitute an easy prey because they are peaceable creatures.

THE MANGROVES

The low coastline that runs from the western shores of the Gulf of Paria and past the delta of the Orinoco was described by Christopher Columbus, after his third voyage, as "the gateway of the Celestial Paradise." The coast is bordered by dark green vegetation, an almost solid forest of exotic trees with rounded crowns that, at low tide, reveal a tangle of arched, elbowed roots sunk in the mud. They are mangroves that thrive along low tropical coasts in many parts of the world but are so characteristic of this tropical flat coast of lagoons and estuaries that William Beebe called the region "the land of the single tree."

La Corona, a peak in the Sierra Nevada de Mérida. (Werner Lüthy)

There are two types of mangrove, members of two distinct families, the black mangrove *(Avicennia nitida)* and the red mangrove *(Rhizophora mangle)*. At high tide, one sees only the rounded treetops and a stout trunk sunk into the water; at low tide, this trunk appears to be shored up by props, thick brown roots curving down into the black mud and sprouting roots in great number. Thus, at the base of every tree is a kind of inverted and elastic basket which, while solidly anchored in the slime, allows the currents of the river and the ocean tides to circulate freely without violently shaking the thick parent trunk. The tree produces still other roots, air roots which sprout from the supplementary, submerged roots, allowing them to breathe; they are a notable feature of the *Avicennia,* which is often surrounded by a kind of forest of these cylinders, some two to five feet long.

Besides its characteristic root growth, the mangrove is peculiar in its germination and seed production. While the fruit is still attached to the branch and after its complete development, instead of detaching and falling in the usual way, it elongates to as much as a foot in length, acquiring the look of a giant haricot bean. The seed has germinated a plantlet, justifying the remark of some botanists that this tree is viviparous. Finally the embryo seedling detaches itself; if it falls at low tide, it sinks into the mud and quickly develops roots that anchor themselves solidly. At high tide, many of the plantlets are lost, but others are swept along by the currents and when water-soaked sink to the bottom and take root, thus dispersing the species all along the coasts favorable to its growth. In the *Avicennia,* the fruit drops into the water before fully developing, then splits in two and ejects a plantlet already quite well developed; this falls to the bottom and immediately takes root.

The mangrove flourishes in conditions that would discourage any other plant life. Veritable pioneers of vegetation, these trees grow in a shifting element that is no longer water but is not yet land. The mangrove creates its own environment and gradually encroaches upon the ocean, for its roots catch and hold the particles of silt borne by the currents and the tides, consolidating gradually what was fluid mud. The fallen leaves also form humus, then a firmer ground that other plants will colonize, thus progressively converting expanses of water into solid earth. Meanwhile, the mangrove itself continues to move on. This constructive work of the mangrove barely suffices to counterbalance the erosion by the sea, as for example at the mouth of the Amazon. But without it, the sea would win the contest with the land. In this work the mangrove has been compared with coral, that other powerful creator of territory.

The mangrove provides a very rich habitat for aquatic life. The dense tangle of roots creates a quiet environment, safe

Left: The jabiru stork builds a huge platform nest in trees and especially in palms. (Karl Weidmann)

Right above: The nightingale thrush (Catharus aurantiirostris) *which owes its name to its melodious song, nests in trees but usually seeks food on the ground. Right: The rusty-breasted antpitta* (Grallaricula ferrugineipectus) *lives on insects found in dense underbrush. Far right: The streaked saltator* (Saltator albicollis), *a sturdy-billed bird, feeds on buds and insects. (All by Paul Schwartz: Photo Researchers)*

from the waves and the great backwash of the tides. Mollusks and crabs are incredibly numerous, and they find shelter in the slime and in the openings among the mangrove roots, as well as in the plant residue deposited by the ebb tide.

Although mammals have not found a favorable habitat here, the same cannot be said of birds, which thrive in great number. The strictly marine species do not make their appearance here, because of the relatively low saline content and the muddiness of the water. Brown pelicans do enter the estuaries, although they prefer the waters of the more open sea.

The birds to be found in the mangroves are marsh birds, and the Ardeidae are the most characteristic. The most ornamental of all the bird population is without a doubt the scarlet ibis *(Eudocimus ruber)*, native to the northwest of South America, from Venezuela to Brazil. Completely red, even to the feet and the beak, this bird was formerly present almost everywhere in numerous colonies that sometimes comprised a thousand individuals. In some regions these birds have been decimated by hunters coveting the plumage as well as the flesh, greatly esteemed by the native Indians despite its oily and rancid odor. Snowy egrets *(Egretta candidissima)* are also numerous.

The arms of the sea and the brackish waters that advance like tentacles among the stretches of mangrove trees are the hunting-grounds of skimmers *(Rhynchops)*. Skimmers are related to terns and are remarkable for the unique formation of the bill, the lower mandible being much longer and flattened like a knife blade. These birds fish on the surface of the water which they skim with a strong and regular beating of wings, literally ploughing the water with their beaks. Fishing at twilight, when the aquatic animals come to the surface, they seize small fish and crustaceans.

The mud flats uncovered by the tide and so rich in living organisms are also the winter quarters of numerous snipes, sandpipers and plovers migrating from North America, this environment being very favorable to their feeding habits. Several varieties of passerines also inhabit the mangroves, especially the insectivorous species. Prominent among these is the yellow warbler *(Dendroica petechia)*.

The delta of the Orinoco, which extends over 160 miles of the South American seacoast and the Gulf of Paria, is not the only region of South America where mangroves flourish. They are to be found in the tropics and the subtropics, wherever there is a flat coastline and brackish tidal waters.

A maguari stork nests with its young. (Karl Weidmann)

Flourishing in such close proximity to the splendid coastal ranges with their temperate forests, and not far from the vast, dry llanos of the Orinoco basin, these mangroves bear witness to the great diversity of Venezuela's habitats.

Angel Falls, one of the highest cascades in the world, drops 3,281 feet from the rim of the Guiana plateau. (Karl Weidmann)

Green Jungle and Humid Lowland

The Guianas

4

Low flat coasts barely emerging from the ocean, surmounted by a dark green line of mangroves, with some wooded valleys that overlook the shore—this is how the Guianas first appear to the voyager approaching from the sea.

The Guiana region comprises all the lands stretching from the Atlantic Ocean to the Amazon basin and bounded on the west by the Rio Negro, the Casiquiare and the upper Orinoco. It forms a vast plateau sloping toward the north, bordered by an alluvial coastal plain, separated from the Amazon basin by a series of mountains. The term "Guianas" is often restricted to the three lands lying east of Venezuela—the independent British Commonwealth nation of Guyana, formerly British Guiana; the Netherlands dependency of Surinam, formerly Dutch Guiana; and French Guiana, now an overseas department of France. Actually, as a natural region, much of Guiana overflows into Venezuela and Brazil.

If we disregard the coastal low country, the Guiana region represents the northern part of the immense Guianan–Brazilian shield, formed of very ancient crystalline rocks, most of it greatly worn down. Mention is often made of the "mountains" of the region but in fact there are no true mountains except in the southern part and in Venezuela. The most notable hills, the Central Guiana Highlands, with an altitude of about 2,500 feet, are in the center of the country. Elsewhere the Guiana plateau is a vast monotonous expanse about eight hundred feet high and consisting of a series of hillocks separated by narrow marshy depressions called *criques*. This marshy land is drained by a complex dendritic stream pattern. Many of these depressions are almost invisible in the forest.

With its steep sides, Mount Duida, rising almost 6,000 feet from the plain, forms a kind of fortress. The plateau at its summit is a temperate island in a tropical zone. (Karl Weidmann)

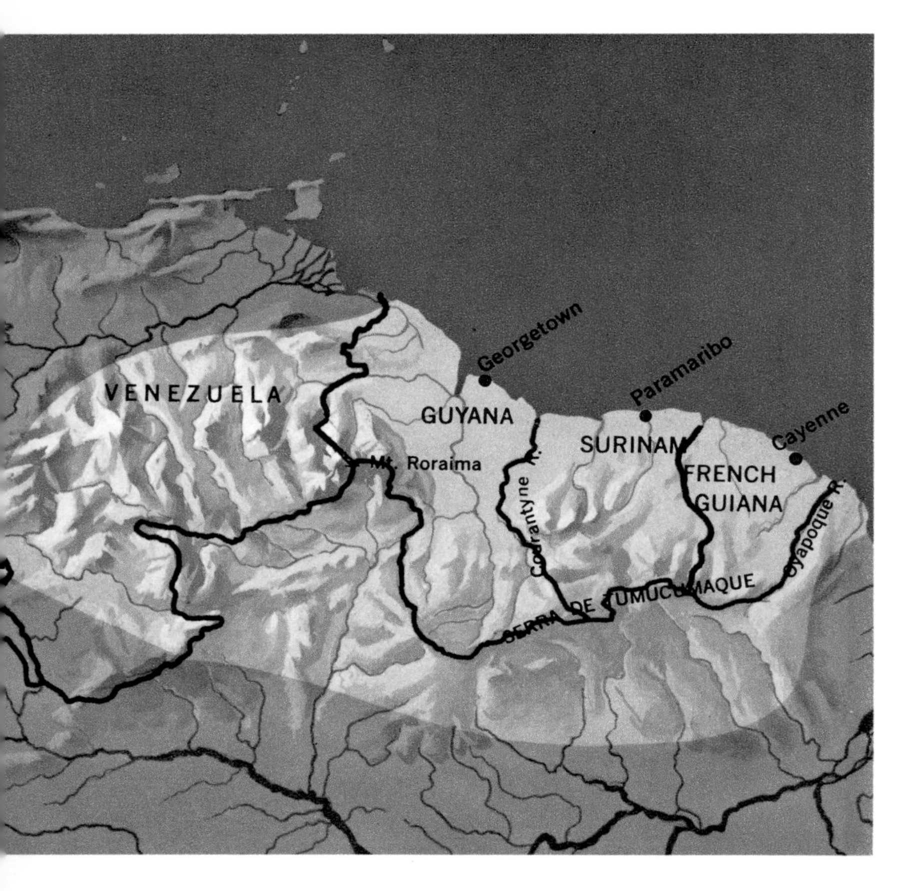

The Guiana Region is made up of a vast plateau of some of the oldest rocks in South America. The plateau is etched by rivers and bordered by low, alluvial plains.

A few widen into alluvial plains representing ancient lake bottoms, in the midst of which one can see the winding outlines of a secondary watercourse. The outstanding features are a number of steep-sided domes about 1,500 or 2,000 feet high; these are granitic inselbergs, the vestiges resulting from the erosion of ancient geological formations. They look like enormous rocks, denuded except for patches of herbaceous or bushy vegetation. Their surface is often marked with deep vertical flutings, like sculptured draperies, produced by the torrential rains that beat down on the bare rocks. Such domes are common here and their summits command striking views of the forest extending to the horizon like a froth of foliage.

Toward the Brazilian frontier, the southern edge of the Guiana plateau rises abruptly into a series of mountains that were long thought to be true mountain chains. The Tumucumaque Mountains in particular were shown on relatively recent maps as a continuous barrier. But aerial reconnaissance has revealed that these hills are two independent masses. The eastern Tumucumaque, located around the sources of the Oyapoque River and in Brazilian Guiana, are wooded hills no more than 1,500 feet above sea level. The western hills, extending over the upper Itany River and then westward into Surinam and Brazilian Guiana, have higher summits, reaching 2,600 feet above sea level, and form a widespread mountain mass. Farther west, on the frontier between Venezuela and Brazil, there are higher and more complex ranges; about these we will have more to say later on.

The Guiana plateau is on the whole uniform, being generally made up of a crystalline base dating back to the Precambrian period. Some of the rocks of which it is formed are the most ancient in all South America. The territory is mainly made up of gneiss and granites.

To the west of the Guiana Highlands, between 4° and 6° Lat. N., there is a discordant formation of sandstone and conglomerates, sometimes as much as 1,500 feet deep, above the Precambrian crystalline rocks. Scarcely affected by erosion, this immense platform culminates in vertical cliffs from which the rivers fall in cascades. One of these, the Potaro, an important tributary of the Essequibo, drops 741 feet over the eastern edge of the sandstone plateau in the Kaieteur Falls, one of the highest falls in the world on a permanent river.

Between the sandstone plateau and the granite mountain mass of Acarai, there opens a deep depression through which the Essequibo River system communicates with the Rio Branco, connecting the Guianas with the Amazon Valley. The tropical forest is broken here, making communication easier. This part of the Guiana region has played an important part in the migrations of the native populations.

The Guiana plateau is thus on the whole very ancient, dating back at least 500 million years, and doubtless much more. Since the end of the Precambrian period several cycles of erosion have taken away all the earlier sedimentary deposits, leaving only those very recently brought down mainly by the rivers, and dating, at the most, from the Pleistocene period. Everywhere along the courses of the streams these deposits form mud banks, or pebbly and sandy shores. Gold is found, sometimes in appreciable quantities, on the sides of the hills beneath layers of sediment recently carried down by the waters. Besides these superficial deposits there are important lateritic clay deposits fifty to seventy-five feet deep, resulting from rock transformed by the action of weather.

Beyond the limits of the crystalline plateau extend the coastal plains. These plains, strewn with bleak-looking rocks, are formed of recent sediments, sandy or clayey, brought down by the Amazon. The equatorial counterflow of ocean currents, driving northwest, turns these sediments toward the Guianas; the rivers of the Guiana region then add their sediments to these. The sedimentation is very rapid and is progressively blocking the estuaries.

A HUMID WORLD

The climate of the Guianas has an unenviable reputation, which it does not really deserve. Some of the blame for this must be attributed to harrowing tales of the penal colony until recently maintained by the French on Devil's Island. As a matter of fact, the climate is rather agreeable, mainly because the nights are relatively cool, a rather surprising circumstance in the torrid zone.

At Cayenne, the average temperature is 80° F, ranging from 72° F at dawn to 86° F at noon. At Georgetown, in Guyana, the average monthly temperature is between 79° and 82° F. It is the rains, much more than the variations in temperature, that determine the rhythm, often very irregular,

A fierce predator meets its match: a caiman caught in the coils of an anaconda, one of the most powerful reptiles of the South American jungle. (John Hoke)

A tangle of lianas in the equatorial forest. (E. Aubert de la Rüe)

of the seasons. The rainy season lasts from December to the end of August, and the dry season from September to the end of November, but only September and October are really dry, and even they have occasional showers or rainstorms. There is ordinarily another dry spell of a few days or weeks in February or March, preceding the great rains of April and May. Rain falls at Cayenne about 150 days a year (averaging 125 inches annually), sometimes in brief torrential showers widely spaced, or one after the other throughout the day, especially in the afternoons. At the height of the rainy season, the rains often last for several days, with rare lulls. The rains create a constantly high level of humidity, except from September to November, but even on clear sunny days in these months the humidity exceeds 90 per cent.

Trade winds prevail, blowing throughout the year from east-northeast to east-southeast. Usually a sudden and sometimes violent windstorm precedes the rain.

RAPIDS AND STAGNANT POOLS

A great many of the numerous watercourses, including the largest rivers, the Essequibo, the Courantyne, the Maroni, and the Oyapoque, rise in the Guiana massif and flow more or less from south to north. In French Guiana alone no less than ten important rivers, many of great volume, empty into the Atlantic along a 220-mile shoreline.

These rivers are all much alike and flow through a monotonous landscape. The upper reaches of the rivers, on the plateau, are often interrupted by rapids, sometimes dangerous, sometimes insignificant, and at rare intervals by waterfalls. Their number varies from river to river, and particularly according to the season. The Tampoc, a tributary of the Ouaqui in French Guiana is a succession of dangerous rapids, but other rivers, such as the Inini, have but one such obstacle to navigation. The number and dangers of the rapids in Guiana rivers have been greatly exaggerated. In any case, as in Amazonia, these waterways are the chief means of travel in this heavily forested region. On some of the rivers—the Berbice, the Courantyne, the Demerara—it is possible to voyage comfortably 60 to 150 miles inland. On other rivers the portages are frequent, long and arduous.

Except for those portions of the rivers interrupted by rapids, the river banks are treacherous, muddy and swampy and filled with amphibious plants, sometimes with thorns; elsewhere the banks are steep, high and dangerous in the dry season when they crumble and bring down uprooted trees across the watercourse. As the pirogue or flat-bottomed skiff plies these rivers, the traveler has the sensation of moving through a green tunnel, for little sunlight penetrates the green vault overhead. Searching for a landing place and a camp site takes patience, and more often than not the boat will be forced up on the rocky shore of a rapid.

Because large ravines and gorges are rare, waterfalls are relatively scarce; the Trois Sauts of the upper Oyapoque is one of the better-known. The larger rapids create a maze of islets and obtruding rocks between which narrow streams flow. These streams, called *bistouris* in French Guiana, allow pirogues to pass except at low water. At the portage points, the passengers disembark and cross the rocky terrain on foot while the pirogues are hauled along by ropes. At high water, however, the river is wide and the volume and roar of the waters are impressive. The volume of water varies considerably from season to season. In the rainy period the rivers race along in tumultuous floods and spread out over the more level stretches of adjacent forests. In French Guiana, the waters begin to subside toward the end of June, very slowly at first, then faster and faster until in September they may drop almost two inches in twenty-four hours. By the end of October some of the river branches are completely dry, while others expose rocky banks. In the course of particularly dry years, some of the calmer stretches are completely blocked, leaving only a succession of pools among sand bars and the rocks of the riverbed. In some of the swampy regions, at low water, the dead and rotting vegetation fills the air with so much marsh gas that it can be ignited with a match. On the other hand, a heavy rain in the rainy season can raise the water level in these rivers as much as three feet in one night.

THE RIVER FAUNA

In the rivers, streams and pools of the Guiana region there is such an abundance of edible fishes, crabs and shrimps that these are the basic foods of the population. In fishing, the natives generally use trained hawks or a bow and arrow but they also employ a paralyzing poison extracted from the roots

Trois Sauts Falls on the Oyapoque River in French Guiana. (E. Aubert de la Rüe)

of certain lianas. The pulp is dropped in quiet headwaters or above a falls and the paralyzed fish soon float to the surface.

Among the best table fish are the pacu *(Metynnis)* and the coumarou *(Curimato)*. Without teeth, and resembling the marine mullet, the coumarou feeds mainly on the fleshy leaves of the river weed *Podostemonaceae*. Also numerous in these waters is the stingray *(Potamotrygon)*, with poisonous spines in its whiplike tail that can inflict painful wounds that are hard to cure. In the calm stretches of the rivers the fish known as the electric eel *(Electrophorus electricus)* is common. And another fish, the aimara or niama *(Hoplias macrophtalmus)*, sometimes attains a length of over three feet. These fishes are voracious and are provided with razor-sharp teeth that can inflict serious wounds. Also present in these waters are the fearful piranhas.

One of the strangest fish of the region is a small one called "four-eyes" *(Anableps anableps)*, a relative of the top minnow. The eyes of this fish, including the cornea and the retina, are divided into an upper and lower part. Four-eyes swims so close to the surface that the upper part of its eyes is above water while the lower part is underwater. Furthermore, the lens of the eyes is oval-shaped, so that an object under water is seen through a part of the lens much thicker than the part above water. Only one other fish in the world has such optical equipment: the three-inch blenny *(Dialommus fuscus)* of the Galapagos. Apparently four-eyes does not look for prey in the air; the upper parts of the eyes merely serve to keep a lookout for predators. With the coming of man, that greatest of predators, this unusual optical equipment is a disadvantage, since a beam of light shone on the upper eyes at night causes them to have a phosphorescent glow.

A still more curious trait of four-eyes is its method of reproduction. All the poeciliids are viviparous, the female giving birth to fully developed young. As with the other fishes in this group, the anal fin of the male is so modified as to be able to deposit sperm within the female. As if this curious adaptation were not enough, it has been found that the anal fin of some males moves only toward the right, while in other males it moves only toward the left, and that the genital aperture of some females opens only toward the right, while in others it opens only toward the left. Thus a "right-handed" four-eyes must find a "left-handed" female for insemination to take place. Fortunately there seem to be an equal number of left-handed and right-handed members of each sex.

PRIMEVAL FOREST

The Guianas, like the Amazon basin, are for the most part densely forested, French Guiana being almost 90 per cent tropical forest. The forests extend upward to a height of 3,200 to 4,000 feet in the Kanuku and Acarai Mountains of Guyana, the Wilhelmina Mountains of Surinam, and the Tumucumaque Mountains in French Guiana, except for patches of granite that rise like rocky islands from the sea of green foliage. This forest is really continuous with the Amazon forest, the differences in plant species between the two being slight. It is estimated that it contains from 7,000 to 10,000 species of flowering plants and ferns.

As in Amazonia, the Guiana forest is composed mainly of giant trees 100 or 125 feet high, which branch out only at about sixty feet from the ground. Beneath these trees grow smaller ones thirty to eighty feet high, along with palms and shrubs belonging to a great variety of families: Piperaceae, Anonaceae, Rosaceae, Violaceae, Flacourtiaceae, and so on. The lianas fasten themselves to the trees, reach the treetops and develop their foliage. Of course epiphytes are numerous—ferns, bromeliads, orchids, arums and even a few cacti. The herbaceous layer, poorly developed as always in great primeval forests, is comprised mainly of saprophytic plants, such as fungi, devoid of chlorophyl.

The scene presented by this forest to anyone traveling up a river is monotonous. The forest is at its grandest in the higher regions where the trees are largest. The undergrowth is not very dense, so that it is relatively easy to walk through these woods. On the other hand, in areas flooded during the rains, especially along the shores of watercourses, the trees are shorter and much of the vegetation is of a type that can endure humidity. Shrubs and palm trees, particularly the assai palm *(Euterpe edulis)*, with graceful and supple leaves, are definitely more numerous, as are the lianas.

The winding rivers often enclose marshy zones where amphibious plants flourish, some of them submerged during

Araceae, epiphytes growing from the branches of huge trees on this river bank, send aerial roots plunging into the river itself. (E. Aubert de la Rüe)

A blue-gray tanager (Thraupis virens), *having preened its feathers and rid itself of parasites, takes flight after a bath. (Paul Schwartz: Photo Researchers)*

Mangroves of the genus Avicennia *growing along the Atlantic coast. (E. Aubert de la Rüe)*

periodic floods. There is in these areas a particular abundance of azingers or moucou-moucou *(Montrichardia arborescens)*, that big Araceae with leaves rising from ten to fifteen feet above the water. Elsewhere, especially in the level and alluvial sections, there are semi-aquatic trees of the leguminous type (called *Pois sucrés*, sweet peas) that invade the channels of rivers and block the passage of pirogues. The river banks that are periodically flooded are muddy and encourage an abundance of mani *(Symphonia globulifera)*, the roots of which ramify and form a net on the soil.

By and large, the Guiana forest is still primeval, with clearings only here and there along the banks of the largest rivers, where Indians and Negroes work some plantations.

SAVANNAS AND COASTAL PLAINS

At higher altitudes there are extensive savannas in southwestern Guyana and in isolated patches in southern Surinam. The savannas of the Guiana Highlands are in fact an extension toward the east of the immense Venezuelan savannas and of the upper Rio Branco of Brazil. On these often undulating plains flourish associations of grasses *(Andropogon, Cymbopogon, Trachypogon, Elyonurus, Paspalum*, etc.), mingled with bushes (especially *Curatella americana)*, sedges *(Cyperus, Carex, Dichromena)*, and herbaceous plants, annuals that develop at the beginning of the rains. Pools and lagoons dot these savannas at random because of the uncertain watershed between the Amazon and Essequibo tributaries, and these furnish a habitat for a most interesting aquatic flora.

The coastal plains are also mainly grassland, but with occasional stands of trees and wooded patches. These coastal savannas, often established on poor, sandy soil, are from ten to thirty miles wide and occasionally extend inland for some thirty miles or so along the rivers.

Immediately before the rains the sedges and grasses on some of these plains, arrested in their development, take on a grayish tint. At this time people light brush fires and burn off the dried-out plants. Those portions of the coastal plains that are periodically flooded by the sea are always humid and sometimes become swampy.

It seems likely that these coastal savannas and palm groves are mainly the work of man rather than nature since there is not much reason for the forest to stop so suddenly when nothing in the topography or soil warrants it. Besides, we know that the Indians had been felling trees for a long time before the white man's first efforts at colonization and this may be one of many illustrations of how quickly a wooded region can degenerate into open country. The annual brush fires and the browsing of cattle would prevent the second growth of trees. However, in certain lower, more humid areas, the soil does clearly govern the character of the vegetation.

This coastal region, especially where the fertile clay is favorable to plantations of rice and sugar cane, has always been a center of human life; it is said that this 10 per cent of the total area of the Guianas supports 90 per cent of the population.

For several hundred yards in from the coast, the saline mud is colonized by mangrove forests made up of the red mangrove *(Rhizophora mangle)* and the white mangrove *(Avicennia nitida)*.

OTTERS AND IGUANAS

Contrary to popular belief and any number of jungle adventure stories, observers have always insisted on the scarcity of animal life in the great tropical forests. The French geologist, Edgar Aubert de la Rüe, has said that it is possible to travel for days and days in some remote districts rarely frequented by man without seeing a single animal. The native hunters, whether Negro or Indian, often return to their encampments empty-handed.

In the kinds of animals in it the Guiana fauna closely resembles that of the Amazon. Among the mammals we find the tapir, peccary, forest deer and capybara; some of the big cats are present, and monkeys of a great many species, the howler, the sapajou and spider monkey among others.

The great network of river systems inevitably favors aquatic mammals, such as otters, which are in some places very numerous. Three species inhabit the Guianas, one of them, the *Lutra enhydris*, being of an unusually light color. The

A rufous-tailed jacamar (Galbula ruficauda) *uses its pick-shaped bill to hollow out a burrow in a bank of loose soil. (Paul Schwartz: Photo Researchers)*

The Maroni River in French Guiana sometimes completely disappears under dense aquatic vegetation. (Carl Frank)

arirai *(Pteroneura brasiliensis)* differs from the other two in having a snout entirely covered with hair and a flattened, widened tail fringed with hairs; it is larger than the others, attaining a length of about four feet, excluding a long tail, with an occasional individual reaching an overall length of seven feet. Its pelt ranges from sepia to chocolate brown and when wet seems almost black. These otters are, of course, amphibious and frequent the banks of rivers or lagoons. Although the first is almost exclusively a night prowler, the arirai is a daylight animal and spends its nights sleeping. Of gregarious habits the arirai lives in groups that fish and hunt together. Unlike most otters, the arirai feeds not only on fish but on small mammals and birds that seek out the banks of pools and rivers. As in Amazonia, these otters are hunted for their furry pelts.

The shores of the rivers are also inhabited by many caimans and countless iguanas. Almost entirely native to the New World, and found elsewhere only in Madagascar and the Fiji Islands, iguanas are represented by many species in the Guianas and in Amazonia. Like European lizards, some are quite small while others are true giants measuring five feet in length. Such in particular are the arboreal species, with flattened sides and long tails that serves as a balance in their leaps from branch to branch. Their feet are provided with sharp claws allowing them to cling solidly. Their scales are often green or yellow, a camouflage that enables them to remain invisible on a branch. These iguanas lay their eggs in sandbanks in holes hollowed out by the females. Some species are vegetarian, feeding especially on fruits and buds; others are carnivorous, taking insects and spiders and other smaller invertebrates.

The larger iguanas are intensively hunted and great numbers are killed in the districts they frequent, so that they are gradually disappearing from these places. Their eggs are likewise prized and hunted.

The saurians are also represented by many species of lizards, some small but others truly gigantic. Such in particular is the great tepu *(Tupinambis teguixin)* and a close relative, the *T. nigropunctatus*, sometimes more than three feet long. Living on small mammals, birds, frogs' eggs, and insects, these huge lizards on occasion wreak havoc in hen coops and chicken yards. Some of these reptiles apparently lay their eggs in big termite nests in trees. In spite of the hardness of these structures—one must use a saw or pick to open them—the female manages to break into the nest and lay her eggs in it. The termites hasten to repair their nest, so that the young lizards, when they hatch, must break it open in order to escape.

Among the snakes, there are not only such giants as the anaconda and the boa constrictor but many others, including the crotales *(Crotalus)*, the fer-de-lance *(Bothrops)*, and the bushmaster *(Lachesis muta)*, all characteristic of the humid regions of the American tropics.

GAUDY BIRDS

The numerous birds of the Guianas belong to groups characteristic of tropical American forests, and most of them, if not all, are very similar to the birds of the lower Amazon. Many are gaudily colored. Hummingbirds of several kinds abound, among them the great topaz hummingbird *(Topaza pella)*, found in abundance even in the suburbs of the city of Cayenne. The parrots, toucans and woodpeckers here rival in beauty the manakins, tanagers, and oropendolas. The cotingas are also well represented. It was from French Guiana that the first specimen of the Pompadour cotinga *(Xipholena punicea)* was sent to Europe in the eighteenth century; destined for France, the French ship was seized by a British privateer and made to put in at an English port. There a British naturalist, George Edwards, gallantly bestowed upon this bird the name of the celebrated marquise. Other species of brightly colored birds inhabit the dense Guiana forests where they especially frequent the treetops or the edge of the forest. They are solitary in their habits but pairs or small family groups are sometimes encountered. The white bellbird *(Procnias alba)* is of the cotinga family and is so called because its call, which can be heard for a long distance, sounds like a gong.

The boa, coiling tightly around branches mainly in dense forest, captures good-sized animals, crushing them in its coils and swallowing them whole. (Edward S. Ross)

The prehensile tail of the South American tree porcupine enables it to get a firm grip on branches. (Lorus and Margery Milne)

Another member of this family in the Guianas is the rather large, whitish-feathered tityra *(Tityra),* which resembles a shrike. It nests in cavities of trees high above the ground, driving out the toucans or woodpeckers that made the holes, evicting the tenants and stopping up the entrance with leaves and twigs. Tiring of the repeated job of cleaning out this accumulation, the original proprietors give up and make their homes elsewhere.

We cannot leave the Guianas without mentioning the many water birds. A variety of herons, egrets and ibises is found here and some less well-known species, such as the sunbird *(Eurypyga helias),* which occurs throughout the Neotropical and tropical forests of Central America and Brazil. This sedentary bird measures about eighteen inches and feeds on small fish, batrachians and insects as it prowls the riverbanks. Like others of the wading-bird tribe, it executes curious processional dances at mating time, displaying beautifully marked wings, which are intricately patterned in black and white, rust and beige.

The agami or trumpeter *(Psophia)* is another long-necked and long-legged bird found throughout the Guianas and the Amazon Valley. Its plumage is dark and silky, but it makes up for the sobriety of its dress by the loudness of its call. A group of these gregarious birds trumpeting can be heard for miles in the densest part of the forest. These birds also perform dances at mating time. They are easily tamed and the native Indians often keep some trumpeters in their poultry yards to give warning of the approach of a predator.

GIANT BEETLES AND GORGEOUS MOTHS

The Guiana region is famous for its insects, especially its butterflies, moths and beetles. Detailed paintings depicting the insects of Surinam reached Europe in the early part of the eighteenth century, thanks to an extraordinary woman, Maria Sybilla Merian, who made the two-month voyage from Amsterdam expressly to study and record the insects of this region. Indeed, no region can rival Guiana and the Amazon Valley in the gorgeous coloring and gigantic size of the insects commonly found there. Among the giants are the buprestids, those elongated wood-boring beetles glittering in their metallic dress; the long-horned cerambycids, and particularly the scarabaeids. Among the long-horned beetles is the *Macrodontia cervicornis,* whose elytra or anterior wings are protectively cream-colored and elaborately striped in brown. The male is equipped with enormous sharp mandibles, and in French Guiana it is called the *mouche-café* because it is mistakenly thought that it cuts off the branches of coffee trees. Other giant beetles common here as well as in Amazonia are the *Dynastes hercules,* armed with a single huge horn, and the *Titanus giganteus.*

Some of the grasshoppers are also gigantic and gorgeously colored. There are crickets three times as large as the familiar ones of the northern hemisphere with green, blue and red wings. The blattids, including the hardy cockroach, sometimes attain a length of four to five inches here. Among the membracids or treehoppers, the forms are often so fantastic as to seem unreal.

The dazzling coloring and immense size of the moths and butterflies defy description. The heliconids, caligos, and morphos rival each other in beauty, with the latter especially prized by collectors. At one time the convicts of the French Guiana penal colony made a well-paid and pleasant pastime of collecting butterflies for fanciers in France. It became so

Like a woodpecker, the red-billed scythebill (Campylorhamphus trochilirostris) *uses its bill to probe bark on trees for insects and larvae. (Paul Schwartz: Photo Researchers)*

profitable for some of the colonists that villages of collectors were formed. The pale silvery blue *Morpho eugenia* butterfly was already threatened with extinction when the market was flooded and the price went down. With the closing of the prison colony at Cayenne, the great butterfly hunt came nearly to an end.

VEINS OF GOLD

It was at one time thought that the subsoil of the Guianas was incredibly rich in gold deposits. The belief is still held by some, despite a century of random and rather fruitless prospecting. Many people now believe that the gold of Guiana is only a myth.

The discovery of small amounts of gold here was, however, responsible for the colonization of the Guianas and the penetration by explorers of the inland areas. In 1853 the precious metal was discovered in the valley of the Arataye River, in French Guiana. Since 1878, similar discoveries have been made in various parts of the Guianas: in the valleys of the Barima, Yuruari, Cuyuni, and Potaro in Guyana, and in the Saramaca Valley in Surinam. The few attempts at industrial exploitation of this precious metal have failed; it is now in the hands of simple artisans, the concessions being worked by a semi-nomadic population of gold-washers.

The exploitation is all of the placer mining type, that is, of gold washed down by the rivers. There is no mining of seams since the veins of gold in the quartz sediment are only about twenty inches deep and often buried under several feet of rock. Gold in the Guianas is often found in very small fragments; nuggets of any size are rare. Occasionally nuggets weighing several ounces have been found in the valley of the Inini.

It is rather hard to determine the gold production of Guiana, since only a part of the total is ever declared. Twenty or so years ago the production in French Guiana was about 3,300 pounds a year but this has since fallen below 500 pounds a year, many placers having been abandoned.

In Guyana the placers have turned out to be richer in diamonds than in gold, especially in the vicinity of the Mazarúni. Other minerals have been discovered, notably a tin-bearing tantalite and some copper, but none in quantities worth commercial exploitation. On the other hand, bauxite is profitably exploited in Guyana and in Surinam.

TEMPERATE ZONES IN THE TROPICS

Approximately on the borders between Venezuela, Guyana and Brazil rises a massif, Mount Roraima, near the eastern end of the Sierra Pacaraima. To the west, in the Venezuelan state of Amazonas, is another mountainous mass of the same type, Mount Duida. These areas interest naturalists because they represent small temperate enclaves in the very midst of the tropics.

Mount Roraima, a table mountain, rises to 9,219 feet, among hills covered with savannas, where forests penetrate deep valleys. Toward the north, the forests occur in the foothills of great cliffs that extend into Guyana. The uppermost plateau has an area of scarcely twenty-five square miles. Formed of red sandstone, on first view it appears to be a flat, monotonous expanse. In reality it has a quiet complex relief, as the traveler crossing it discovers, for the rock has been deeply eroded. Expanses of gigantic blocks are furrowed by ravines surrounded by cliffs in strange forms. At some points the rock has disintegrated and created sandy expanses where water collects in swamps. Humus has accumulated in these, forming deep peat bogs.

Mount Roraima is surrounded by a cloud-forest zone characterized by low gnarled trees of various species—*Lauraceae, Guttiferae, Composites* and palm trees, all of them burdened with epiphytic plants. The summit of the mountain is in great part bare, except where soil has accumulated in hollows or ravines. At this altitude grow various kinds of bushes such as *Ilex, Myrcia, Befaria* and *Phoradendron,* some trees, and a great many ferns and herbaceous plants. The conditions on this mountain mass make possible the most impressive assemblage of endemic plants of any locality in South America.

Mount Duida is Roraima's western counterpart. It is like a great fortified castle surrounded by almost vertical cliffs rising six thousand feet above an eroded plain. It forms an immense plateau, almost perfectly square. Even during the dry season, it is almost always shrouded in cloud and fog; only early in the morning can its dizzyingly steep sides be admired. During the rainy season, the sun appears only for one or two hours a day on the summit. The foot of the mountain is surrounded with forests and savannas that must be crossed before one can start the difficult climb up the precipitous sides.

Abundant rains, subtropical temperatures, and a rich, deep soil have permitted a much more luxuriant vegetation on the whole range. This forest of trees and bushes, covered with mosses, extends up the slopes but somewhat less luxuriantly. The summits are covered with a tangle of bushes and cushions of herbaceous plants.

These islets of vegetation at high altitudes in the midst of tropical zones have provided habitats for a fauna very different from that of adjacent districts. Of all the animal life here, the birds are best known, having been the subject of careful studies. All are characteristic of subtropical zones, but a few species are clearly of temperate zone origin. The contrast between the fauna of the lower and tropical regions with that of the summits is particularly marked on Mount Duida because of the steepness of its sides and the difference in altitude between its base and summit.

Although these mountains are not comparable in height to the Andes, many isolated species on the summit of Mount Duida and Mount Roraima originally came from the High Andes of Peru and Colombia. The best example is that of Duncan's seedeater *(Idiospiza homochroa),* common on the moors of the temperate parts of the Venezuelan and Peruvian Andes, the corresponding species in the Andes being so close as to be barely distinguishable. The same applies to the goat-sucker *Systellura ruficervis* and a small tyrant, *Mecocerculus leucophryx,* a species most characteristic of the temperate areas of the Andes from northern Argentina to Venezuela.

It is a striking fact that of the eighty-five bird species found on Mount Roraima and Mount Duida, only twenty-two have come from the neighboring tropical areas while thirty-nine have close relatives in the temperate and subtropical zones of the Andes. It is completely unlikely that these birds have flown all the way from the Andes over lands lacking in all the conditions these birds require. Such "migrations" are

The tamandua, like such other edentates as the sloth and the anteater, has arboreal habits. (Patricia Caulfield)

contrary to all that we know of such sedentary birds. Moreover, any theory that these isolated mountains once formed part of a complex mountain range that linked them with the Andes runs counter to all that is known of the geological past of this part of America. We are thus led to the conclusion that tremendous modifications have taken place in recent geological time in the zone lying between these mountains and the Andes. Probably these birds, having spread from the Andes of Venezuela and Colombia, found themselves isolated when the tropical climate once again moved into the intermediate regions. Some Andean species may have disappeared from these isolated mountains, while others persisted. Such examples of discontinuous distribution are known elsewhere in the world.

The Great River

The Amazon and its Tributaries

5

In the Peruvian Andes, at the foot of the Cordillera Blanca and at an altitude of about 15,300 feet is a small lake, only some one hundred yards in diameter: it is called Niñococha, meaning "Little Boy Lake." Slabs of snow border its shores, for a glacier plunges into it, sliding down the great surrounding mountains. Out of this glacier flows a small stream: the Amazon at its source (discovered by the French explorer Bertrand Flornoy)—so to speak, the infant Amazon. It would be impossible to imagine a setting more solitary or a cradle more modest for the greatest river in the world, the river that drains four tenths of South America and has carved and shaped all the northern part of the continent.

Of course that torrent is not known as the Amazon; it acquires that name only after traversing a chain of mountain lakes, gathering volume from several tributaries, and then flowing down the eastern side of the Andes. At any rate, this river, which has its source only about one hundred miles east of the Pacific, first of all flows north through some precipitate mountain gorges, then turns east and enters the Amazonian plains, an enormous, almost flat drainage area of 2,722,000 square miles.

The Amazon basin, shaped by the river and its tributaries, is abundantly watered throughout the year, not only by precipitation but from the ground in springs and rivers, and the high temperature is also constant. Because of this, the vegetation is of a luxuriance unequaled anywhere. A rain forest forms an enormous cloak over the whole of the Amazonian plain, the largest expanse of forest in the world, including not only the giant trees but an almost infinite amount of smaller vegetation. The fauna of this green paradise teems in unimaginable number and variety. Nowhere else except perhaps in the forests of the Malay Peninsula does the traveler experience such a sense of bewilderment at the grandeur of the scene and the exuberance of living things.

Crossing this territory is difficult; the soil is marshy and often flooded. Great rivers and myriad streams block the traveler's progress; he feels drowned in the midst of a vegetation so dense and high that the sky is invisible. No wonder, then, that knowledge of these regions is still very incomplete even today. Amazonia is one of the rare portions of the world still in a primeval state, one of the great blank spaces on the demographic maps of the globe.

Before modern times, it was inhabited only by some very scattered tribes of Indians subsisting on what food could be gathered and on a very superficial agriculture. These primitive groups fiercely resisted any invasion by Europeans, and the tribes are still hostile to each other.

The true discoverer of the Amazon was the Spaniard Vicente Yañez Pinzon, who accompanied Columbus on his first voyage to "the Indies" commanding the *Niña*. On a later voyage, in 1499–1500, he discovered the Amazon estuary. The name he bestowed upon the river was Rio *Santa Maria de la Mar Dulce* (Holy Mary of the Freshwater Sea).

Some forty years later the river was explored when Francisco de Orellana, a friend of Gonzalo Pizarro, left Quito to go toward the east, and in descending the eastern slopes of the Andes reached the Napo River and finally the Marañon. Struggling against countless difficulties—the climate, sickness, and attacks from native tribes—he navigated the river to its mouth on the Atlantic, where he arrived in August, 1541, thus being the first to cross this green continent. He reported that on this voyage he was attacked by a troop of female warriors, whom he referred to as Amazons, as in the classic myth, and that has remained the name of the most powerful river in the world, although the incident it commemorates belongs only to legend.

The story of the Amazonian plains begins a very long time ago, before the Silurian period. Up to the Carboniferous period, or about 250 million years ago, a vast gulf opened wide on the Pacific Ocean, bordered on the north by the ancient shelf of the Guianas, on the south by the great central plateau of Brazil. The sea extended to where the rain forest now is. Freshwater cetaceans still swimming between the trees of inundated forests, and fish such as the ray and the skate, seem to be survivors of that epoch, having remained after the withdrawal of the sea. This took place in the Carboniferous period, when the waters began draining toward the Pacific Ocean.

The folding or uplift of the Andes began in the upper Cretaceous period, blocking the passage toward the Pacific and forming an immense inland lake. During the Tertiary period, the Andean Cordillera attained its full height and permanently obstructed the passage of waters toward the west. Then it was that the passageway between the Guianas and the Brazilian plateau opened, allowing the waters to empty into the Atlantic. Thus a new hydrographical system was established, flowing in the "right" direction, this time. Simultaneously an active erosion of the Andes tore off material and filled the Amazonian lake. Little wonder, then, after all these shifts and changes, that the waters of the Amazonian basin are often still, almost hesitating in what direction to flow!

Amazonia, an incontestable geographic unit, thus forms a vast basin, an immense plain of low undulations, bounded by the Andean range and the plateaus of Guiana and Brazil. To the north it is bounded for a good distance by walls of sand-

Water and forest have shaped the Amazon region, slow-moving muddy rivers carrying sediment from one area to another in time of flood. (Jerry Frank)

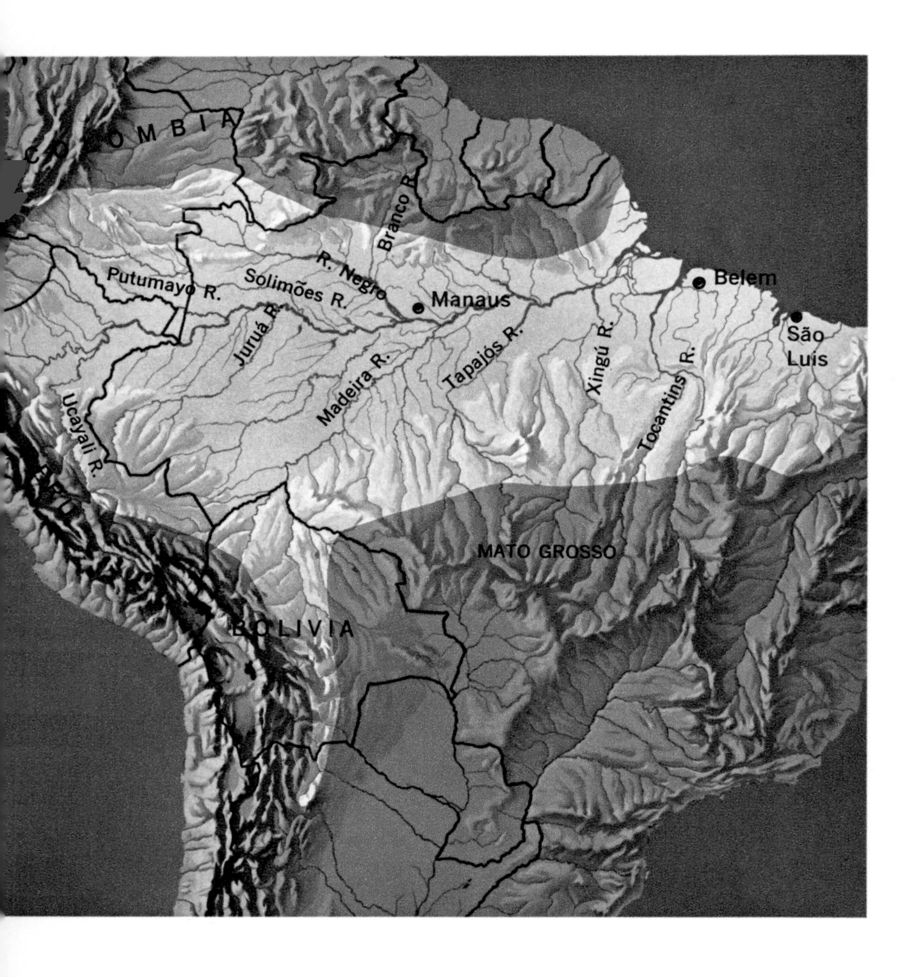

The Amazon Valley is a vast basin bounded by the Andes and the plateaus of Guiana and Brazil. Luxuriant rain forest covers this immense plain, making it the largest forest in the world.

stone, forming an escarpment of from three thousand to four thousand feet in height.

The structure of the Amazon basin, complex in detail, is simple in its broad outline. The cover of the ancient, primary platform is comprised of layers of alluvial sand and clay forming a succession of plateaus and low plains smoothed by the waters. The alluvium deposited by the rivers is mainly clay, for often the flow of the watercourses is too weak to transport heavier particles. However, when the floods renew the strength of the rivers, they bring down sands from the sandstone plateaus that hem in the basin on the west and north. The general relief and incline are extremely slight, but a difference in altitude of one or two hundred feet between neighboring localities is enough to modify the environment by changing the humidity and the level of water in the soil; the vegetation clearly manifests these differences.

If Egypt owes its all to the Nile, no other region of the world is more closely dependent upon a river and its affluents than is Amazonia. In length the Amazon River comes second to the Nile, measuring only 3,915 miles from its source to its mouth. But considered by its volume of water it surpasses all other rivers, comprising a fifth of all the flowing water of the world. At least 4.2 million cubic feet of water per second is emptied by the Amazon into the Atlantic, which is seven times more than the Mississippi empties into the Gulf of Mexico. It drains four tenths of South America, bringing down water from Peru, Ecuador, Colombia, Venezuela, and the Guianas, besides of course Brazil. It has more than one thousand tributaries, seventeen of them more than a thousand miles long and thus vast rivers in themselves.

At its source, before entering Brazilian territory, the Marañon, as the upper course of the Amazon is named on most maps, is swollen by several rivers of comparable importance. All come from the cordillera, and have carved out deep ravines and narrow canyons, such as the Pongo de Rentema and the famous Pongo de Manseriche, in the upper reaches. Below Iquitos in Peru, the river, often called Rio Solimões as it first enters Brazil, is joined by a mighty tributary, the Rio Napo, coming from Ecuador. Several hundred miles to the east, near Manaus in Brazil, it is joined by the huge Rio Negro, which drains a good part of northern Brazil and parts of the Guiana plateau. The Amazon then acquires its classic name and is swollen by a multitude of tributaries winding through the dense jungle with countless ramifications. A "land journey" through Amazonia is in fact mainly a voyage on innumerable rivers and streams.

The Brazilians distinguish between two types of rivers, naming them according to the color of their waters. The turbid rivers, burdened with clay sediment and for this reason white or ochre, are termed *rios blancos*. These flow through alluvial zones, where the ground cover is easily carried along and the river beds are thus perpetually being reshaped.

The *rios negros,* on the contrary, have the purest water, charged with organic substances which give them their "black" or dark green color, along with a higher percentage of acidity. The rivers Xingú, Tapajós, Negrò, Téfé, and Trombétas are all rios negros, and they flow over harder terrain with outcroppings of rocks that create rapids.

The differences in the color of the waters is particularly noticeable at the confluence of the two types of rivers. For instance, below Manaus, the dark clear waters of the Rio Negro contrast sharply with the muddy waters of the Amazon, and for miles and miles after the Rio Negro enters the Amazon the two rivers seem to flow side by side in the same bed before finally mingling. The nature of the waters and their physical characteristic affect, moreover, the life which inhabits them: certain fish of the rios blancos never enter the clear rios negros, and vice versa.

All these rivers have, however, a common trait: except where rapids occur, they flow sluggishly, because of the very slight incline of the Amazon basin. The rivers of the Amazon basin seem to loiter in veritable lakes of irregular form. Also, as these watercourses ramify, their arms embrace islands and spread out beyond the main river bottom. This complex hydrographic system is thus in a constant state of change.

Because of the low inclination of the basin the tides are perceptible as far inland as Obidos, 600 miles from the Atlantic. For the same reason there are fearful tidal waves, called in Brazil *pororocas,* that advance with a speed of fifteen or more miles an hour, with a breaking wall of water from five to twelve feet high.

The river system becomes still more complicated at the mouths of the Amazon. The river would seem to have freely communicated at one time with a river coming from the Brazilian plateaus, the Rio Tocantins, called at its mouth the Rio Pará. The two river courses are now almost completely independent as a result of sedimentation, communicating only through narrow and sinuous canals that sometimes look artifi-

A part of the Amazon known as the Solimões River, about seventy-five miles upstream from Manaus. (Weldon King)

cial. The Amazon and the Rio Pará hug between their powerful arms the island of Marajó, the largest island in the world surrounded by fresh or brackish waters, with a surface larger than that of Denmark.

Although the mouth of the Amazon is on the Equator, rains do not fall regularly all over the basin. The southern part, notably that drained by the Madeira, Purús, and Juruá rivers, gets rain especially during the summer months of the Southern Hemisphere (October to April), while the northern part has its rainy season during the Northern Hemisphere's summer.

The dry season likewise varies in duration. In the forested region it is neither long nor noticeable. At Belem, and at Obidos and Manaus, there is no more than a single month of relatively dry weather. Throughout this region the climate is marked by humidity even in the heart of the dry season.

The recurring rains determine the annual rise and fall of the rivers: the Amazon River system throbs like a heart. In its upper portion, in Peruvian territory, the river has two annual floods under the alternate influence of the upper tributaries that descend from the Peruvian Andes where the rains come during the summer months of the Southern Hemisphere—October to January—and the tributaries on its left bank, descending from Ecuador and subjected to the rainy season of the northern tropics—March to July. This alternation of high and low water simplifies as one goes downstream, the two seasons of high water gradually merging into a single one which moves down slowly in a gigantic wave from November to June.

In reality the phenomenon is still more complicated, since each of the giant affluents of the Amazon hurries on or holds back the high water according to the seasons of rains and the topography of its own basin. The height of the floods becomes constantly lower as one moves downstream. At Ega, the difference between the high and low water mark is fifty feet and at Obidos, above the mouth of the Tapajós, it is no more than twenty to twenty-five feet.

The width of the river varies, of course, to the same extent: in the rainy season it spreads out over the lower portions of the basin sometimes twenty-five miles beyond its banks. Exceptional floods may drown the forest for fifty or even sixty miles beyond the main river bed, well beyond the lateral lagoons and the lowlands which normally act as moderators.

The annual rhythm of the floods exerts more influence on the biological cycle than does the temperature, which does not

vary very much in the course of the year. Contrary to widespread belief, the heat is not excessive. At Manaus, the maximum observed is 98.4° F, and the mean annual temperature is 81° F. The annual fluctuations are very slight, and this is of prime importance.

In spite of local differences, the Amazon basin displays an emphatic geographical and biological unity. This is due above all to a river system unequaled in its extent and complexity. Land travel through this region is extraordinarily difficult, because the roads are constantly barred by rivers. In contrast, 50,000 miles of rivers are navigable, despite occasional rapids, and it is by these water routes that merchandise is transported. Manaus is a veritable maritime port and ships from the high seas can navigate as far as Iquitos, not far from the foothills of the Andes and 2,300 miles from the Atlantic Ocean.

On the other hand, the Amazon and its great tributaries often constitute barriers against the dispersion of plant and animal species, many of which are not distributed throughout the Amazonian basin. Plant and animal species well-known on the right bank of the Amazon have not penetrated to the left bank. Since the rivers of Amazonia are routes of travel for some species and barriers for others, they are a prime factor in the genesis and distribution of living things throughout the largest natural region of South America.

GIANT FISH AND ELECTRIC EELS

The Amazon waters present an extraordinary variety of characteristics—torrential in some parts and sluggish in others, sometimes clear and elsewhere burdened with silt and organic debris. Considering this variety and the vast extent of the river system, it is not surprising that the aquatic life includes almost countless species.

The fish are particularly numerous and diversified. It has been estimated that at least 2,000 of the 2,500 species known in South America inhabit the basins of the Orinoco and the Amazon, as well as the tributaries of the Rio de la Plata with which certain Amazonian streams are more or less interconnected. In a twenty mile radius around Manaus, seven hundred species have been found, a figure that surpasses the known number of species in all of North America. And the inventory is far from complete. Most of these fish are peculiar to the Neotropical region. The catfish, characins, and cichlids are the best represented.

The most famous fish of the Amazon, a member of the Osteoglossidae, is the giant redfish or *pirarucú,* called *paiche* in Peru and *arapaima* in Guiana *(Arapaima gigas)*. It is one of the largest species confined to fresh waters; individuals attain a length of fifteen feet and a weight of 200 pounds. The average pirarucú brought to the markets weighs fifty to sixty pounds. Its heavy and massive body is greenish at the head and bright red toward the tail. Much esteemed as food, it is intensively fished or, more accurately, hunted with arrows

Left: The Guamues River, a tributary of the Putumayo and one of the many rivers that cuts a channel through the Amazon forest. (López M. Nereo) Right: For some distance after the great Rio Negro joins the Amazon, its dark waters flow in a separate current side by side with the whitish, silt-laden waters of the Amazon. (E. Aubert de la Rüe)

and harpoons. Cut up and dried, its flesh gives rise to a very active commerce.

Certain catfish (for example, *Brachyplatystoma filamentosum),* a group that includes several hundred Neotropical species, surpass it in size and weight. Others, smaller, are protected by a veritable armor of bony plates; they feed on rotten vegetation or algae which they detach from the rocks with the mouth which forms a kind of rake. Others, not longer than an inch, are carnivorous and feed on the blood of other fish that they attack at the gills.

The Characidae includes some of the most famous and dangerous fish in South America, the piranhas or pirayas *(Serrasalmus, Rooseveltiella* and *Pygocentrus),* one species of which attains twelve inches in length. Although related to vegetarian forms—as for example the pacus or silver dollar fishes *(Metynnis)* that feed on water plants and fallen fruit—the piranhas are exclusively carnivorous. The usual food of the piranhas is fish, generally other characins. But they also attack mammals that venture into the water. Their jaws are so strong and their teeth so sharp that they can cut a piece of flesh like a razor and can snap off a finger joint with one bite. They are all the more dangerous because of a speed and an aggressiveness beyond belief, and they always attack in schools of several hundred individuals. Attracted by any splash in the water, and excited by blood, they pounce upon any animal that ventures into the water. It is on record that a capybara weighing one hundred pounds was reduced to a skeleton in less than one minute.

In the marshy regions of the Amazon River system is found a large fish of the same order as catfishes which so resembles the eel that it has been dubbed electric eel *(Electrophorus electricus).* It attains a length of from three to six feet and sometimes has the thickness of a man's leg. It is capable of producing electric discharges of well over 350 volts and can administer a shock sufficient to stun very large animals. Its electrical organs are in the ventral posterior region—which comprises four fifths of the total length. They are modified longitudinal bundles of muscles, arranged in series like the elements of a battery or a condenser. The electric eel's head is the positive pole, and its tail is the negative. An encounter with the fish it preys upon sets up a distortion of the magnetic field, the batteries are discharged, the prey stunned. It is quite probable that some unexplained deaths of explorers or native Indians may have been caused by this fish.

The electric eel has still another peculiarity: it obtains oxygen by breathing, instead of using the oxygen dissolved in water, as most fish do. It comes up for air every fifteen minutes, the oxygen entering its system through the many folds in the mouth cavity. This respiratory system is very different from that of the lungfishes (one of which is found in the Amazonian basin), which have true lungs.

While many Amazonian fishes attain gigantic size, others rank among the smallest in the world. There is a wealth here of minuscule fish, some of them vividly colored. The guppy *(Lebistes reticulatus),* a Cyprinodont native to Guiana and northern Brazil, has been introduced into tropical waters throughout the world as a destroyer of mosquitos. It is named after its discoverer, the Rev. Robert J. Lechmere Guppy; but it certainly earns its other common name, million-fish, on account of its extraordinarily high rate of reproduction. The small characins are numerous, particularly the tetras, of which the most vividly colored, the neon tetra *(Hyphessobrycon innesi),* inhabits the clear watercourses of the forest. It is not surprising that fanciers of exotic fish have drawn abundantly upon the Amazonian waters to fill their aquariums.

LEGENDS OF THE INIA

Contrary to generally accepted opinion, cetaceans, aquatic mammals of which the best-known are the whale and porpoise, are not peculiar to salt water. Some few highly specialized species live exclusively in the great tropical rivers. One of them, the inia *(Inia geoffroyensis),* a dolphin-like animal, is found in the Amazon, the Orinoco, and their tributaries. It has a rather short body, cylindrical in form, with a long head on a clearly distinguishable neck, a characteristic that sets it apart from other cetaceans. The beak or snout is long and conical, entirely covered with short and close-set hairs, and the mouth, with immovable lips, is equipped with from 132 to 136 teeth. The total length of the animal may exceed six feet.

The inias feed mainly on fishes. Like all Cetacea they come to the surface periodically to breathe. Every intake of air is quite noisy, as voyagers who have camped by night on the shores of the Amazonian rivers have related. The female gives birth to a single young which follows her until it reaches maturity.

Countless legends have gathered about this cetacean. The Indians of the region will assure you that it can sing melodiously, like the sirens of antiquity. They also say it can transform itself into a woman as beautiful as a goddess, with long silky hair, and that this woman prowls the shores at night in search of a man to seduce, and that she takes her victim down to her watery realm and drowns him. The Indians never hunt the inia, which they regard as taboo. Oddly enough, the same attitude prevails in southeast Asia—a strange convergence of beliefs on the part of peoples whose origins are very different.

The presence of this creature in Amazonian waters within Bolivia and Peru, as far inland as 1,500 miles, is one of the most astounding features of this river system.

Another strange mammal, the manatee, a member of the Sirenia order, is found in the Amazon. The species, *Manatus inunguis,* which attains a length of ten feet, is found in the river from the island of Marajó to Iquitos. It differs from its counterpart in the Orinoco in having a larger head, several skeletal peculiarities and a total absence of fingernails on its flippers, but otherwise the two species are biologically identical.

ENDANGERED TURTLES AND HUGE CROCODILES

As might be expected, the Amazon waterways are rich in aquatic reptiles of all kinds, but most particularly in turtles, and in their predators, the crocodiles.

The river turtle called here the arrau *(Podocnemis expansa)* sometimes attains, in the female, a length of nearly three feet. Baron von Humboldt was the first to describe it, and later in

The scarlet ibis (Eudocimus ruber) *constitutes one of the most beautiful ornaments in Amazonian waters, especially around mangroves, where they gather in great colonies. (Harald Schultz)*

The payara (Hidrolycus scomberoides) *is about eighteen inches long, and as a result of a strictly carnivorous diet has a formidable set of teeth. (Karl Weidmann)*

the nineteenth century the great British naturalist, Henry Walter Bates, made a very detailed study of the species, in his time still numerous but now considered to be threatened with extinction. The native Indians hunted both the young and the adult turtles and ruthlessly collected their eggs for the oil that could be extracted from them and used in lamps and for cooking purposes. Bates estimated that at least 48,000,000 eggs were collected in one season.

The arrau is still astonishingly numerous, at least in the Orinoco, judging from recent studies by Janis A. Roze of the University of Venezuela. But he, too, predicts the eventual extinction of *P. expansa* unless the hunting of the species is controlled. In the mating and egg-laying season they assemble on the low islands in such crowds that they obstruct some natural canals and the sound of their shells jostling together can be heard at a distance. As in Bates' time, the hot sand of the higher islands where the females bury their eggs beyond the reach of flood waters is sometimes dark with turtles. The average female lays about eighty-five eggs in the hole she digs. After laying the eggs, the females return to the river, leaving the hot sand and sun to hatch the young, a process that takes at least forty-five days. In two or three more days the soft-shelled young come to the surface and begin their run down to the water. The worst enemy of all is man. Besides the native Indians and Creoles, the white man now esteems arraus as delicacies and hunts them with increasing intensity.

Besides the giant arrau, the Amazon River system is the habitat of several smaller species of turtles, among them the strange matamata *(Chelys fimbriata),* usually about eighteen inches long, with a deeply engraved shell. The jaws of the matamata are so weak that it must feed itself as fish do, by swallowing whole its prey—small fish, tadpoles, and crustaceans. This turtle is equipped with a kind of trunk, a respiratory tube which allows it to breathe while submerged.

There is an impressive population of crocodiles in the Amazon River system. One of the largest, the Orinoco crocodile *(Crocodylus intermedius),* found both in the Orinoco and Amazon, sometimes attains a length of twenty-four feet.

The caimans are still more numerous, South America having been a center of evolution for this group of reptiles. Most abundant among these are the *Caiman latirostris,* with a broad snout, and the jacare *(Caiman crocodilus),* with a bony crest seeming to join the two eyes, giving it the look of wearing spectacles. Jacares average about six feet in length but some are ten feet long; they are found in all the calm waters of the Amazon basin. Unlike the jacares, the smooth-fronted caimans, *Paleosuchus palpebrosus* and *P. trigonatus,* frequent deep and rapid waters with rocky bottoms, their thick hide able to take the knocks and bumps in such conditions. The black caiman, *Melanosuchus niger,* twice as big as the former species, can be dangerous to human beings and domestic animals, and for this reason roundups are often organized in the lower Amazon to reduce their number.

A SPLENDOR OF VEGETATION

Constant warmth, water in profusion, and high atmospheric humidity provide this region with the optimum conditions for vegetation to attain an unequaled luxuriance. The vegetation of the Amazon basin is a three-dimensional universe. Plants here reach a remarkable height. Enormous trees with straight trunks, almost rigidly vertical, carry to a height of 150 feet a continuous vault of leafage, interrupted very rarely by clearings or the gaps made by rivers. Seen from a pirogue voyaging up a watercourse, the forest looks like two high green walls draped and hung with tropical creepers. These trees are always green, the constant warmth eliminating the seasonal fall of leaves. And woody species far exceed the herbaceous species, which represent at most only a fifth of the flora.

Virgin forest is the name bestowed upon this region and the romantic name was probably suitable until recently. Nowadays, however, the forest has been to some extent despoiled by man. Exploiters of the source of rubber called latex, naturalists, and travelers have traversed it despite the difficulties presented by the dense vegetation.

No longer virgin, but still extending from the foothills of the Andes to the coast of Guiana, this remains the greatest forest of the western world. The Amazon rain forest, or *Hylaea amazonica,* as Baron von Humboldt called it in 1800, covers

The Victoria regia, *a giant water lily, has huge, flat round leaves with a graceful, narrow rim. (López M. Nereo)*

1.6 million square miles in Brazil alone, that is to say, almost 49 per cent of this vast country. The southeastern line of the forest is located at São Luiz de Maranhão, not far from the point where the Rio Tocantins meets its affluent, the Rio Araguaia; it follows the left bank of the Araguaia as far south as the State of Mato Grosso, where it turns west and then envelops the high basins of the upper affluents of the rivers Juruena, São Manuel, and Xingú, toward latitude S. 14°. The southernmost point of the forest is west of Rio Cuiabá, where it meets the marshes of upper Paraguay. Roughly this area corresponds to the Amazon basin and the lower basin of the Tocantins River.

This forest is characterized by its giant trees, some of which exceed a height of three hundred feet, with low-branching and well-buttressed trunks having a girth of more than forty feet. The great trees of the Amazon have an average height of 150 to 180 feet. The trunks are columnar, branching only at 65 to 100 feet above the ground. The foliage sprays are usually staggered, for the closeness of the trees to one another restricts their lateral development. However, the giants that have soared above the vault of the forest have more room to develop and they spread out in flattened domes resembling great green umbrellas. The continuous vault of foliage prevents sunlight from penetrating to the ground, which is shrouded in semi-darkness. The trees in such forests generally have superficial roots that crawl on the ground like great serpents. Other trees are flanked by powerful flying buttresses like tortuous draperies. The main roots, sometimes together with the adventitious roots connecting with the branches above, form a system of moorings for the trunk and its branches.

A COMMUNITY OF OUTLAWS

In the temperate zone we are used to seeing homogeneous associations of plant life. When we speak of beech woods or oak groves, we visualize the particular kind of plant life that associates with those trees. This is not so in the primitive forests of the tropics, where countless species exist in great confusion. As the great French naturalist Roger Heim has written of African forests: "The primeval tropical forest is an undisciplined army, composed of rigid giants and quivering dwarfs, an army without anyone to command or obey, an army of outlaws."

When I first entered a tropical forest after crossing the dry woodlands of the upper Marañon, I expected a grand spectacle, but not the awesome sight that greeted my eyes. As in all the rain forests of the world, the Amazon is composed of an almost incredible variety of species in the greatest disorder. In one area of less than three acres, there were counted 423 trees belonging to 87 species, and in another similar area 654 trees belonging to 60 species. An analysis of the flora throughout the Amazon forest would yield similar results; this is quite different from the situation in the United States or in Europe where a maximum of five or six species of trees forms a deciduous forest. And if we include lesser plant life, aside from the giant trees, the figures are still more spectacular: in one square mile of rain forest close to three thousand species of trees and bushes have been identified, a figure that could never be approached in any temperate region.

Some botanists squared off the region of Manaus and studied all the plants greater than a yard in height, which would exclude most herbaceous plants, and found no less than 21 families. They found 24 lianas belonging to 13 species ranged in 8 families. On about 1,900 square feet, they found 1,652 plants (that is to say, 23,000 per acre) belonging to 107 species in 37 different families. The ligneous and erect species accounted for 77.6 per cent of the individuals, with 69 species

Right: Like other rivers of the Amazon region, the Ucayali, here shown in Peru, comes down from the foothills of the Andes and meanders lazily up and back across the Amazon basin. (Robert Lawrence Pastner) Below: The river turtles (Podocnemis expansa) *gather at breeding time. Right after they are hatched, the young mingle with the adults, often perching on the backs of the parents. (Karl Weidmann)*

Several spectacled caimans warm themselves in the sun while in the background a few hoatzins perch on low branches of trees. (Karl Weidmann)

belonging to 25 families, while the herbaceous plants accounted only for 6.7 per cent with 11 species belonging to 6 families. These inventories clearly show the heterogeneous character of the vegetation.

This incredibly rich forest flora varies, of course, according to the localities. Although some species are strictly limited in their distribution, others are to be found over vast expanses. The species of trees change from one part to another, but the forest retains the same aspect. Seen from the air, the forest appears like waves of verdure interrupted by gray spots where trees are momentarily stripped of leaves, or bright yellow or purple spots that indicate trees in flower.

THE FOREST LEVELS

The depth of this ocean of green waves is unguessed by the air traveler. Like all rain forests seen from the air, it reveals only the most superficial portion.

A stratum of low herbaceous plants grows on the level of the ground, often stunted for lack of light. Less than one per cent of the rays of sunlight penetrate that far and in these conditions chlorophyllic plants cannot flourish. However, some of them, including the most decorative, have adapted to this penumbra. Among others, some begonias and arums are white spathed, or brightly colored. Various phylodendrons and monsteras with jagged leaves also occur here.

In the middle level are found small trees, palms and some arborescent ferns. Above this level are the true trees which support the almost continuous leafy vault, dominated here and there by the giants of this vegetable universe—the only inhabitants freed from the suffocating atmosphere below.

This division is of course rather arbitrary, for the strata often merge and become indistinguishable. And the whole of this cloak of vegetation is threaded with lianas, many attaining the diameter of a human body. Some lianas climb directly, like stretched cables; others crawl tortuously along the ground until they find a trunk around which they can wind. They do not unfold their first branches until they reach the treetops where, eager for light, they cover themselves with leaves and flowers, and sometimes fall to the ground under their own weight. They hang in festoons and their infinite variety gives to the Amazonian forest its look of exuberance.

Among the very numerous species of lianas are some that rank as useful plants, for example the *Paullinia cupana,* a Sapindaceae that produces seeds used in the preparation of *guarana,* one of the beverages of Brazil which has a higher caffein content than coffee. Most of them use trees simply as support, without causing any harm. However, such is not true of the so-called "stranglers," among which the *Clusia* are the most widely distributed. Their seeds sprout like those of the epiphytes on a tree branch and put forth long roots that sink into the soil. Then the plant thrusts up toward the sky and at last forms a treelike growth that twines round the original tree and literally chokes it to death.

A list of the trees of Amazonia would fill many pages. In Brazil alone, 846 species belonging to the Leguminosae have been counted. Among these are two of the forest giants: the angelim *(Dinizia excelsa)* and cedro rana *(Cedrelinga catenaeformis).* Palm trees are also numerous, especially in the more humid sections, and some of them play a very important part in the Amazonian economy. The moriche *(Mauritia flexuosa),* for instance, provides an edible fruit; a sap that is made into wine; pith that is made into a kind of bread; fiber useful for fishlines, ropes, and hammocks; leaves that make an excellent thatch for houses; and wood that is hard enough to be used in building.

Other trees of the Amazon basin useful to the economy are the cacao *(Theobroma cacao),* which grows in the lower levels of very humid forests, and yields cocoa and chocolate; the castanheira *(Bertholletia excelsa),* which produces the Brazil nut; and rubber-producing trees belonging to a variety of families.

FORESTS OF THE AMAZON

The forests of the *igapos,* or swamps, of the lower region, where the ground is inundated or very marshy throughout the year, have a dense undergrowth, along with bushes, palms, ferns, and trees perched on stiltlike, prop roots that allow them to maintain equilibrium in unstable ground. Still other trees, like the *Symphonia globulifera,* are provided with respiratory roots that allow the submerged parent root to breathe. The trees here are, generally speaking, lower than in the drier regions. The characteristic trees of these marshy localities are, among others, the jacareubas *(Calophyllum brasiliense),* the araparis *(Macrolobium acaciaefolium),* the abiuranas *(Lucuma sp.),* the piranheiras *(Piranhea trifoliata)* and the louros do igapo *(Nectandra amazonum).* Lianas are rare here, but the epiphytes are abundant.

The *varzea,* that is, forests inundated only at the annual floods, border the rivers, varying in extent from a few yards to hundreds of miles, depending upon the topography. The trees in these sections are higher than in the swampy regions but they almost never exceed sixty-five feet in height, although an occasional one-hundred-foot tree may flourish here. There are a great many palms but they represent only a few species, notably the euterpes with their great bouquets of graceful pinnate leaves, the pachiubas *(Socratea exorrhiza)* perched on stilts, and the small palms of the *Geonoma* genus that make the undergrowth impenetrable.

The species in the riverside forests are many and quite diversified. Nearest the water grows the oeirana *(Alchornea castaneifolia).* Adjacent to these are the imbauba *(Cecropia sp.),* comparatively tall and so numerous at times as to form almost a stand. Under their sheltering branches grow the tachis *(Triplaris sp.),* the mutambas *(Guazuma ulmifolia),* the assacus *(Hura crepitans),* the pau mulato *(Calycophyllum Spruceanum),* and the jauari palms *(Astrocaryum jauari).* The heveas or serengueiras *(Hevea brasiliensis)* are also found in the varzeas, especially on the right banks of the Amazon and its southern affluents. Lianas abound, particularly the one the Brazilians call *escada de jaboti,* turtle's staircase (classified with leguminous plants of the genus *Bauhinia),* because its flat stem with bands of wood gives it a stepped appearance.

These plant associations pass progressively to those of the drier zones where the forests are never submerged, no matter how high the rivers rise. These forests of relatively high altitude are characterized by the urucuri palm *(Attalea excelsa)* and by arborescent species such as the cumaru *(Coumarouna odorata),* the sumauma *(Ceiba pentandra)* and the muiratinga *(Olmedia maxima),* the latter sometimes growing to a height of 130 feet.

The forests of true terra firma are rich in hardwoods: acapus *(Vouacapoua americana),* pau amarelo *(Euxylophora paraensis),* pausanto *(Zollernia paraensis),* massaranduba *(Mimusops sp.),* jaranas *(Chytroma sp.),* matamatas *(Eschweilera sp.),* are only the best known. The caucho *(Castilloa ulei)* and the castanheira *(Bertholletia excelsa)* are characteristic of these forests, where the ground is in places covered with stemless and spiny palms.

A close-up of a young caiman in eastern Peru emphasizes the largeness of its eyes. (Rolf Blomberg: Full Hand)

HANGING GARDENS

As we make our way through the dim Amazonian forests, we encounter only a few flowers. In the occasional clearings, there are just a few bushes and herbaceous plants bearing brightly colored flowers. The strelitzias, relatives of the banana trees, display curious bright red and translucent bracts like the beaks of herons while a few corollas here and there sparkle like amethysts or rubies in a ray of sunlight. But they are only isolated bright spots in a green sea.

However, as we raise our eyes toward the upper canopy we see tree trunks that are almost completely covered with epiphytic plants bearing leaves and flowers unequaled anywhere else in their exuberant coloring. These plants, which depend upon the tree merely for support, without in any way being parasitic, require a saturated atmosphere: they absorb the needed water and minerals from the rain that falls from the sky and not from moisture drawn up from their roots. They are very abundant in the most humid forests, almost forty per cent of the trees wearing a garment of epiphytes. These plants have undergone a long series of adaptations to this extremely specialized way of life, as can be seen particularly in the bromeliads, the roots of which serve the plant as anchoring cables rather than organs of nutrition. At the time of flowering, they are reduced to dried and blackened ropes, clinging to the bark. Depending upon the sky for moisture, its base has been transformed into a cistern. The long narrow leaves are arranged in rosettes or bouquets, their edges upturned, the concave interior forming a channel that carries the rain to the center of the plant; there it accumulates to be drawn upon as needed. I recall that in collecting such plants in the Peruvian Andes I was subjected to a veritable shower, sometimes evil-smelling, each time I separated the bromeliad from its support, although rain had not fallen for several days.

A microscopic examination of a bromeliad leaf reveals a thick waxy cuticle that acts like an impermeable lacquer, and beneath this a network of absorbent cells gorged with water, reminding one of the structure of succulent plants or even aquatic plants. And indeed, the epiphytic plant does have the characteristics of both aquatic and xerophilic plants, thus enabling it to avoid both the dangers of being soaked with water and being dried out for the lack of it.

The Bromeliaceae produce flowers in spikes of vivid yellow, dead white or bright red and the fruit, often fleshy, is much sought after by birds, bats and monkeys.

Bright as are the flowers of the Bromeliaceae, they are rivaled in splendor by the hues of the Orchidaceae, their neighbors in this habitat.

Left: A liana seems to be strangling the palm around which it has wound itself. (Karl Weidmann)

Right above: The strelitzia are related to banana trees, common in the Amazon jungles. The vivid bracts surrounding the flowers are shaped like a stork's beak and show up brilliantly in forest clearings. (Edward S. Ross) Right: These splendid orchids (Cattleya) *grow in symbiotic union with microscopic mushroom. The flowers are pollinized by insects. Far right: Passion flowers owe their name to a spikelike stamen that recalls the Crucifixion. (Both by Karl Weidmann)*

Immediately after being hatched on a sandy bank, river turtles (Podocnemis expansa) *head straight for the water. (Karl Weidmann)*

THE MIRACULOUS MILK—LATEX

One of the valuable products of the Amazonian forests is rubber, or caoutchouc, made from a secretion of several tropical trees. The derivation of these names is of some interest.

When Columbus returned to Spain after his second voyage to the "Indies," he mentioned having seen the native Indians handling balls made of a black vegetable gum. Later voyagers described these balls as bouncing like living things. The Indians called the elastic gum *cahuchu,* meaning "weeping tree," and the early Spanish, Portuguese and French explorers incorporated that word, with slightly altered spelling, into their languages. It was not until the eighteenth century that it was given the term "rubber," when the English scientist, Joseph Priestley, found that it "rubbed out pencil marks."

Among the several trees that are commonly known as "rubber trees," the bully tree *(Mimusops globosa)* secretes a milky liquid, which, coagulated, results in a rubber, called balata, still used in the manufacture of golf balls. The caucho *(Castilloa elastica)* secretes a similar liquid. But the most important of these trees are the heveas, or Pará rubber trees, of which many species exist throughout the Amazonian forest. *Hevea brasiliensis* is the most common as well as the most valuable and occurs almost exclusively on the right bank of the Amazon, being replaced in the north by twenty other species. These Euphorbiaceae attain a height of one hundred feet and have lobed leaves and pale green flowers. The fruit forms capsules that explode upon reaching maturity, scattering their three seeds to a distance of fifty or sixty feet. The trees are tapped, an incision being made just deep enough to reach the latex-secreting canals that lie beneath the bark, and the juice is collected in receptacles. The rubber suspended in this milky juice is coagulated by heating.

In the nineteenth century the uses of rubber were very limited, and exportation of latex was difficult because of its unstable nature. Then the American inventor Charles Goodyear discovered a way of stabilizing it, incorporating sulphur in it during a process called vulcanization. The demand for rubber soon became so great that there was a mass immigration of fortune-hunters into the Amazon Valley, particularly into the Pará estuary and, far to the west, along the right bank of the Juruá, Purús, and Acre rivers. The territory was divided up into vast concessions, and armies of workmen were bound by contract to the owners.

Brazil had a monopoly of rubber production until in 1873 a British subject managed to elude the law and export the hevea seeds to the famous botanical gardens at Kew, near London. After several futile trials the seeds germinated and produced plants that were transported to Ceylon and other Far Eastern areas, where the tree now flourishes. Soon Brazil lost its monopoly, since plantation rubber almost entirely supplanted natural rubber. Although rubber is still a valuable product of the Amazon basin, many of the *sereingueiros*—the skilled workmen who tapped the trees—have had to find other work.

THE DEADLY ROOT

In the heart of the tropical forests of both the Orinoco and Amazon basins grow woody bushes, from three to six feet high, with tough vinelike branches and roots that secrete a virulent poison, *Strychnos toxifera.* Long known to the aborigines as curare, it is used by them to poison the tips of their arrows. "Curare" means "the one to whom this comes, falls." In 1595 Sir Walter Raleigh brought it back from Guyana.

The natives prepare the poison by grinding the outer layer of the taproot to a powder and then soaking it in water. Filtering leaves a gummy red liquid that turns thick and brownish when heated to the boiling point. Concentrated by a second boiling, the product becomes a thick hard paste. In some parts of the Amazon region, the aborigines prepare a more complex mixture by adding the poison of toads. Its toxicity can be high, for it contains several alkaloids that act upon the nerve endings, producing cramps, asphyxia, and death. Deer and monkeys are paralyzed by it in a few minutes; the tapir resists the effects of the poison for several hours before collapsing. Research with laboratory animals indicates that curare may eventually be useful in treating epilepsy and tetanus.

Mature river turtles come out of the water to warm themselves in the sun. (Janis A. Roze)

CLEARINGS IN THE FOREST

The luxuriance of the Amazonian vegetation knows no equal except perhaps in southeast Asia. In the sluggish rivers, the pirogue sometimes moves through a sea of green and purple vegetation—water hyacinths *(Eichhornia crassipes).* In some regions of the world where it has been introduced as an ornament, this plant has become a pest almost beyond control. Sometimes the riverside is an almost solid wall of leafage, so that the pirogue seems to be moving through a vast green tube. And in some marshy regions, one is also surrounded by giant Araceae, such as the aringas *(Montricardia arborescens).*

Even the rocks that form the rapids are covered with a highly specialized vegetation, as if nature were trying to carpet the entire Amazon basin. However, this vast expanse of green is broken up at some points by "dry" forest, bush country, and grassy clearings, veritable enclaves of savannas within the great forest. These are found mainly in the lower Amazon around Santarem, Monte Alegre, and Amapa.

Some of these grassy clearings, where low trees grow, may represent the first stage of land formed in the conquest by vegetation of river sand. Others may result from local soil or climatic conditions. And mankind's penetration of these regions has also contributed to the formation or extension of these clearings. In former times the Indian population was more numerous, especially in the Santarem region, as evidenced by an abundance of pottery artifacts uncovered by archaeologists. The most favorable parts of the forest for settlement were those where the soil was driest, and the cutting down of trees as well as the repeated building of fires started the classic process of soil erosion.

These savannas generally occur on stretches of white sands thinly covered with humus as well as with dense thickets called by the Brazilians *carrascos,* masses of vegetation about eighteen feet high, dotted here and there with trees only a very little higher. The undergrowth is very dense with numerous lianas and epiphytic plants.

OILS OF THE BABASSU PALM

Although the limits of the Amazonian forest are clearly drawn for the most part, at times the plant associations form

a transitional stage with the *campos*. Such is the case with the "forest of babassu" in the State of Maranhão, south of the Amazon, adjacent to the arid caatinga of Piaui and Ceará. The babassu *(Orbignya speciosa),* one of the tallest and most majestic of all the Brazilian palms, carries a great plume of wide-spreading leaves some thirty-five feet in length, and a brownish fruit, the size of an egg, containing a kernel with seeds from which one of the clearest and best oils for the manufacture of soap is extracted. This oil is put to the same uses as coconut oil.

Dense groves of this palm cover hundreds of square miles to the south of São Luiz. The same palm occurs in portions of the states of Amazonas, Bahia, Pará, Piauí, Ceará, Mato Grosso and Goiás. It is estimated that a billion babassu palms grow in the State of Maranhão alone. The distribution and predominance of this palm have puzzled botanists. In reality these palm groves owe their existence to man, for they existed in the undergrowth of dark forests and it was only when those portions of forest were cleared and sunlight reached the babassu that it achieved its vigorous growth, rapidly exceeding in height the surrounding vegetation. Since then the babassu has multiplied in geometrical progression, becoming the dominant and sometimes the only species of tree in this part of Brazil. Toward the east, the babassu zone dwindles, giving way, in the vicinity of Caxias, to the dry or caatinga type of forest.

A green lizard waits for its prey in dense undergrowth near Yarina in eastern Peru. (Rolf Blomberg: Full Hand)

THE CAMPOS OF THE UPPER RIO BRANCO

Between the frontier of Guyana and the Amazonian forest of the lower Rio Branco extends a rather extraordinary region, a succession of low mountains, severely eroded, rocky, and arid. These are covered with parched savannas that have narrow fingers of forest, comprised of the moriche palm *(Mauritia flexuosa),* thrust into them.

These campos resemble grassy steppes, the tufts of tough grasses *(Paspalum)* dotted across expanses of gray sandy soil, with here and there bogs covered with Cyperaceae and flooded in the rainy season.

The dense rain forest begins suddenly south of Boa Vista, heralded only by a few copses on the hills. Bordering the rain forest is a palm grove, where the great inaja palm *(Maximiliana regia)* reigns in company with several thorny species. Elsewhere, notably in the Sierra Taiana, to the northwest of Boa Vista, a dense dry forest, semi-deciduous or deciduous, covers the slopes and the lower lands.

These associations of plant life are in balance with the very special climate of a "good weather" area occurring between the tropical zones of Guyana and Brazil. The climate is characterized by a short rainy season and a prolonged dry season. In the month of November, the average rainfall at Boa Vista is about $1^1/_2$ inches while at Georgetown in Guyana and at Manaus it is 6 inches. In January the figures are respectively $1^1/_2$, 8, and 10 inches. Thus a traveler going from the south to the north, from Manaus to Boa Vista, sees tropical storm clouds suddenly replaced by the clear skies of the upper Rio Branco.

The Amazon forest is so dense that one can appreciate its luxuriance only from a river. (Rolf Blomberg: Full Hand)

The Great Rain Forest

The Amazon Basin

6

When one considers the hot and humid climate, the exuberant, well-watered vegetation, and the constancy of these conditions throughout the year, without any seasonal break or abatement, it is obvious why animals proliferate in the Amazon basin as nowhere else on earth.

The number of species is markedly greater here than in other parts of South America, except certain tropical mountainous regions with a more varied climate. This is essentially the result of the extraordinary variety of habitats in the great forest. Within this many-dimensional green universe a great number of animals have been able to differentiate, and each one has chosen its place in a complex community. In the view of ecologists, the great forest is a very complex mechanism, unlike the savannas or the deserts. This very richness make its study difficult. Biologists are still far from understanding exactly how the equatorial forest "operates."

Although there are many species, there are not many individuals; in fact, the total population is very small. Some Amazonian species are known only by a few preserved specimens, even among birds, which have been the subject of intensive studies. The lack of specimens is caused partly by the difficulties of observing and collecting the fauna in an environment which provides them with a thousand hiding-places. But it is also due to the scarcity of individuals. An entomologist noted that he had collected in the Amazon basin in a single day twenty-eight species of one family of butterflies, the Riodinidae; he had thus collected twice the entire number of species known in North America, but his hunt comprised no more than half a dozen specimens of the commonest species, and most of the rest were represented by only a single specimen.

The physical factors of the Amazonian environment have

The tapir leads an almost amphibious way of life. A kind of living fossil, it uses its flexible trunk to browse on foliage and gather water plants. (James Simon)

deeply influenced the morphology and biology of each one of the species that live there. The humidity is such that Amazonia is without doubt one of the points on the globe where the passage from aquatic to terrestrial life took place. Typically aquatic or amphibian groups—for example, certain crustacea, the leech, and even arboreal batrachians—can still lead a terrestrial life here thanks to the humidity. Furthermore, the heat, which seems to accelerate the evolution of living creatures, frees them from a great many contingencies and allows, among others, cold-blooded animals and the invertebrates to attain sizes greater than those of their relatives in temperate climates. Many of the Amazon Coleoptera and butterflies are giants. Finally, the amount of light available has a profound effect upon the vertical distribution of the forest animals. The dark undergrowth is inhabited by animals of dark colors, fond of coolness and humidity. The canopy is on the other hand luminous. Most of the forest animals remain there and some of them never descend to lower levels or to the ground. It is among these that nature has surpassed herself in bestowing the brightest and most variegated colors.

Since this great forest tract has existed since the Tertiary period, this relatively stable environment has allowed an archaic fauna to survive. Indeed the Amazon forest is a refuge for "living fossils," including certain reptiles, the sloths, such birds as the trogons and the hoatzin, and countless invertebrates. Amazonia, then, constitutes a paradise for the naturalist.

This "green continent" is above all else stamped with two dominant elements: water and trees. And in fact the animals are aquatic or arboreal, sometimes both. Many of the animals such as the fishes and the batrachians, are almost innumerable. Predators flourish at their expense, notably the birds, whose colonies are established all along the rivers. The mammals themselves have partially adapted to the aquatic environment, and even the marsupials have an amphibian representative. The otters are numerous and their pelts constitute one of the riches of Amazonia. The large terrestrial mammals, notably the tapir, spend a part of their life in the water. All the terrestrial animals must know how to swim, for otherwise any movement overland would be impossible for them.

Many animals have become arboreal and an entire book could be written on their adaptations. Restricting ourselves to the vertebrates, we may call attention to the adhesive pads of the batrachians, notably the tree frogs, which can move across the surface of the smoothest leaves thanks to these tiny suckers. Lizards have very elongated fingers ending in powerful claws, often opposable to each other to form a pincer for gripping branches. The reptiles include many tree-dwellers.

Among the mammals we find similar adaptations; many have prehensile tails, constituting a fifth limb and assuring them a safe hold among branches. The prehensile tail is most common among the monkeys and is also seen in the sarigues

Left above: The woolly opossum usually hunts insects and other tiny prey at night. Its highly developed eyes are adapted to nocturnal vision. (Patricia Caulfield) Left: The agouti (Dasyprocta), *a rodent of the forest depths, has long front legs which cause it to resemble the smaller antelopes of the African forests. (Paul Schauenberg) Right:* Mauritius flexuosa, *which thrive mainly in flooded areas, are characteristic palms of the South American forests. (E. Aubert de la Rüe)*

(a South American opossum) among the marsupials, and the potos or kinkajous among the carnivores. Needless to say, most of the birds are tree-dwellers.

Many animals are able to camouflage themselves in dense vegetation. Certain insects for example, resemble leaves or bits of wood. Butterflies and moths are colored like the bark against which they flatten themselves. Such mimicry may also be observed among the birds, notably among the potoos *(Nyctibius)*, relatives of the nightjar. Flying only at night, during the day they remain motionless on a branch, their mottled gray and brown plumage making them resemble tree bark or even weather-beaten old wood.

INSECT GIANTS AND MIMICS

The insect population of the Amazon basin is so large that many new species remain to be discovered in most groups. The diversity is incredible. The American zoologist Marston Bates reported that in a radius of ten miles around a laboratory in eastern Colombia he encountered 150 species of mosquitos, while only 125 species are known throughout the United States and Canada.

Some Amazonian insects are known for their large size, others for their beauty and many others for their curious habits. Nothing better illustrates giantism than the enormous Hercules beetle *(Dynastes hercules)*, in which the males have a huge thoracic horn. These insects measure up to six inches in length and have a horn about 2 to 2$^{1}/_{2}$ inches long. They rank, along with the *Titanus giganteus*, among the largest coleoptera in the world.

The spiders rival the insects in size. For example, the tarantula has a body often three inches long. With legs of extraordinary length, it measures ten inches across and looks even larger than it is because of its thick hair. The female is said to live as much as twenty-odd years, but this has been questioned. It feeds in part on small vertebrates, batrachians, reptiles, birds, and small mammals.

The butterflies are noted not only for their size but their spectacular beauty and the number of species—more than all other species of insects. Seven hundred species have been collected within an hour's walk of Belem, and Henry Walter Bates collected five hundred in the environs of Ega far to the west. Many groups of Lepidoptera, for example, the Ithomiidae, the Heliconiidae, and the morphos, are native to this part of the world.

The Heliconiidae, very common in the Amazon basin, are particularly interesting for they are part of a complex group of original butterflies and their mimics. These were studied by H. W. Bates in the light of Charles Darwin's theories. They are well protected against predators, since they have a very disagreeable smell or taste and may be poisonous. Such butterflies as the Nymphalidae, the Papilionidae, the Geometridae, and others, seem to have adopted the same coloring, perhaps to deceive predators into thinking that they too are inedible.

The most widespread pattern of coloration among the Heliconiidae is black stripes and borders contrasting with a basic bright brownish-orange, often adorned with white or yellow dots. The mimics have adopted this coloration to such perfection that only a careful anatomical study can reveal the differences. Originals and mimics undergo parallel geographical variations wherever they are found. And the imitators enjoy at least partial immunity, thanks to what is called "Batesian mimicry."

The morphos rank among the most beautiful butterflies in the world. Always large, attaining a size of slightly over seven inches, they comprise fifty or so species, and their wings are of an extraordinary shimmering and almost unreal blue. So large are the morphos and so bright is the light reflected from their wings that they are sometimes visible from low-flying planes. As with birds of metallic plumage, these colors are caused not by pigments but by reflections from microscopic structures in the scales.

Many of the morphos inhabit the highest stratum of the Amazon vegetation and never descend lower. Their caterpillars are very downy and covered with stinging hairs; they metamorphose into chrysalids enclosed in a kind of purse, spun collectively by a colony of caterpillars.

Amazonia is also the domain of strange insects. For example there is the owl butterfly *(Caligo eurylochus)* which is distinguished by an eye spot on the underside of each hind wing, giving it the look, when seen from below, of a nocturnal bird of prey. Presumably the sight terrifies certain of its predators, who are then preyed upon by the owl. Other strange insects that are particularly abundant are the Membracidae, commonly referred to as "tree hoppers." These creatures suck the sap of branches and have developed thoraxes which assume so many forms—thorn, crescent, stem surmounted by a bubble—that they defy description. These structures often imitate the excrescences of the plant on which they feed, thus helping to camouflage themselves—although in some instances the disguises are useless and may be the result of an evolution that has gone astray. In any case, many of these insects look as though they were conceived by a surrealist painter.

LEAF-CUTTER AND DRIVER ANTS

As for strangeness of habits, perhaps no insect is more interesting to study than the ants. These are remarkably numerous in Amazonia and play an essential part as transformers of organic matter and as links in the food chain. Mark Twain once said that the ants are the stupidest of all living creatures. He was completely wrong, for these insects are in fact the most highly evolved and the best-organized of all the invertebrates. The species of Amazonian ants are countless and each fills a particular function in the natural communities. Two deserve special attention.

The ants of the Attini group are fungus-growers and fungus-eaters and are commonly called leaf-cutters, or *saubas* as the Brazilians know them. They do indeed cut leaves and collect them with such extraordinary concentration that they can strip a tree of its leaves in a single night. Despite their small size, they are fairly conspicuous in the forest because they

Right above: Pacas (Cuniculus paca) *are large rodents of the dense forest that live near water and feed on aquatic plants. (Carl Rettenmeyer) Right: This toad of the genus* Bufo *is one of a great variety of amphibians found in the marshy parts of the Amazon. Far right: This tree frog, so called because of its arboreal habit, has suction pads on the undersides of its feet that enable it to get a hold on the sleekest leaves. (Both by Harald Schultz)*

move from one place to another in long columns, each individual carrying a piece of leaf above its head. Hence they are sometimes called parasol ants. They carry the leaves to their ant-hill where worker ants reduce them to a spongy paste which they place in special rooms, sometimes a yard long and a foot wide. Here the fungus-grower species cultivates a kind of mushroom in a curious association of plant and insect; the ant's saliva, it seems, contains antibiotics favoring the kind of fungus it has selected and checking the growth of any other. Neither the mushroom nor the ant can do without the other. Equipped with mandibles as sharp as clippers, these ants play havoc with some plantations and are regarded as pests. The colonies of fungus-growers may contain as many as 600,000 individuals and sometimes occupy hundreds of square yards. All around these colonies the vegetation is completely stripped of its leaves, which obliges the ants to constantly search for new feeding places.

Quite different are the army or legionary ants, for they are carnivorous and nomadic, differing from the fungus-growers exactly as the desert nomad differ from the sedentary agriculturist. These extraordinary ants, like true gypsies, build no nests and are continually on the move. They sometimes remain in one place for twenty or so days, then become migratory for about seventeen days, during which they "pitch camp" each night. The physiological rhythm of the queen ant's ovaries conditions these moves. During the nomad period the queen participates in the group's migration, since her abdomen is not weighted down by a charge of eggs. The workers carry the young larvae that have just hatched, and hunt food for them. At the end of a certain time, the larvae reach maturity, spin their cocoons and become transformed into nymphs. The migration is then interrupted and the colony enters a sedentary phase. At this time the queen's ovaries have become active, and a week after the stabilization of the colony she begins to lay eggs. In less than a week she lays up to 25,000 eggs, which hatch in a few days. The ant colony, now augmented by a great number of larvae and young workers, again enters into a migration phase. During the nocturnal stops, the colony does not build a nest but simply gathers in a mass beneath some natural shelter. This teeming mass, containing up to 160,000 individuals, forms a kind of living nest, with its own galleries and its rooms. The central part is occupied by the queen, who is thus protected by the bodies of her subjects.

These army ants are savage predators and attack any small animal in their path. Climbing trees, they kill young birds in the nest; upon the ground they attack lizards and other reptiles; even small mammals do not intimidate these omnivorous raiders.

THE BATRACHIANS

Warmth and humidity are all that is needed to attract the batrachians, since they are susceptible to desiccation. They are particularly numerous both in species and individuals throughout the Amazon basin. Like other forest animals they show a strong tendency to live in trees wherever the humidity enables them to forego a true aquatic life. This is evident in the abundance of toads of the Hylidae family. These look like frogs and are often small—3/4 inches to 1 1/4 inches—but many species attain a length of four inches or so, as for instance the Brazilian blacksmith frog *(Hyla faber)*, so called from the anvil-like sound of its call. Typically arboreal, the tree frogs have an adhesive on the underside of their "toes." These suction pads assure them a solid hold on leaves and branches. Among the most highly evolved, the thumb is apposable to the other fingers as in the primates, thus assuring a still more solid hold. This is particularly true of members of the *Phyllomedusa* which move from branch to branch like lemurs. With other species of the *Hyla* genus, the membranes that unite the "toes" are highly developed and constitute miniature parachutes which check the speed and prevent an abrupt drop as they leap from branch to branch.

The tree frogs' methods of spawning also illustrate their liberation from aquatic life. Some species spawn in the water like other batrachians, but sometimes in a curious way. The male blacksmith frog builds small receptacles of mud with steep, polished sides in shallow, quiet water. Mating, laying eggs, and development of the tadpoles, all protected by the wall from carnivorous fish, takes place in this enclosure. In other species, the female carries the cluster of eggs on her back until the tadpoles are completely developed. In the less-evolved species, the eggs are simply held in the wrinkles of the skin; in some species these dermal folds develop into shapes like purses, with the opening a mere slit on the outside. The female marsupial frog *(Gastrotheca)* sometimes carries as many as fifty or more eggs on her back, from which the young emerge fully metamorphosed.

Among Amazon batrachians the Leptodactylidae are also very numerous, as are the toads (Bufonidae), comprising many aquatic or terrestrial species. Their nocturnal songs of love are a prominent part of the music of these forests.

MYRIADS OF BIRDS

To describe the countless birds that inhabit the Amazonian forests would fill more than a book, for these vertebrate have here attained an almost incredible diversity of species. Indeed, birds are so numerous everywhere in South America that it has been termed "the bird continent." One should add that they are not only numerous but beautiful, for here the hummingbirds, trogons, cotingas and tanagers rival each other in vivid color and shimmering metallic plumage.

The beauty of the plumage has not escaped the notice of the Indians, who make rich ornaments, such as collars, head-dresses, capes and stomachers, of bright-colored feathers. They utilize especially the feathers of the toucans and parakeets, but also those of the trogons and of passerines such as the pipras and the tanagers.

Although few studies have been made of the number of species of birds in Amazonia, in the Purús River Valley, an affluent of the Amazon, an ornithological expedition encountered no less than 458 species, and no doubt a considerable number escaped observation. This wealth is evidently due to the enormous amount and variety of available foods. The birds have thus been able to enjoy a most varied choice of diets. Many of them, such as the trogons, the toucans, and the parakeets are principally fruit-eaters while others, such as the hummingbirds, are nectar-feeders.

For the flesh-eaters there is an abundant supply of insects. The insectivorous birds are therefore also highly diversified, each species having adapted to a particular prey. Ants are uncommonly numerous in the Amazon Valley and so an

Capybaras are huge rodents (adults may grow to three feet or more) that resemble guinea pigs and prefer to live near water. (Karl Weidmann)

entire family of passerines, the Formicariidae, or ant birds, has adapted itself to feeding on these arthropoda and even derives its name from its prey.

Other insectivorous birds, such as the tyrant flycatchers, catch insects on the wing. From a safe perch they wait for their prey and like the flycatchers of the Northern Hemisphere dart out upon any flying insect that comes their way. Others hunt for insects in the trees, as for instance the vireos and the warblers, minutely exploring the leaves and branches. Still others, like the tody flycatchers *(Todirostrum)* of broad and flattened bill, confine themselves to low bushes teeming with the insects disdained by high-flying flycatchers.

The constancy of this damp and hot climate throughout the year explains the sedentary character of the Amazon birds. Vegetation flourishes all year long, as do the insects and small animals upon which the birds prey. Hence, conditions are quite different from those in parts of the tropical zone where there is a periodical alternation of wet and dry seasons, and especially different from the temperate zones, where winter and summer cause great fluctuations in animal and plant life. Amazon birds thus move about only within a very restricted perimeter. At the most, some birds, such as the parakeets, will move from one part of the forest to another in search of a specially prized fruit as it ripens. The practice of remaining in one place has affected the physical characteristics of the birds; aside from the insectivorous species which need a rapid flight to capture their prey—birds such as the swallow and martin, for instance—most Amazonian birds have short, rounded wings capable of bearing them slowly over short distances. They do not need the long and pointed wings characteristic of the migrants; they have widened wings that will facilitate maneuvers between tree trunks and other obstacles.

Amazonian birds have also adapted to arboreal life, most of them becoming perching birds, with short tarsi and long curved claws assuring a solid grip on the branches. And since the tree trunks abound in insects such as wood-borers and their larva, this has attracted many birds such as the woodpeckers. Woodpeckers are very diversified in the Amazon and include a large series of species competing with a family of primitive passerines peculiar to the New World, the Dendrocolaptidae or woodcreepers, which are very numerous in the Amazon. The woodcreepers have strong feet with powerful curved claws and tail quills that are stiffened to form a prop on which the bird partially supports itself when climbing. They can thus search in peace for the insects hidden in the interstices of the bark, passing almost unperceived on account of their predominantly rust-brown color.

The characteristics of the large crested hoatzin might perhaps be explained as adaptations to arboreal life. The anatomy of this anachronistic bird, its heavy and clumsy flight, and its habits have puzzled ornithologists who have classed it in an order apart. The hoatzins resemble the pheasant in outline, and live among the bushes that border the edges of the forest and the watercourses, where their nest is a kind of platform above the water. When hatched, the nestlings are unique in having, at the end of each wing, two well-developed claws that permit them to cling to branches with four "feet" like young quadrupeds. These claws disappear in about three weeks. This primitive characteristic cannot but remind us of the Archaeopteryx, the hoatzin's primitive ancestor, half way between reptile and bird.

Aside from that, the hoatzin presents highly evolved characteristics, among them an enormous crop, well muscled, where it digests the leaves of arums, its main nourishment. This organ is so voluminous that it has modified the body to such a point as to cause a reduction in the size and muscles of the wings. In fact, the bird is barely able to glide from tree to tree and is therefore very sedentary. The fact that it has remained close to home along the Amazonian rivers from time immemorial indicates the antiquity of these forests. No doubt as protection, the adult hoatzin has a strong musky odor, which has earned it the name of "stinkbird."

The tendency of the Amazon birds to nest in knot holes and other tree cavities is another example of their adaptation to arboreal life. Some of the birds such as the woodpeckers, equipped with beaks strong enough to act as a drill, peck out cavities for themselves. Whole families, including the barbets, trogons, parakeets, woodcreepers and puff-birds have adopted this habit.

We should also mention the countless aquatic birds established along the rivers and lagoons, especially on the sandbars uncovered at low water. As in the Guiana region and Venezuela, ducks, herons, egrets, ibises and tree-ducks are here in immense numbers.

FROM TOUCANS TO HUMMINGBIRDS

All these thousands of birds have a tendency to inhabit different strata of the forest vegetation according to their food preferences and needs—some at ground level, others in the

Iguanas, mainly arboreal, camouflage themselves by clinging motionless to a bough. (Kurt Severin)

middle or upper branches, still others in the very tops of the tall trees. Studying the birds of Costa Rica, the American ornithologist, Paul Slud, distinguished five parallel zones or layers, and studies in the Amazon forest reveal a similar stratification.

The Amazon forest shelters significant number of ground-living birds, such as the rufous tinamou *(Rhynchotus rufescens),* resembling the quail and, like it, feeding on grains, fruits, and insects on the ground and nesting casually under bushes. Some species are indigenous, as for example the variegated tinamou *(Crypturellus variegatus).* The hocco, a gallinaceous bird resembling the turkey in size but less heavily built, has similar feeding habits, but perches in the trees at night and takes refuge there at the least sign of danger.

Birds of the undergrowth are particularly numerous. They include a notable number of passerines of the ant bird family that prey upon the insects routed by the army ants, following these nomads for days or even weeks at a time.

In these dense thickets we also find the cock-of-the-rock *(Rupicola rupicola),* the male bright orange and crested, the female warm brown. This genus of the Cotingidae has attracted attention not only for its beauty, but for its curious courtship display, in which many members of both sexes assemble at mating time in clearings for what are called "dancing parties." While the females perch in low branches, the males, each having chosen its particular terrain, go through a series of solemn-looking movements. Before the dance begins the males let out a kind of sonorous cawing, which can be heard at a distance. Then one at a time, the males take various attitudes: each spreads his tail and slowly bows, remaining in this position for several minutes, then hops up and down for a while. These birds nest on the ground or at the entrance of sheltered caves, the female taking full charge of the work, carrying damp clay to the site and patiently building it up. The edifice may weigh ten or more pounds.

However, most of the birds, and the gaudiest, are found in the high treetops—as in most tropical forests—as if they wanted to display their bright dress in the open. In those treetops the many-hued hummingbirds gather their nectar, their plumage glinting and shimmering. There too are countless parrots, from the tiny chattering parakeet to the large mackaw or ara with its long tail.

The toucans, distributed from southern Mexico to northern Argentina, are particularly numerous in Amazonia. The toucan's enormous beak is as big as the bird itself, vividly colored—red, yellow, blue or green—and light in weight, being made up of fibrous matter. The beak is used as a weapon when disputing berries and other fruits with another toucan. Their ear-splitting screams make them the noisiest bird in the Amazon jungle, and they behave like clowns.

The liveliness of the toucan contrasts strongly with the more subdued behavior of the trogon, a moderate-sized bird with short, rounded wings and curiously squared-off tail. This bird abounds in the tropics of the Old World as well as the New, and is notable for its extremely sedentary habits; it can remain motionless for minutes at a time, becoming almost invisible in spite of a dazzling plumage in which metallic red and green predominate. The trogons remain motionless in order to catch the passing insects with which they supplement their diet of fruit. Their flight is rapid but short and spasmodic.

The jacamar is another consumer of insects. It frequents the edges of the forest, and its shimmering plumage rivals the

The coral snake (Micrurus) *is a poisonous reptile with vivid markings. Several harmless snakes are protected from their enemies by similar markings. (Paul Schauenberg)*

The jararaca (Bothrops jararaca), *a close relative of the fer-de-lance, is about five feet long and has a deadly venom. (Othmar Danesch)*

glitter of the hummingbird, while its long slender body and long sharp beak enable it to catch and seize its elusive prey—dragonflies and butterflies such as the large and brilliant morphos. The puff bird has a rather heavy-looking silhouette, which has earned it several nicknames such as *Joao Bobo* (John-the-foolish) or lazy-bird, and it too waits for insects to pass nearby, snaps them up, then sits motionless again, with feathers puffed out.

The barbets are as colorful as the parakeet, and the bristles around their stout bills give them a bearded look. The motmot (pronounced "mo-mo") is a bird named from the sound of its call. Motmots have bright blue heads, the body feathers being a mottled black, brown and rufous; they are notable for a long, curious-shaped tail. The honeycreepers *(Diglossa)* with long beaks adapted to sucking nectar from the flowers, and the tanagers of incomparably bright plumage are here in an abundance of species, but certain species are so rare or at any rate so little known that museums are apt to possess only a few specimens. Hanging from the trees are the huge bag-nests of the oropendolas, this type of nest placing the nestlings beyond the reach of enterprising tree-snakes.

Hummingbirds are to be found throughout the Americas, practically from Sitka to Tierra del Fuego, and in the Amazon Valley are represented by a splendid series of species. Some, like the *Phaethornis,* are very soberly dressed, their plumage streaked with gray, brown and black. They haunt the dark undergrowth of the forest, never flying high above the ground and preferring to remain among the bushes and the tangle of lianas. They also avoid all other birds, and this has earned them the name of "hermit." Elsewhere the hummingbirds are more social and more gaudily dressed. The *Thalurania,* because of their beauty, are called "nymphs of the forests," and surely in all the world there are no hummingbirds that equal in beauty two species found in the Amazon, the crimson topaz *(Topaza pella),* and a related species, the *T. pyra,* natives, respectively, of the lower and upper Amazon. Their bronze-red plumage shades into green-gold on the rump, and their black velvety hoods are set off by a green and gold breast; it is easy to understand why these birds are constantly described as winged jewels. They frequent unusually dense forests on the shores of rivers, finding a choice environment in the thickets and lianas that form a living wall through which the waters flow. And unlike other hummingbirds, which are generally rather unsocial, the females build their nests not far from each other.

Some of the species of Amazon birds form temporary associations, scouring the forest in search of food. H. W. Bates wrote in 1863: "One may pass several days without seeing many birds, but now and then the surrounding bushes and trees appear suddenly to swarm with them. There are scores, probably hundreds of birds, all moving about with the greatest activity—woodpeckers and dendrocolaptidae (from species no larger than a sparrow to others the size of a crow) running up the tree trunks: tanagers, ant-thrushes, hummingbirds, fly-catchers, and barbets flitting about the leaves and lower branches. The bustling crowd loses no time. . . . In a few minutes the host is gone, and the forest paths remain deserted and silent as before." These observations have since been confirmed, ornithologists having counted at least thirty-two species that regularly form mixed bands having what amounts to a social structure. The advantage each species obtains from this association is that as one of these "gangs" of birds passes, the various insects flee in disorder and each of the winged predators chooses its favorite prey.

This association of the forest birds for the chase is one more example of their adaptation to the habitat.

TAPIRS, ANTEATERS AND OTHER MAMMALS

The mammalian fauna of the Neotropical region, sparse in comparison with other parts of the world, consists of a small number of terrestrial species, often aquatic or at least able to swim, and a larger number of arboreal species.

The larger land mammals are poorly represented here aside fom the sloth and a few of the feline predators. The Cervidae, or deer family, are relatively unimpressive in size: the mazama *(Mazama rufa),* for example, is scarcely twenty-eight inches tall, and its antlers are simple, not branching, and less than five inches long. Like many forest deer, the mazama is solitary in its habits. It takes unhesitatingly to the water when in danger and has been known to swim across rivers more than 1,000 feet wide. It lives side by side with the white-tailed deer *(Odocoileus virginianus),* thus testifying to its extraordinary powers of adaptation.

Instead of the duikers, the small antelopes so common in tropical Africa, there are many highly evolved rodents, such as the agouti *(Dasyprocta),* short-tailed, long-legged and graceful animals that attain a length of twenty inches. Their short rough pelt, brown or rufous, recalls that of the small

Left: The tayra or Eira barbara, *a member of the weasel family, is a ferocious carnivore but when domesticated becomes as gentle as a dog. (Paul Schauenberg) Right above: The huge, hollow bill of the giant toucan* (Ramphastos toco) *plays an important role in the bird's courting display. Right: The bill of the toucanet* (Selenidera maculirostris), *although smaller than that of other toucans, is well adapted to the bird's fruit-eating habits. (Both by Harald Schultz)*

antelope in both texture and color. The pacas *(Cuniculus, Dinomys)* are close cousins of the agouti, and have similar habits, but their flanks are spotted with white. These plant-eaters live in small communities either in the heart of the forest or on the shores of the rivers.

The ungulates are also represented in the Amazon Valley by two interesting species of peccaries, the white-lipped peccary *(Tayassu albirostris)* and the collared peccary *(T. tajacu)*. The latter species is found as far north as Texas and Arizona, an instance of the adaptability of these relatives of the domestic pig. The two peccaries frequent the same habitats but never intermingle; they have the same mode of life, being nomadic, traveling in bands of a hundred or so individuals, feeding mainly on fallen fruits, bulbs and roots, particularly the bulbs of certain Araceae that the Tupi Indians call *taya*. This vegetarian diet is augmented by any prey they can seize, from insects to smaller vertebrates, dead or alive. The white-lipped peccary is the more aggressive of the two and in fact is one of the most dangerous animals of the Amazon.

The strange form of the tapir *(Tapirus terrestris)* astounded the first explorers. It was quaintly described at the beginning of the sixteenth century by Pietro Martire d'Anghiers in his *De orbe decades octo,* as having trunk and ears like an elephant, the color and size of a steer, and the hoofs of a horse. With its rudimentary tail, stocky almost hairless body, its snout prolonged into a proboscis, its three-toed hind feet, the tapir is a very odd-looking creature. It belongs to a group formerly widespread and not confined, as now, to Central and South America and the impenetrable forests of southeast Asia.

Although not amphibians, the tapirs prefer swampy forests and the shores of rivers, taking readily to the water, especially at the least sign of danger. The paths they follow are clearly visible; sometimes they take the form of tunnels. Hunters of course take advantage of these routes. Nocturnal animals, tapirs seek their food at night, feeding mainly on leaves, young shoots, bulbs, and fallen fruits. They are solitary creatures, living either alone or in small family groups. The female gives birth once a year, usually producing a single infant.

Another large mammal inhabits the Amazon forest: the great anteater or ant bear *(Myrmecophagus tridactyla)*. It measures four feet in length, not counting a bushy tail about thirty inches long. The body is narrow, with a long and tapering snout; the mouth is very small, merely big enough to allow the long protractile and mobile tongue to pass through. This tongue is covered with a sticky saliva that allows the anteater to capture ants or termites that it encounters on the ground or digs out of ant-hills with its strong curved claws. So large are these claws that the anteater is obliged to walk on the sides of its feet, which gives it a peculiar gait. A solitary animal, it is found in groups only at the time of rut or when the mother is accompanied by her cub.

The anteater inhabits the swampy forests of Central and South America as far south as the northern part of Argentina. Other species of smaller size have become arboreal; for example, the tamandua is never larger than an average house cat. Its claws are particularly curved and sharp, truly hooks for climbing trees, and its tail is prehensile, enabling it, when attacking an enemy, to have a solid anchorage while it uses its forefeet. Another and still smaller anteater is the *Cyclopes didactylus,* about the size of a rat, with a softer pelt and a shorter snout. This little creature is completely nocturnal, spending the days curled up in the fork of a tree branch.

The rodents, numerous here, also prefer to hunt at night, and are semi-aquatic and semi-arboreal. Among them are the capybaras *(Hydrochoerus),* the largest rodents in the world, sometimes measuring over three feet in length. They are regarded by the Indians as good to eat.

The Amazon forest is inhabited by many species of squirrels, rats, mice and porcupines. Among the latter is the coendou, a small porcupine with prehensile tail and, unlike the porcupines elsewhere in the world, exclusively arboreal.

Left: The ocelot (Felis pardalis), *one of the largest felines in tropical America, reaching a size of almost three feet, is easily recognized by eyelike spots in longitudinal bands on its fur. Right: A young ocelot showing the species' characteristic preference for a life in the trees. (Both by Paul Schauenberg)*

Another distinctive feature of this porcupine is the presence of soft hairs among the sharp quills that cover its body.

The marsupials, likewise arboreal, are represented in the Amazon by five or more species of opossum, some of them resembling those of the United States. Others are much smaller, but all are strictly arboreal and nocturnal. As in all marsupials, the young are carried in the mother's pouch until they are strong enough to cling to her by means of their claws and prehensile tail; they then hang on to the mother's shoulders or cling to her tail which she curves upward and over her back. They feed upon insects, fruits, and seedlings.

Quite different are the habits of the cuica *(Chironectes)*, the only aquatic marsupial in the world. This small animal has a thick gray and black pelt, lives at the edge of calm rivers, and hunts at night, feeding on frogs, crustaceans, and fish. It swims with great ease by means of its webbed hind feet.

THE MONKEY KINGDOM

Although monkeys are found throughout tropical America, from Mexico to southern Brazil, the majority are found in the Amazon basin, but they are unevenly distributed because these arboreal primates cannot cross rivers. The Neotropical monkeys (Platyrhinians) are very different in form and anatomy from the monkeys of the Old World (catarrhinians and anthropoids), having evolved in an entirely independent way. The New World monkeys have an additional molar, and their nostrils are more lateral. The common ancestor of the two groups dates at least from the Eocene period, and probably came from North America during the Tertiary.

The monkeys of the American tropics are more attractive and much more diversified than their counterparts in Africa and Asia. Some of them are quite small, particularly the wistiti or marmoset, that Lilliputian of the primates. The pygmy marmoset measures only about four inches in length, excluding the tail, which is not prehensile. Its coat is soft and silky, and on its cheeks it has tufts of fur resembling sideburns. It has sharp canine teeth, and it is equipped, unlike other monkeys, with claws rather than nails on all toes except the big one. These small monkeys live in bands or family groups dominated by an adult male, and they seem to carry on genuine "conversations" as they run about in the trees. The amazing variety of sounds they utter suggests a high evolution of intellect. Their diet is exceptionally varied, including small reptiles, birds and bird's eggs, fruit and young seedlings. When they are raised in captivity this varied diet has been found to be absolutely necessary for them.

We do not have space to deal with all the monkeys in this area, but certainly the douroucouli *(Aotes)* should be men-

Left above: The blue-headed parrot (Pionus menstruus), *one of the most widespread species in the Amazon, feeds mainly on the larger fruits that it crushes with its powerful beak.* *Left:* Thiridia themisto, *a vivid example of the butterflies and moths in the Amazon forests. (Both by Harald Schultz)* *Right: Anteaters such as this* Tamandua tetradactyla *live in trees and feed by breaking into ant or termite nests with their powerful claws and gathering insects on their long, sticky tongue. (Carl Rettenmeyer)*

tioned. Hardly more than twice the size of a squirrel, it has a disproportionately large, round head with eyes so bulging that it has earned the name of "owl monkey." Because of its strictly nocturnal activity, it is also sometimes called "night monkey." Its fur is very dense and soft, a brownish-gray in color, and its tail is long and bushy. Rolled into a ball, as it sleeps the daytime hours away in the fork of a tree, it is almost invisible. But at night it is exceptionally active and calls to its companions in unexpectedly loud and varied tones. Its diet includes fruits, grain, nocturnal insects, and mollusks.

Despite its rough coat, the saki is closely related to the owl monkey. It is noted for its prodigious leaps from bough to bough, and its diet includes bats.

The uacari *(Cacajao),* which is exceptional in having an extremely short tail, has a grotesquely disheveled look, with an emaciated and entirely hairless head, and a scarlet face that becomes even redder when the animal is excited. This monkey seeks the most humid parts of the forest, lives in bands or groups of its kind, and feeds mainly upon fruits. Its relative, the bearded saki *(Chiropotes),* has a head covered with long hairs that grow all around the top of the cranium, falling in bangs over the forehead. It also has a long beard and a dense wooly coat.

Found especially at the edges of the forest or in the forest lining some of the river shores, is the saimiri *(Saimiri),* called the squirrel monkey because of its small size and habits. It lives on fruit but is also eager for the flesh of crabs and larva buried in the ground and comes down from the trees to search for this food. It is particularly gregarious, moving from place to place in groups that seem to be well organized. Its tail is very long and exceptionally prehensile and is used as a fifth limb, so that these monkeys are referred to as "hand-tailed."

The cebus monkey is nervous, inquisitive, sly and brazen. (Rolf Blomberg: Full Hand)

The capuchin *(Cebus),* a long-tailed monkey almost as intelligent as the chimpanzee, is found in the American tropics from southern Mexico to northern Argentina and a great number have settled in the Amazon forests. These monkeys adapt to life in captivity and may be seen in many zoos, where they always fascinate visitors with their dexterity, the "wise-old-man" expressions created by the wrinkled forehead and the head of hair like a monk's cowl.

The woolly monkeys *(Lagothrix),* whose thick fur makes them look like teddy bears, live in groups of from ten to twenty-five. Their enormous appetite has earned them the name *barrigudos* (big-bellies) in some parts of South America. Their strong jaws allow them to crack the hardest of nuts, which are the basis of their diet.

The spider monkey *(Ateles)* distantly resembling the tailless gibbon of the Old World, is likewise well adapted to tree life, and is intelligent. Everything about it is unusually long—body, legs, tail. The tail is prehensile and is used to pick up objects even as small as a hazel nut. Normally these monkeys walk on all fours, the tail rolled up over the back, and are capable of making leaps of more than thirty feet, stretching out their long limbs and tail to facilitate the jump. The spider monkey is found as far north as southern Mexico, but nowhere south of the Amazon basin.

The howler monkeys *(Alouatta)* make their presence known: endowed with greater vocal powers than any other primates, their roars can be heard for miles. Besides this, they are the heaviest and largest of the ceboids. They live in groups usually of three adult males and eight females, along with about seven young and immature monkeys. Apparently there is no definite hierarchy; the males seem to join in defending the territory occupied by the clan. They communicate with a great variety of calls. Their consumption of leaves and fruits is enormous; one howler can eat as much as three pounds at one feeding.

WORLD OF BATS

Bats are most abundant in the tropics, and, as might be expected, there is a dense population of these flying mammals in the Amazon forests. The Chiroptera order is here represented by at least eighty species, with all nine of the bat families of the western world represented.

The lush vegetation provides them not only with abundant food—fruits, insects and even fish—but shelter during their daytime sleep, when they fasten their claws to a support and hang head downward, their membranous wings wrapped around their bodies. The fruit bats *(Artibeus jamaicensis)* and the *Uroderma* also cut a "V" near the median vein of a palm leaf in such a way that the ends of the leaf fall vertically, making a kind of tent into which they can retire for the day. Some bats are insectivorous, hunting on the wing at twilight, and other bats are purely carnivorous, feeding on rodents or the blood of cattle. Such is the false vampire bat *(Vampyrum spectrum),* which has a three-foot wing span. Others, such as the *Glossophaga* and the *Anoura,* have unusually long tongues and feed on nectar, thereby assisting in the pollination of several plants. But whether they feed on insects, animal blood, pulpy fruit or nectar, all are crepuscular or nocturnal.

The puma, which has adapted to a wide range of habitats including the forests of the Amazon basin, is carnivorous and likes the blood of its victims. (Kurt Severin)

And all bats seek a safe hiding place—leafy branches, hollow trees, caves—wherein to suspend themselves during the day. One highly evolved type deserving special mention is the *Noctilio* or bulldog bat, of average size but with particularly long sharp claws. To the usual diet of insects the bulldog bat adds small fish, seizing them as they swim close to the surface.

The Desmodontidae or vampire bats are found from southern Mexico to northern Argentina but are particularly numerous in the Amazon region. The teeth of the *Desmodus rotundus* are veritable lancets for puncturing thick skin. They will attack any warm-blooded animal including other bats, but they prey on domestic animals—horses, cattle, goats, barnyard fowl, and man. A repeated attack from these bloodsuckers can be disastrous. One of these bats can absorb two ounces of blood in a night and the intake of blood by a single bat has been measured at up to ten gallons a year.

Although the vampire bat would naturally be the first to be suspected of transmitting rabies or other diseases, in the decade of studies made on Trinidad up to 1963, the fruit bat, not the vampire, was found to be infected!

However, repeated vampire predation is debilitating, and since as many as five hundred vampires may congregate in a single roost they present a health problem and in cattle-raising areas an economic problem. Methods of control are actively being studied in Mexico and in Central and South America.

THE SLOTH—NATURE'S IDLER

The summit of the trees of the Amazon is the habitat of one of the most curious mammals in the world—the sloth. Resembling at first glance a small bear because of its rounded form, it has a globular head, a short snout and very long limbs. Its body is covered with a thick coat of long, rough and brittle hair. This coat ranges from brown to whitish gray but it is often strongly tinted with green by a microscopic algae that

The kinkajou (Potos flavus), *which early travelers mistook for a monkey, is a fierce little arboreal predator. (Paul Schauenberg)*

lodges in the hair and flourishes in the forest humidity. This unique condition is made all the more curious because this algae is in turn host to the larvae of a moth; even the adult insects with quite normal wings thrive in the sloth's fur.

Few animals are as strictly arboreal in their way of life as the sloth. Shunning descent to the ground, where it is hopelessly out of its element, this long-limbed creature is most at home hanging upside down from branches. Long, curving claws on its toes—the ai *(Bradypus tridactylus)* has three toes on each foot and the unau *(Choloepus hoffmanni)* two toes on the forefeet and three on the hind feet—are a great help in scaling the tree trunks and swinging from branches.

The famous American naturalist William Beebe, who taught us so much about the creatures of tropical America, once followed a sloth continually for a week and found that its routine consisted of eleven hours of feeding, eighteen of just moving slowly about, ten hours for rest and the remaining 129 hours for sleep. "Some would call this the ideal life," comments Beebe.

Indeed, even during its waking hours the sloth moves about so languidly that it reminds the observer of a slow-motion film. Yet its endurance is outstanding and it is capable of traveling considerable distances by passing from one tree to the next—although an ancient tale would have it that it clings to the same tree until it exhausts the food supply and then dies.

It is not easy to raise the sloth in captivity, if only for its highly selective vegetarian diet. The Bradypus disdains all but the leaves of the Cecropia tree, that giant tropical relative of the temperate-zone mulberry. To digest this bulky diet, the sloth's stomach is equipped with several chambers, and has powerful muscles in the first chamber for churning, and other sections for chemical breakdown. Constantly filled to capacity,

Right above: White-faced monkeys live together in bands remarkable for their organization. (James Simon) Right: The spider monkeys (Ateles) *with long supple limbs and a tail that acts as a fifth limb are well equipped for life in trees. Far right: The woolly monkey* (Lagothrix) *has short powerful paws that enable it to crack the toughest nuts. (Both by Harald Schultz)*

this huge stomach may constitute as much as 30 per cent of the sloth's body-weight, reminding us, in certain respects, of the digestive habits of the ruminants. It takes a long while for the sloth to digest a meal, sometimes as much as a week; it eliminates great quantities of excrement at intervals of seven or eight days, when it descends to the foot of a tree.

Are we to think of this creature, without a single close relative in today's animal kingdom, merely as some degenerate form? The eighteenth-century French naturalist Buffon considered the sloth not only lazy, but wretched—an evil creature. And yet, if some of the sloth's ways seem primitive, others are actually highly specialized adaptations.

In the far past the group was far more versatile, and huge ancestors of the sloth, the megatheriums and mylodons, once roamed the American plains. Of the group, the arboreal sloth alone remains, perhaps because of its rigid adaptation to a unique ecological niche, and one where it has no competition. The sloth also happens to have remarkable powers of resistance to deep wounds and even to serious mutilation. Once again, the mighty Amazon forest has played a vital role in the conservation of a unique creature that might otherwise have been doomed to extinction.

THE PREDATORS

Where there are many animals there will be many predators. The Amazon Valley is one of the world's great centers of reptiles and they are the most active hunters in this area. Besides innumerable crocodiles and caimans, there are very many snakes, including some giant species. The huge anaconda *(Eunectes murinus)* may attain a length of twenty-five feet or more—but never the fantastic lengths described by the more imaginative of amateur explorers. Although surpassed in length by the Asiatic pythons, the anaconda exceeds them in diameter and is certainly one of the largest serpents in the world. It is part arboreal and part aquatic, waiting in the water toward nightfall to feed on the birds and mammals that come down to drink. The boa constrictor *(Constrictor constrictor)* is another giant, but it rarely exceeds twelve feet in length. It wraps itself around a branch and catches small animals and birds that carelessly venture too near it. All boas kill their prey by coiling themselves around the body of the victim and crushing its bones before swallowing it whole. The emerald boa *(Boa canina)* with its green skin striped with white or yellow is the most strictly arboreal of all the South American boas. Its camouflage and its ability to climb swiftly in trees make it a formidable hunter of its main prey, birds.

Of the many smaller reptiles in the Amazon basin, the arboreal forms include some slow-moving species such as the

Left: The great Amazon forest is occasionally broken by a grassy, tree-strewn savanna, such as this one between Macapa and the Rio Araguari, Amapa territory. (E. Aubert de la Rüe) Right above: Lantern flies, related to the cicadas, get their name from the light given off by certain bacteria under the skin. (Rolf Blomberg: Full Hand) Right: Longicorn beetles (Acrocinus longimanus), *with front legs and antennae far longer than the rest of the body, illustrate the bizarre forms taken by some insects. (Paul Schauenberg)*

liana-serpents *(Oxybelis)* and the snail-eaters *(Sibon)* as well as some swift-moving green serpents *(Thalerophis)* that live in the trees.

Many of these reptiles are remarkably camouflaged and are almost invisible amidst the dense growth. Among these are the beautiful but venomous coral snake *(Micrurus)*, with its pattern of black, yellow, and bright red rings, and the enormous bushmaster *(Lachesis muta)*, most venomous of pit vipers, colored gray with brown losenge-shaped markings. The bushmaster preys upon all mammals, but the sloth is its preferred victim.

The Amazon Valley is of course an excellent hunting ground for birds of prey, and vultures, eagles and hawks abound. One of the giants among these is the harpy eagle *(Harpia harpyja)*, which hunts by day and preys mainly upon sloths and monkeys. Slow and heavy in flight, it has an unusually powerful bill and talons. Its distinguishing mark is its erectile crest on a white head. The wings are rounded and rather short, enabling it to fly among the trees, where its mottled gray plumage provides effective camouflage. As elsewhere in tropical America, vultures are found throughout the Amazon basin. Besides the common black variety, called carrion crow, and the turkey buzzard, the Amazon forest is the favorite hunting ground of the bizarrely colored king vulture *(Sarcorhamphus papa)* with its enormous gray-white and black body, naked head, and a neck like a rainbow: red, yellow, and gray-blue.

Of the many carnivorous animals in the Amazon forest, some of the smaller mammals are among the most ferocious. Such is the margay *(Felis tigrina)*, which is marked like the ocelot and has a similar tail but is usually only about two feet long. It spends most of its time in the trees, hunting at night for birds in the nest, but on occasion it descends to the ground to seek out the tinamous and small mammals. The true ocelot *(Leopardus pardalis)* is also found here. Its pelt, marked with eye-spots (as the name ocelot indicates) is thick and beautiful. The ocelot is distributed over a wide territory from Texas to the Chaco, and as an arboreal animal obviously finds the Amazon forest much to its liking. Nocturnal like most felines, it hunts animals of all sizes, including the snail. Another small mammal, the jaguarundi *(Herpailurus yaguarondi)*, unlike the true jaguar, has a uniformly brownish gray pelt and short feet. Like other Mustelidae (minks, weasels, martens), the taira or eira *(Eira barbara)*, has a dense brownish fur, is about two feet long, not counting a long furry tail, and can be domesticated. Then there are various members of the Procyonidae, such as the raccoon, already mentioned, and the crabier or mayuato *(Procyon cancrivorus)*, both carnivorous, the coati *(Nasua rufa)*, the strange cuataquil *(Bassaricyon)*, one of the rarest of New World carnivora, and the least well known, the potto *(Potos)*. Nearly all of these are arboreal but each occupies its own particular ecological niche.

The Amazon Valley has very few large carnivores. However, a small number of two large-sized feline species are found either in the heart of the dense forest or in the high bare Andes: the puma *(Puma concolor)* and the jaguar *(Panthera onca)*. Both animals have an unusually wide distribution, the puma ranging from Canada to Patagonia, the jaguar from Texas to Patagonia, each being called by a different name in the country in which it is found. The puma's coloring, uniformly tawny on the upper parts, dirty white on the under parts, has earned it the name of "mountain lion" in the Northern Hemisphere, and sometimes even "panther." The French refer to it by the name *couguar*. Although the puma's coloring resembles that of the lion, in size, form and habits it corresponds more closely to the Old World leopard. It averages about forty inches in length not counting the tail, which has some bushy hairs—it is not a tuft—toward the tip.

Although it can climb trees it is not arboreal and seems to prefer the bush country of the higher altitudes. It preys upon

Left: Papaya trees (Carica), *native to tropical America and resembling palms, bear edible fruits of melon size. Both fruit and leaves contain a ferment, papain, capable of digesting meat. (Paul Schauenberg) Right: Like a monkey, the female three-toed sloth* (Bradypus) *moves about with her young clutching her undersides. The large, curved claws keep a strong grip on branches. (Carl Rettenmeyer)*

a variety of animals, some of them aquatic, and roams along the river shores at night. Contrary to some of the tales told about it by hunters, it is not a ferocious animal and rarely, if ever, attacks man.

The jaguar is the largest feline on the American continent, averaging a length of over five feet. Tan-colored, with black spots, it is thickset and has short legs but is nevertheless swift and agile. Ranging from Texas to Patagonia, it has acquired, like the puma, many common names. Most South Americans refer to it as *tigre,* but some in Brazil call it *cangsu,* meaning "big head" because its head is noticeably large in proportion to its body.

Most big cats avoid water, but the jaguar is a notable exception for it seems to like rivers and is a good swimmer. This fierce and adaptable predator will climb, when pursuing an arboreal victim, but is at a disadvantage in trees because of its heavy build. No animal of any size is safe from the jaguar's nocturnal sorties. A dexterous fisherman, it seems to prefer the caiman; but the capybara and large mammals such as the tapir and the deer provide appreciated meals, and when opportunity offers it will take cattle. Aside from man, the universal enemy of the animal kingdom, it has no natural enemy, and is therefore at the top of the pyramid of predators. Along with the anaconda and the harpy, the jaguar is one of the kings of the Amazon jungle.

The predators, from the jaguar and anaconda down, are not being cruel or ferocious when they hunt and devour smaller creatures; they do so only to survive and almost never kill except to feed. They are merely obeying a law of nature. The Amazon Valley, teeming with such a variety of living things, makes one especially conscious of this law. And it is from the interlocking of death and life that the balance of nature is maintained everywhere. The great rain forest of the Amazon has changed in the course of hundreds of centuries; yet since the Tertiary, this region has maintained a remarkable stability in the midst of conditions wonderfully favorable to the development of life in all its forms.

Left: The jaguar, unchallenged king of the Amazonian jungle, is found in many habitats, but prefers river banks, where it sleeps by day and hunts at dusk. (Karl Weidmann)

Right above: Although a very powerful feline, the jaguar avoids a long chase, preferring to lie in wait for his prey and then pounce on it. Right: Of all the cats, the jaguar shows the strongest preference for water and is capable of crossing the wide rivers so common in the Amazon basin. (Both by Sasha Siemel)

Arid Plateaus and Clay Deserts

North-eastern Brazil

7

Far from being uniformly humid, tropical regions encompass many extremely arid areas. Nowhere is this contrast more striking than in northeastern Brazil. Here, not far from the great Amazon rain forest, is a plateau region where scrub forest, the *caatinga,* alternates with large stretches of desert, in which nothing grows but plants that can store moisture in their thickened stems and leaves. Geographers trace this aridity far back in time, ascribing it to an erosion of the plateaus that long ago carried away rich clay and top soil, leaving only a covering of pebbles or sand—a naked and furrowed landscape resembling formations in western Africa, especially the Sudan.

This dry zone of the Brazilian Highlands, set close to the coastal plain, extends inland to the upper reaches of the Rio São Francisco, taking in the greater part of eight states (Piauí, Ceará, Rio Grande do Norte, Paraíba, Pernambuco, Alagôas, Sergipe, Bahia, and a large portion of Minas Gerais), and covering an area of about 580,000 square miles. The entire area is geologically a part of the great Brazilian plateau, formed of crystalline rocks and separated from the Guiana tableland only by a threshold through which the Amazon flows to the Atlantic.

In the north this plateau slopes gently down to the sea, especially in the state of Ceará, where it is barely one hundred feet above sea level. Toward the sources of the Rio Paraíba and on the high plateau of Borborema, it rises in the south to an altitude of about 3,300 feet. Here and there these highlands are crowned by short ranges of mountains or hills.

THE RIO SAO FRANCISCO

South America has three great rivers: the Amazon, La Plata (actually a gulf), and São Francisco, in that order. The São Francisco rises in southern Brazil in western Minas Gerais and flows northward for about one thousand miles before curving eastward into the Atlantic about sixty miles northeast of the port of Aracajú. It is almost two thousand miles long and it is navigable for almost one thousand miles in its upper section and for about 150 miles in its lower reaches, its course being interrupted by occasional rapids and the 279-foot Paulo Afonso falls. This river has been the main artery of communication between northeast and central Brazil since colonial times, and it is still important enough to warrant a program of dams that will regulate its flow and make it even more useful.

THE ARID NORTHEAST

The northeastern portion of Brazil, by far the most arid of this country, has been called the "Job of the North" because of its extreme poverty. This region frequently suffers from an almost complete lack of rain because of erratic winds. During the summer it gets the trade winds and in winter it gets winds from the southwest that act as counter-monsoon winds. Winds of this type do not bring rain, merely passing over the land without condensing except when they strike a mountain barrier. Only a narrow coastal region south of Natal, including Recife and João Pessoa, receives any significant rainfall. This relatively humid region, formerly wooded, is now entirely devoted to agriculture. Northwest of Natal, this region becomes progressively narrower, until southeast of Fortaleza the sandhills along the seaside have scarcely any vegetation, except for groves of palm trees between the mouth of the Rio Assu and Cape Calcanhar.

As one leaves the coast and moves into the interior, the average annual rainfall decreases rapidly except in the highlands around the upper reaches of the São Francisco. In the most arid sections the dry season lasts from four to seven months, and the average annual rainfall is less than twenty inches.

The climate of the lower reaches of the São Francisco, and the interior of the states of Pernambuco, Alagôas, and Sergipe, is less arid, the seasons are less marked, and the rains fall over a longer period. Only on the highland slopes exposed to the trade winds are rains more abundant; in the Chapada Diamantina in Minas Gerais and on the slopes of the mountain range of Ceará and Serra do Araripe the rainfall is quite abundant, thus favoring the growth of true forests of more or less deciduous trees, and even some evergreens, usually cleared, by now, for cultivation. These regions are veritable oases in the midst of the caatinga.

The worst feature of the climate of northeastern Brazil is the irregularity of the rainfall. In some years the rainy season fails altogether; crops and domestic animals perish in the drought and the region becomes a disaster area. The inhabitants then migrate to more prosperous areas in search of work, a movement that the government is trying to check.

HARDY VEGETATION

The character of the climate is reflected in a striking way in the vegetation, and above all in the contrast between the

The São Francisco, third-largest river in South America, runs for part of its course between steep banks, carving deep gorges in the Brazilian plateaus. (James Simon)

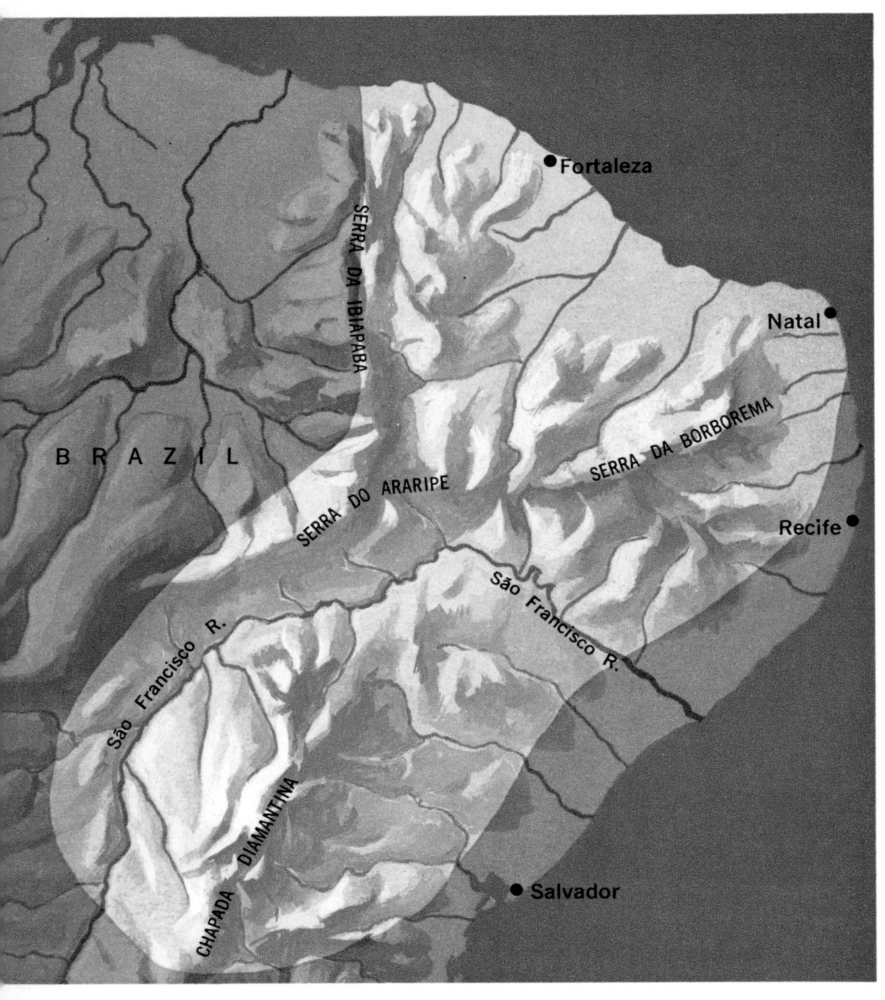

The arid, northeastern portion of Brazil is geologically a part of the Brazilian Highlands. The region is largely scrub forest and desert, the acute lack of rain being due mainly to erratic winds.

humid coastal region and the pronounced aridity of the rest of the country.

The coastal zone was once covered with semideciduous rain forests. These forests were, however, never continuous, and on sandy stretches, in particular, they were replaced by a poorer vegetation, mainly of shrubs. The forests rarely extended more than thirty or so miles inland and never beyond the first mountain range. These woods were almost entirely cleared in the course of the exploitation of the timber, and the land was turned to pasture. Except for some woods that were reserved by the Portuguese Royal Navy or for private building, broad plantations, especially of the sugar cane that made the fortune of this part of Brazil, took the place of the forests. Thus, the forest has almost entirely disappeared, especially in the region of Bahia; so have the patches of woods on the better-watered slopes of the sierras.

Elsewhere on the arid plateau, the most common vegetation is that of open forest or a dense thicket called caatinga (a combination of two Indian words—*caa,* meaning forests, and *tinga,* meaning white—which well describe this forest when stripped of leaves).

Generally the caatinga is a type of stunted forest formation that is classed with those equipped to resist drought. Mingled with xerophytes in the more arid expanses are thorny bushes and trees, succulents, cacti, euphorbias, bromeliads and annual grasses. The caatinga is distinctly different from the *cerrados,* or isolated forests of tall trees, in the abundance of thorny vegetation and in a ground cover that is for the most part spotty and temporary. The plants, covered with small leaves, are leafless during long periods. Only a few trees, for instance the joazeiro *(Zizyphus joaseiro),* keep their leaves throughout the year. Some of these yield useful products: for example, the *Anacardium occidentale* bears the cashew nut, which is exported in great quantities especially to the United States, where it is a delicacy and its oil is used in paints.

A large portion of the caatinga is a dry dense forest which the Brazilians call *mata seca.* This growth covers especially the slopes exposed to the trade winds. To a great extent this forest has been cleared, but it once represented a transition zone in eastern Maranhão between the Amazon forest and the deteriorated thickets of the drier eastern regions. The babassu palm tree has in part taken its place as a result of man's activities. What remains of the *mata seca* consists of trees no taller than twenty feet and of big bushes, often with a very dense undergrowth of shrubs. Elsewhere the caatinga takes the form of thickets, the *carrascal,* with here and there a few taller trees.

The caatinga thus represents inferior forms of a dry, thorny forest, more or less dense, that must have extended throughout northeastern Brazil before the intervention of man.

The flora of the caatinga is in large part endemic and rich in species. The Leguminosae abound, particularly the catingueras *(Caesalpinia)* and juremas *(Mimosa).* The euphorbias are also numerous, including the faveilero or *pinhao bravo (Jatropha),* a shrub not without beauty but more dangerous than the worst nettles on account of its stinging powers. Some crotons and some *Bombacaceae,* among them the famous barrigudas *(Chorizia)* with trunks bulging like barrels and covered with conical points, complete the arboreal vegetation. The undergrowth includes a great many bromeliads, their long, prickly-edged leaves arranged in rosettes, at times a vivid yellow or red. Some of them, such as the caroas *(Neoglaziovia variegata),* are valued for the long fibers that can be extracted from their leaves.

A spectacular and essential plant of the caatinga is the cactus. One of the most remarkable and widely distributed in arid, rocky zones is the xique-xique *(Cereus gounellei),* easily recognized by its grayish stems covered with hairs and its complicated intertwinings. Others are like trees, reaching heights of fifteen feet and sometimes even twice that. Such are the mandacarus or cardeiros *(Cereus jamacaru)* and the fecheiros *(C. squamosus),* species whose tall "candles" dominate the landscape. The opuntias are likewise abundant and cover the ground along with the prickly balls of other cactus, such as the *Melocactus.*

The caatinga is thus a dense concentration of plant life. Although lianas are almost absent and epiphytes very rare, except for some lichens and clusters of *Tillandsia,* trees, bushes and the great number of prickly or thorny plants often

Xique-xique cactus (Cereus gounellei) *near Itaretama in the dry caatinga region. The remains of a volcano loom on the horizon. (E. Aubert de la Rüe)*

The young shoots of the xique-xique cactus, common in northeastern Brazil, are used as fodder for cattle. (E. Aubert de la Rüe)

form an impenetrable tangle. Because of this the vaqueros who herd cattle in the caatinga—the counterpart of the Argentine gauchos—are clothed entirely in leather.

In the midst of this vast expanse of thicket especially in some of the mountain regions, there are patches of greener forests, the *mattas,* resulting from a greater humidity. These greener islets are perhaps the remains of a forest that extended over the entire region when the climate was less arid.

On the level bottoms of the valleys great palm groves are set out, consisting mainly of the carnauba palm *(Copernicia cerifera),* great fan-shaped trees cultivated for the wax often used in manufacturing floor and furniture polishes. The fronds are covered with a thick layer of this wax, which serves to lessen the intense evaporation that occurs in the hot dry climate that prevails for most of the year. Up to 15,000 tons of this wax are produced annually in Brazil, which has a world monopoly of this product. The presence of the carnauba palm is all the more interesting since the caatinga is generally poor in palm trees, except for the catole *(Cocos commune),* which is very abundant all around the coastal city of Fortaleza.

The effect of man on the caatinga is obvious in certain regions that the Brazilians call *agreste* (as against *sertão,* meaning uninhabitable desert land). Many of the dense thickets of today are only the degraded form surviving from the primeval forest. The need for wood, clearing for plantations, overgrazing, goats, and bush fires have all ravaged the original ground cover. The importance of man's impact on this region must not, however, be exaggerated, because the paucity of natural resources in the caatinga has tended to discourage settlement.

There are similarities between the vegetation of northeastern Brazil and that of the African *sahel* but there are also distinct differences, notably the presence in the caatinga of cacti and bromeliads, which have no true equivalents in Africa. On the other hand, the mimosa tree *(Acacia)* so common in the African landscape, plays only a very minor role in South America. The result is that although the two regions greatly resemble each other, they have a quite different flora.

The caatinga and the sertão are obviously not suited to agriculture. At the most, they have made possible a form of shifting cultivation, except of course on the more fertile open mountain slopes and in the more humid lowlands bordering the rivers. On the other hand, they have favored cattle raising. In 1711, it was estimated that the sertão of Bahia grazed 500,000 head of cattle and that of Pernambuco 800,000. The vaqueros were kept very busy, especially in getting the cattle to the few watering places in the region.

The caatinga, so near to and so easily reached from the coast, thus contributed to a well-balanced economy, with a profitable exchange between a cattle-raising area and a farming area. The baroque splendor of the buildings in the oldest cities of the coastal plains testifies to the great prosperity that this produced in colonial times.

ARMADILLOS—ARMORED MAMMALS

This region is only moderately rich in animal life, and the most noteworthy species are also found in the Amazon Valley. Of mammals, there are various marsupials, a rather large group of rodents—the capybara lives here but in very small numbers—and such carnivores as the skunks *(Conepatus chilensis).* A few monkeys, among them the titi *(Callithrix jacchus),* which resembles the squirrel monkey, frequent the more wooded districts.

Isolated stands of carnauba palms (Copernicia), *with broad, leafy crowns, grow in the most humid zones. A wax coating on the leaves is used in furniture polish. (Hilgard O'Reilly Sternberg)*

Probably the most remarkable of the mammals in this area is the tatu or armadillo. Armadillos are found everywhere from Texas to Patagonia and from dense rain forests to almost desert regions. Three species occur in the caatinga: the three-banded armadillo *(Tolypeutes tricinctus),* the common nine-banded armadillo *(Dasypus novemcinctus),* and the weasel-headed armadillo *(Euphractus sexcinctus).* Armadillos are encased in an armor composed of overlapping buckler-plates and movable bands, like medieval chain-mail, encircling the middle of the body. The head and tail are also protected by plates. The plates are horny in the young animal, bony in the adult. Despite its rigid "armored-tank" appearance, an armadillo employs a highly developed muscle system to contract and roll itself into a ball, with the head and tail plates meeting, thus making it almost impregnable. It can also run very rapidly. It is, moreover, remarkably adapted to rooting in the earth, or rather in ant-hills, its feet being provided with strong, very long claws. With these it can also anchor itself so stubbornly that it takes great strength to pull it free, as native hunters do, for they esteem it a great delicacy. In spite of the physical effort required in digging, the armadillo is able to hold its breath for three or four minutes while its snout is buried in the earth—a notable adaptation which prevents soil from entering its lungs.

Armadillos live in burrows from two feet to fifteen or twenty feet long, at depths of from one to five feet. Often these have as many as a dozen openings. One room in these burrows is lined with grass and leaves, and there the animals usually spend the day, coming out during the night to hunt, although some armadillos indulge in daytime activity. They feed mainly on insects but they also eat mollusks and even frogs and small reptiles, and if need be, carrion; they balance this diet with some vegetation. From every point of view, the armadillo is truly an extraordinary animal.

BIRDS OF THE PLATEAUS

Few Amazonian species of birds appear in the forests of the plateaus of northeast Brazil. One group found here is the tinamous, which resemble the partridge of northern climes. Among these are the *Crypturus,* which lays its eggs in small hollows in the ground, and the *Rhynchotus,* which is also present in the Mato Grosso. Doves are abundantly represented, many of them characteristic of the arid zones of South America.

Many species of parrots are indigenous to this part of Brazil, among them the golden parrot *(Aratinga aurea),* which nests in holes in trees but also at times hollows out a nest in the huge termite structures found in some trees. The termites immediately seal off the tiny galleries opening into this nest cavity and seem to live comfortably with the birds, a strange association which proves to be entirely to the advantage of the parrots.

The open character of the landscape of northeast Brazil has attracted many of the flickers *(Colaptes campestris)* that are so common in Argentina and the Mato Grosso. Many passerines that like a habitat of bush and thicket, particularly the ovenbirds, are also found here. Conspicuous among the grayish green foliage is the yellow finch *(Sicalis flaveola).*

The ceiba tree is leafless for much of the year, thus avoiding loss of water during dry spells. (Rolf Blomberg: Full Hand)

The giant anteater is found in South America wherever there are ants. (Karl Weidmann)

THE UNDESIRABLE GUEST

As if man hoped to make nature over, he has often transported plants and animals from one part of the world to another. Sometimes this has been done unwittingly, especially with insects, and particularly since travel has become so swift. The accidental and catastrophic introduction into northeast Brazil of a malaria-carrying mosquito, the *Anopheles gambiae,* is a case in point.

In about 1930 a mail boat from Dakar arrived at Natal, the seaport in Brazil's Rio Grande do Norte, bringing some stowaways—several mosquitos representing one of the two principal malaria carriers common in much of Africa. They immediately became acclimatized, and by March, 1930, two thousand of their larvae were collected in Natal. By April, malaria presented a serious problem in Natal, and by January, 1931, there were ten thousand malaria cases among the twelve thousand inhabitants of Alecrim, the slum area of the city. Following this there was a period of quiet while the mosquito was spreading up the valleys into the state of Ceará and throughout Rio Grande do Norte. In 1938 a terrible malaria epidemic broke out in the region, the most disastrous of all Brazilian epidemics of this disease, which has always been endemic in this region. The cases numbered in the hundreds of thousands and it is estimated that more than twenty thousand inhabitants died, and in the contaminated regions, industry, commerce and agriculture came to a standstill.

The bulging trunk of barriguda trees (Chorizia ventricosa) *was once wrongly believed to collect water. (E. Aubert de la Rüe)*

The Brazilian government, with the aid of the Rockefeller Foundation, began an intensive campaign to stamp out the disease—at first containing it, then undertaking to eliminate it from the contaminated region. By November, 1940, it had been completely eradicated from Brazil. But meanwhile tens of thousands had died and many millions of dollars lost—only one more example of how the introduction of even a tiny insect can upset the balance of nature and provoke catastrophe.

THE COAST AND THE ISLANDS

Along the shore southeastward from the mouth of the Amazon, the Atlantic waters are brown with sediment from the great river. As one approaches the shores of Ceará, the waters become clearer and take on their natural greenish or bluish hue.

Thus one arrives at Ponta do Calcanhar, the northeastern tip of the continent. From here the coast slopes southeastward to Cabo de São Roque, a promontory of white sand, where the New World approaches closest to the Old (except of course in the Arctic). Here the width of the Atlantic is only 1,775 miles whereas the average width of the Atlantic is 3,750 miles. This nearness to Africa no doubt explains the similarities in the fauna and especially in the sea birds on the two shores.

The coastline from Fortaleza to Salvador, a distance of 1,250 miles, is fringed with a barrier reef which was for a long time believed to be exclusively coral. In reality it is made up of sandstone consolidated with calcareous deposits. It is very wide along the coasts of Bahia and Espirito Santo, giving the impression of a gigantic sea wall. Fishermen have taken advantage of this barrier, working from fragile *jangadas,* mere rafts equipped with sails. The boats keep to the lagoons created by the natural dike, against which the waves break in a border of foam.

The Brazilian coast is flanked by a few island outposts, including the only coral atoll in the South Atlantic, Rocas Reef. About 140 miles from Ponta do Calcanhar, the island is only four or five miles in length. Here the sooty tern *(Sterna fuscata)* nests in large colonies, as does the noddy *(Anous stolidus);* frigate birds and boobies are also found here.

Still farther east, about 220 miles off the Brazilian coast, is an extinct volcano, Ilha Fernando de Noronha, rising almost 1,100 feet above the sea. When Charles Darwin visited it in 1832, the entire surface was wooded, and the volcanic, well-watered soil was fertile. This vegetation suffered greatly from a colonial settlement, and especially a penitentiary, but where it has survived, a large number of indigenous species have persisted. The animal life here is also very interesting, the most noteworthy being a legless lizard *(Amphisbaena ridleyi),* a relative of some reptiles of the West Indies. Among the sea birds are two species of tropic-birds, three boobies, one frigate and four terns, including the lovely fairy tern, which nests regularly on the island. There is also one species of dove, a vireo, and a flycatcher.

Almost as curious as Fernando de Noronha is the St. Paul Rocks, a rock only a thousand feet long rising from the sea about 540 miles from the Brazilian coast. This rock is peculiar in that it is composed neither of coral nor lava, but is the summit of a mountain more than 13,000 feet high. Only three species of birds nest here, the white-bellied booby and two species of noddies. A few insects and spiders complete the fauna of these rocky islands in the outlying waters of the South Atlantic.

Right above: The buffy-browed guan (Penelope superciliaris), *which feeds on fruit, is equally at home on the ground and in trees. (Harald Schultz) Right: An armor of solid but movable plates protects the nine-banded armadillo* (Dasypus novemcinctus) *against its enemies and the hard walls of its deep burrow. (Francisco Erize)*

Gems, Orchids and a Great Cascade

The Brazilian Coast and Plateaus

8

As our plane slowly circled the airport, night was falling and great aureoles of light wreathed the rugged outlines of the coastal mountains and made a necklace of islets shimmer in the bay. Rio de Janeiro lay stretched out below us, with the lofty mountains that come steeply down to the shore giving the site a majestic beauty.

The mountains that enclose the city, the Serra da Carioca, rise up as rocky masses (called horsts by geologists), which have been isolated by the sinking of surrounding portions of the earth's crust. Some of these mountains (locally known as *morros)* such as the Pico de Tijuca are more than three thousand feet high. Behind the city rises another range, separated from the coastal range by more or less swampy, alluvial plains, now partly drained but still containing a few lagoons. The sea has partially invaded this complex topography. Guanabara Bay, at Rio de Janeiro, is strewn with countless islands and huge rocks; Pão de Azucar (Sugar Loaf), 1,296 feet high, and the Pico do Corcovado, 2,310 feet high, are the most famous. The beauty of this harbor, one of the safest and largest in the world, is due precisely to the rocky remains of shoreline mountains together with a coastal plain and beaches enclosed by other mountains covered with tropical forests.

The natives of Rio de Janeiro, the Cariocas, are justly proud of their city, declaring that "God made the world in seven days, but two days were devoted to creating Rio alone." Even more fanciful is the French poet Paul Claudel's little story that an angel interrupted God while He was making this bay the most perfect landscape on the earth with the result that some of the mountain peaks were set in askew.

Viewed from the ocean, the entire coast of Brazil between Natal and Rio de Janeiro or even as far as the State of Rio Grande do Sul, seems to be an unbroken chain of mountains. Indeed, a part of this range is called La Serra do Mar (the Mountains of the Sea). Properly speaking it is not so much a mountain range as the steep eastern edge of a great plateau, plunging sometimes 2,600 feet down almost vertically to the sea. But in the states of Rio de Janeiro and Espirito Santo, the Serra do Mar becomes a true mountain range. One of its summits, the Pico da Bandeira, rises to 9,386 feet, the highest point in all of Brazil. Great rivers, particularly the Paraíba, Doce, and Jequitinhonha, have pierced this mountain wall and carved out valleys opening into the sea. The mouths of some of these rivers have in turn been submerged by the sea, forming deep gulfs, as, for instance, the Bahia de Todos os Santos, on which the city of Salvador is located.

In front of this mountain wall there are very narrow coastal plains; sand dunes alternate with depressions where the waters accumulate in lagoons and marshes. Lagoa Mirim and Lagoa dos Patos in Rio Grande do Sul belong to this system. Except in the sections where the cliff drops off directly into the sea, as in the vicinity of Santos, the port of São Paulo, the coast is bordered as far as the eye can see with white sand beaches edged with coconut palms.

TROPICAL FORESTS

The narrow coastal plain and the Atlantic slopes of the Serro do Mar from Natal to the State of Santa Catarina have a very humid climate. Unlike most tropical regions, where the rainy season is generally in the summer, the rains here come mainly in autumn and winter, that is, from April to July. This anomaly results from the condensation that occurs when masses of polar air moving northward from the Antarctic meet the trade winds. In southeastern Brazil, the rains tend to be almost continual throughout the year, the rains of the southern winter being followed by the tropical rains of summer. The mountain ranges also play an important role in these rainy seasons: the vapor-charged air coming from the sea is chilled as it rises on the mountain slopes, causing the vapor to condense. Although the best-watered sectors receive only fifty-five inches of rain annually and Rio de Janeiro receives only forty-four inches, this region is covered by a flourishing forest vegetation because the rain is distributed almost throughout the year, fogs are frequent, and the dry season never lasts longer than two months. As everywhere, the dense tropical forest can do with relatively little rainfall provided the air remains humid throughout the year.

Because of the humid climate, a continuous band of forests once extended from northeast Brazil to the extreme southern portion of the country. This band was flanked on the west by the caatinga and on the south by the Brazilian plateaus. It was these forests that gave Brazil its name when Amerigo Vespucci in 1501 and Goncalo Coelho in 1503 took back to Portugal great quantities of a wood called *braza* from the tree now known as *pau brasil (Caesalpinia echinata)*. The King of Portugal promptly gave Fernando de Noronha the exclusive right to exploit this valuable timber, and that enterprising gentleman had five thousand trees cut down and the wood sent to Portugal in the year 1519 alone.

This forest was gradually ravaged in the process of clearing the ground for tropical agriculture, which eroded the soil and destroyed the magnificent vegetation that protected it. A few beautiful forests still persist in Bahia and Espirito Santo, but even these are always being diminished by encroaching

Around Rio de Janeiro the coastal mountains plunge almost vertically down to the sea and are broken up into isolated masses gracefully sculptured by erosion. (Virginia Carleton)

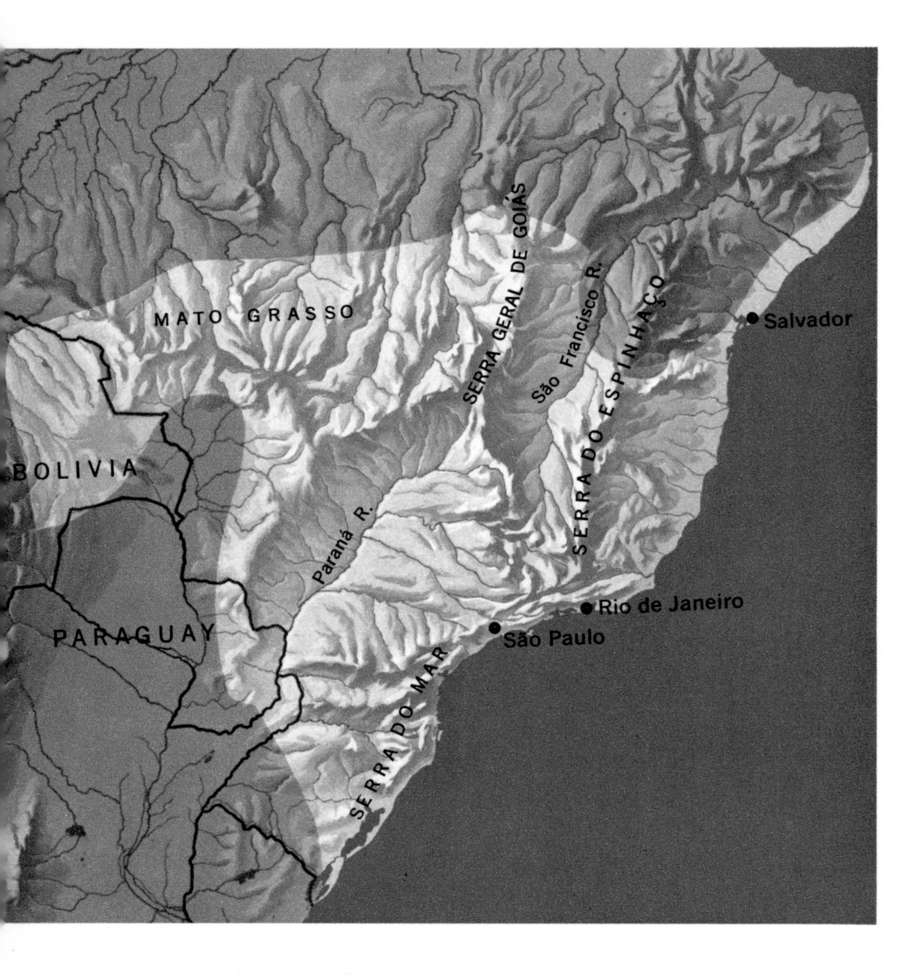

Humid, forested mountains stretch along the entire Atlantic façade of Brazil. Behind these, vast plateaus cover the eastern portion of Brazil as far as the Bolivian frontier.

plantations or by the exploiters of timber. Fortunately the Brazilian government has at last recognized the threat of such activities and has created reserves in some areas and reforestation projects in others. The constant humidity of the climate enables these forests to regenerate quickly. Thus some mountains, such as Tijuca, near Rio de Janeiro, which were completely denuded in the nineteenth century, are once more covered with dense forest. Although mostly man-made, these wooded slopes are of great interest to the newly arrived traveler for they give him his first contact with luxuriant tropical vegetation.

Although the tropical forests of eastern Brazil resemble those of the Amazon basin, the trees never attain such giant size. This may be explained by the fact that the soil is drier. Of the species found here, some are very beautiful and of great economic importance; for example, the jacarandas *(Dalbergia nigra)*, the ipe *(Paratecoma peroba)*, the zebra-wood or *goncalo alves (Astronimum fraxinifolium)*, the purple wood or *pau violeta (Dalbergia cearensis)*, the rosewood or *pau rosa (D. frutescens)*, and one already mentioned, the pau brasil.

The forests of eastern Brazil also differ from those of the Amazon in the extraordinary development of the epiphytes—plants that attach themselves to other plants but are not parasitical—such as the bromeliads, the orchids, many ferns, and even some cacti. The abundance of tree ferns, a characteristic of submountain climate and cloud forests, is especially striking. This vegetation closely resembles that of certain tropical mountains in Africa, especially the epiphytes and ferns found in the high forests of the Nimba Mountains in Guinea.

The most intensive botanical studies have been carried out in the south in the national parks of the Serra des Organos and the Itatiaia. The slopes of the latter are covered with a humid subtropical growth of trees that retain their leaves. The lowest level, extending upward for over three thousand feet, is now covered with secondary growth, having been reforested after the early exploitation for charcoal and railroad ties. The influence of man is particularly evident in the abundance of the quaresmeiras *(Tibouchina)*, which is covered with purple flowers in blossom time, the *Cassia* with its yellow flowers, the *Cecropia*, and the palm, *Euterpe edulis*. From 4,000 to almost 6,000 feet up, the forest becomes dense thicket; at 7,500 it is intermixed with araucarias *(Araucaria angustifolia)* in single specimens or small stands. Above 8,000 feet, the scene reminds one of steppes: the ground is covered with grasses, sedges, including some shrubs and dwarf bamboos *(Chusquea pinifolia)* whose narrow, bunched leaves give them the look of conifers. The bushes shelter from the wind behind rocks, and belong to a high-altitude tropical flora, particularly myrtles and various plants of the heath family *(Ericaceae)*. Although the composition of this flora has been modified by the fires that in early times ravaged these summits, it has kept an original character, if only because of various antarctic and Andean elements, which stand out in this tropical area.

ARAUCARIAS: A BOTANICAL ENIGMA

One of the most interesting forests in all of Brazil occurs on the great plateau in the south—that of the araucarias, called locally *pinhos de Paraná* (Paraná pine). These strangely shaped conifers belong to a group very widespread in the mountains of Chile as well as in far-off New Caledonia in the South Pacific. The araucaria forest formerly extended over a vast area between the Rio Paraná and the sea, reaching beyond the Curitiba in the north, and, in the south, to Pôrto Alegre and the Misiones territory in Argentina. Above 1,500 feet all the plateaus were covered with this forest. Unfortunately these forests have been subjected in southern Brazil to considerable exploitation and twelve million acres have disappeared.

The araucarias range from sixty-five to eighty feet in height with trunks about three feet in diameter at the base. They dominate a dense tropical forest embracing conifers of the genus *Podocarpus* and such deciduous trees as the imbuia *(Phoebe porosa)*, used in cabinetmaking, and the herva maté *(Ilex paraquayensis)*, the leaves of which are used in brewing the beverage known as *maté*, sometimes called "Paraguay tea." The undergrowth is thick. This mingling of conifers and tropical deciduous trees is the strangest feature of an area rich in many botanical enigmas. Depending on sunlight, the

This plant louse has not yet reached the adult stage but already has a vivid color pattern, warning its enemies that it is poisonous. (Othmar Danesch)

araucaria does not regenerate in dense forests. The theory has been advanced that they are the pioneer colonizers of the *campos,* or cleared fields, and that these areas were then gradually invaded by other vegetation which eventually displaced the araucaria.

ORCHIDS: DAUGHTERS OF THE AIR

The tropics are famous for luxuriant vegetation, but no other plant equals in splendor the Orchidaceae, the best-defined and the most numerous family in the vegetable world. According to the most conservative estimate, there are at least fifteen thousand species of orchids, and doubtless many more. The orchid is ubiquitous, and is found even in our north temperate zones, but it is in the tropics that this family attains its most wonderful development and its greatest diversity and beauty. Only in the tropics do we find the epiphytic kind, those the Indians call "daughters of the air." Tropical America, especially the Amazon basin, and the warmer slopes of the Andes, is very rich in species; but some species are found at high altitudes in the cordilleras, the *Epidendrum frigidum* growing at more than fourteen thousand feet in the Andes of Quito.

The forests of eastern Brazil, warm and humid, are particularly well provided with orchids. Although the visitor must often walk far through these forests before discovering an orchid plant, what a marvel it is when one comes upon it perched in a tree or growing in a sunlit clearing! Some are bizarre, almost monstrous, reminding one of a bird or a butterfly. Others are enormous—a diameter from four to six inches is common—while still others, such as some *Coryanthes,* attain ten inches or more. Still others compensate for their small size by growing in tremendous clusters. The coloring of orchids is of infinite variety, ranging from bright reds and yellows to virginal white or marvelous soft harmonies of white, mauve and pink.

Even within a single species there is a great variety of characteristics, especially in coloring. *Laelia purpurata,* a native of Santa Catarina Island, is known in three hundred variants, and rarely are two specimens alike. By clever hybridization, the orchid growers have multiplied even further the natural diversity of these incomparable flowers. Unlike most of those in temperate zones, few orchids in the tropics grow on the ground. Most tropical orchids are epiphytes and grow clinging to the trunks of trees, particularly trees with rough bark. Some tropical orchids grow on rocky cliffs, braving both the relative aridity and the pitiless sunlight. For these orchids are, above all, plants of sunlight, climbing along the trunks of trees to find light and fleeing the lower, darker levels of the forest.

This search for sunlight presents orchids with many problems, especially that of obtaining enough water and mineral substances. Unlike ground plants, they do not have true roots capable of supplying them with moisture and minerals, and since they are not parasites they draw no sustenance from the trees to which they are attached. They solve the problem of obtaining water by drawing on the atmospheric humidity of tropical forests, especially in the cloud forests. They capture moisture by means of free-hanging aerial roots wrapped in a network of dead cells that protect the roots from drying out and can absorb the smallest drops like a sponge. The precious water is then stored in the large bulbs—sometimes six or eight inches in diameter—at the base of the plant. The leaves of the orchid are tough and leathery, acting as a thick skin to protect the pulpy centers; sometimes when the center is swollen with its store of water, the leaves become almost cylindrical.

Another striking example of the orchid's adaptation is its method of reproduction. The single stamen is enormous and rises above the lip of the richly colored flower. Instead of forming a powder, the grains of pollen join in compact masses mounted on a sticky pedicle. The insects, attracted by the orchid's strong perfume—and occasionally by a fetid odor that is in sharp contrast to the beauty of the flower—come to suck out the nectar secreted at the base of the flower. The insects can light on the orchid's lip and thus immediately come into contact with the stamen and its pollen masses. Sometimes the least pressure on the lip will depress the stamen and cause it to drop its pollen on the head and back of the insect, which then carries it to another flower.

The fruit then develops, the seeds being contained within capsules that open when ripe. These grains or seeds are the smallest in the vegetable world, so minute that often two or three seeds weigh only one millionth of a gram. A breath of air can carry off the seeds like dust and hold them in suspension in the forest atmosphere. Since the chances of landing on a favorable place are slight, the orchid compensates for this by producing capsules containing, for example, in the *Cymbidium,* an average of 1,500,000 seeds and sometimes, in certain *Anguloa,* almost four million seeds.

Left: Beyond the humid marshes of the coast rise the foothills of the Brazilian plateaus. Right: The female tarantula (Lycosa), *a huge spider, carries her eggs in a sac beneath her abdomen and, after they hatch, bears the young on her back. (Both by Othmar Danesch)*

Even if a seed does manage to fasten itself on a tree trunk, it must still germinate and find an associate of a very particular kind—a mushroom! And each type of orchid must, moreover, find a particular species of mushroom. For orchids live in harmonious association, or symbiosis, with microscopic fungi that shelter within the roots of the plant. The fungi live in the plant's tissues not in a parasitical but in a mutually beneficial association: the mushroom helps itself to sugar synthesized by the orchid, while the plant benefits from certain substances, such as proteins, liberated by the fungus. Horticulturists were unable to grow orchids until they realized how essential was the relationship between these two very different plants. Normally the seedling grows rather slowly and it does not flower until after two years, at the soonest, and sometimes, in such species as the *Cattleya,* not for six years.

The orchids, glory of tropical forests of the Old and the New World alike, are truly part of a strange universe. Not only do they form hanging gardens high in the trees but they have been colonized by tiny animals, especially certain ants that establish themselves in openings of the plant's tissues or in the hollow bulbs, but without disturbing the plant's growth. Many minute or microscopic aquatic animals also flourish in the water collected at the base of the plant.

Orchids form a world of natural beauty that has long attracted mankind. Since the end of the eighteenth century the cultivation of orchids has been going on in Europe, and especially in England. The number of orchid fanciers has multiplied amazingly. New and rare species of the flowers are sold at fantastic prices; a variety of *Odontoglossum* brought 1,720 guineas in England just before World War II. The intensive collecting has contributed to reducing the number of wild orchids. Hunters have not even hesitated to cut down trees in order to obtain plants growing beyond reach. One prospector collected ten thousand specimens of the beautiful *Odontoglossum crispus* of Colombia by cutting down four thousand trees. Such massacres are all the more regrettable because they also destroy the habitat of these marvellous flowers.

BIRD LIFE

The forests of eastern Brazil shelter wildlife similar to that of the Amazon area but with some important differences. Because the two great forests were long ago separated by immense open savannas, steppes and even semi-deserts, their fauna has evolved independently. Some species are strictly indigenous to the Amazon, others to the wooded districts of eastern Brazil; often the same types are represented in the two regions by distinct species.

The best-known birds are, as usual in many parts of Latin America, particularly diversified. In the region of Mount Itatiaia 248 species have been counted; but the number of individuals is, unfortunately, not high, for the fauna has declined as a result of the destruction of forest habitats.

The traveler arriving in Rio de Janeiro is greeted by a myriad of tropical birds. Frigate birds and boobies fly over the bay, and on the shores stand dazzling great white egrets. On the avenues and in the parks of the city one sees a great number of very common species, among them the Brazilian sparrow *(Zonotrichia capensis matutina)* and the rufous-bellied thrush *(Turdus rufiventer),* which fills the place of the European blackbird and the robin of the United States.

The forests surrounding the city, such as that of Tijuca, provide a habitat for a great variety of birds. The Brazilian tanager *(Ramphocelus brasilius),* with its bright red and black plumage, frequents humid thickets and undergrowth and is even more common in the coastal region than in the mountainous interior. A distinct localization of species may be seen in the high mountains, especially in the Itatiaia mountain mass. The lower slopes are inhabited by tropical birds, including many parrots, sun-birds, tanagers, manakins and flycatchers. The capueira partridge *(Odontophora capueira)* is found in great numbers in the thickets and their monotonous call may be heard from morning to night. At high altitudes,

Left: Cloud forests, most humid of all forests, foster a luxuriant vegetation, including many mosses, ferns and orchids. (Rolf Blomberg: Full Hand) Right: The trunk of this Erythrina *is covered with epiphytes, orchids and bromeliads, which look like parasites but live on whatever is carried by rain and wind. (Karl Weidmann)*

where the temperature may descend to the freezing point, bird life is scarce. However, some very interesting birds are found here, among them a pipit *(Anthus brasiliensis)*, a solitary wanderer at from 7,000 to 8,000 feet. The presence of this passerine, a type found throughout the temperate regions of the world, demonstrates that this is an islet of temperate climate in the midst of tropical or subtropical forests.

HUMMINGBIRDS AND COLLECTORS

The forests of eastern Brazil, like those of the Amazon, have a large population of hummingbirds. For a long time this wealth has interested not only naturalists but also, alas, dealers. Salvador was formerly a center of the export of bird skins for the fashion industry, and the skins of hummingbirds were exported to Europe by the hundreds of thousands. Certain species were even known only by specimens collected locally, with no indication of their exact origin. This was notably true of a very rare species—it was for many years thought to be extinct—called by the famous ornithologist John Gould the hooded visor-bearer *(Augastes lumachellus)*. The source of the few skins in museums was indicated only as "Brazil." However, Dr. Augusto Ruschi, a great ornithologist and the director of the Mello Leitao Museum of Biology, which he founded at Santa Teresa in Espirito Santo, finally traced a specimen to Morro de Chapeu, a 4,000-foot hill in the extreme north of the Serra do Sincora, on the edge of a dry *sertão* zone. His first searches were fruitless. Then he came to the Cachoeira do Ferro Doido, a waterfall 650 feet high and three quarters of a mile wide, and with understandable excitement became the first scientist to observe this rare species of hummingbird alive and in its natural environment. He collected a dozen birds that subsequently flourished in aviaries.

An authority on all the birds of eastern Brazil, Dr. Ruschi has evolved an ingenious method of capturing his subjects. Adapting a device employed by the Indians, as described in the earliest chronicles, he uses a long, flexible pole tipped with sticky birdlime that traps the hummingbird as it hovers over a flower. Thanks to this device, Dr. Ruschi's aviaries are filled with boarders that he can study at leisure.

THE BRAZILIAN PLATEAUS

Behind the Atlantic façade of Brazil, with its timbered ranges, extends a series of vast plateaus which cover the entire eastern portion of Brazil. This topography of elevated plains strewn with low hills and small mountain chains stretches from the eastern part of Maranhão as far as the Bolivian frontier. The area may be regarded as the southern part of the Guiana plateau, the dividing line being the Amazon River.

This plateau, belonging to the Precambrian era, is made up of the oldest known rocks; it is formed of granites, gneiss and metamorphic schists that have been folded and broken by faults. Such rocks are weak and their erosion creates hills with gentle slopes. These tablelands are bordered by steep escarpments. Such, for example, is the vast sandstone tableland in the watershed between the tributaries of the Rio Tocantins, the Rio São Francisco and the Rio Parnaíba, where hills and hillocks of uniform sandstone lead to a border of cliffs. Brazilians often give the name of *rapadura* to these sandstone formations, which they feel resemble the lumps of coarse brown sugar used by the inland people.

Farther south is the Mato Grosso, a tremendous sandstone plateau covered with lateritic clay, a decayed rock (the Brazilians call it *canga)* in the form of shifting sands that make walking difficult. Toward the north, the sandstone gives way to micaschists, gneiss and granites that extend to the limits of the lower Amazon.

In the south, a vast part of the plateau is covered by basaltic lavas. When exposed, this rock disintegrates into the famous red earth, *terra roxa*, a very dark crimson in color. This rich soil favored the growing of coffee, for which this part of Brazil became famous. Unfortunately, this land, exposed to rains and unprotected against erosion, has deteriorated rapidly. The "coffee front" has constantly pushed toward the west, leaving behind it a ruined country.

These complex formations have been further complicated by river systems—the principal watercourses draining these plateaus are the São Francisco, Paraná, Paraguay, Tapajos, Xingú, Araguaia, Tocantins and Parnaíba—that flow in all directions. They and their many tributaries have hollowed out valleys, cut up the plateaus, and uncovered some ancient layers. These layers vary in their resistance to erosion and for this reason many cascades break the flow of the rivers over much of the plateau. The Rio Paraná, for example, cascades from a great height at the Salto das Sete Quedas (Guaira Falls); but the most famous falls are those of Iguaçu, which we shall discuss shortly.

For man, the plateaus of eastern Brazil present all kinds of problems; in particular, the climate makes agriculture difficult and the soil is poor. They have few of the riches of the coast, nor do they have the luxuriance of the Amazon region. As a result, the population is sparse.

And yet these plateaus constitute the heart of immense Brazil. From their heights rivers flow toward the Rio de la Plata or the Amazon, or directly into the Atlantic. Situated between a coast transformed by man and the Amazon Valley still untouched by civilization, they are without a doubt Brazil's future center of gravity. It is therefore not at all surprising that Brazilians, under the leadership of political leaders and enthusiastic architects, have decided to establish here a new city and a new capital, Brasilia. This is one of the most daring and promising social enterprises in all Latin America.

GOLD, GEMS AND MINERALS

The ancient Brazilian bedrock is very similar to that of southern Africa, another very ancient part of the world. And, like southern Africa, this part of Brazil is very rich in valuable minerals. The veins of pegmatite that thread the old plateau are rich in gold and precious stones that can be mined profitably. Elsewhere these veins have been eroded and their precious substance carried away as sediments in streams, but some of this can be sieved out by goldwashers.

Gold brought prosperity to several states—Minas Gerais,

The blacksmith frog (Hyla faber), *a tree frog, gets its name from its call, which resembles the hammering of an anvil. (Othmar Danesch)*

The Araquaia River in the Mato Grosso has humid banks clad in dense forest. (Peter Matthiessen)

Goiás, and Mato Grosso—in colonial times. Discovered in 1698 in Minas Gerais (which in Portuguese means "general mines"), it was extracted on a large scale for more than a century; then production rapidly diminished as a result of the exhaustion of the lodes at the beginning of the nineteenth century.

Diamonds were discovered in 1727 at Caete, to the east of Belo Horizonte, and then in various localities, some now bearing the name of this precious stone. Many of the diamonds, very distinctly tinted—the *carbonados*—are suitable only for industrial use. Others are of considerable value as gems. To the northeast of Goiás, the alluvium of the Rio Bagagem, a tributary of the Tocantins, produced in 1853 the Estrella do Sur, a diamond that weighed 254.5 carats in the rough, and in 1857 the Dresden diamond, weighing 117.5 carats. These precious stones are found on a good part of the plateaus, but more especially in the region of Diamantina where they are taken from the Quaternary alluvia on the shores of rivers or in mountain ravines.

Other precious or semiprecious stones abound in this region, notably topazes, tourmalines of various colors, beryls, aquamarines (one of these weighed over fifteen pounds), chrysoberyls, along with garnets and sapphires. This wealth lured a horde of prospectors (the so-called *bandeirantes)* beginning in the eighteenth century, an immigration exactly like that of the Klondike gold-rush. It not only enriched Portugal itself, but such old Brazilian cities as Ouro Preto or Salvador owe to it a part of their splendor.

The gold is now worked out, and precious stones no longer play their old role in the economy. But the Brazilian plateaus contain other mineral treasures much more valuable to the economy of the modern world. Nickel and cobalt abound in Goiás and Minas Gerais. The eastern part of Minas Gerais holds lodes of magnetite and hematite consisting of 50 to 65 per cent of iron and therefore estimated to contain thirteen trillion tons of iron. One district alone, that of Congonhas to the south of Belo Horizonte, contains 20.7 billion tons of hematite, representing 15.2 billion tons of iron. These regions thus hold out a splendid industrial promise for the South America of tomorrow.

THE CAMPOS CERRADOS

The Brazilian plateaus, especially those in the interior, suffer from relatively severe weather, typical of what meteorologists call a tropical savanna climate. This climate is characterized above all by the alternation of a rainy season and a very marked dry season. The average annual rainfall varies from about 40 inches to 70 inches, but this is of less importance than the length of the dry period. This climate has greatly affected the vegetation. The inland region, from the escarpment forming the Serra do Mar to Mato Grosso, is the *campos cerrados* of Brazil. Although their aspects may vary, these are fundamentally woodlands or more or less wooded savannas. This plant formation, which occupies vast expanses in central Brazil, is bounded on the north by the Amazon forest, on the northeast by the caatinga, on the east by the coastal forests and on the southwest by the vast marshy expanses of upper Paraguay.

The typical landscape, then, of a Brazilian plateau is a grassy savanna strewn here and there with wooded portions consisting of medium-sized or small trees, the density of the woods varying according to local conditions. The lower and more humid portions are forested, the trees thinning out and giving way gradually to bushes on the slopes, then gradually

Facing page, left above: The striking colors of some caterpillars such as this Isognathus *serve to warn predators that they are toxic. (Othmar Danesch) Right above: One of the* Araceae, *typical of the exotic beauty of tropical plants. Right: Many butterflies found in dense forest have colonized the zone near Iguaçu Falls because of the humidity. (Both by Edward S. Ross)*

vanishing and being supplanted by grasses and sedges. Some of the summits are practically bare. In the southern part of the state of Rio Grande do Sul, the extremely level land is covered with grassy savannas, providing excellent pasturage. Such purely grassy savannas are rare elsewhere on the Brazilian plateaus.

In some districts the campo cerrado gives way to a dense forest of low, very thorny, almost impenetrable *Mimosa*. At the bottoms of the valleys are ribbons of forest, and these are at least in part made up of Amazonian species. The hevea, or rubber tree, is exploited in the upper basin of the Juruena tributaries. Palm trees are numerous there, especially the *Mauritia*.

On the whole, the soil is poor, the climate harsh, and the landscape very monotonous on these plateaus. Cattle raising is the most profitable occupation, along with the utilization of forest products such as rubber. The southern plateaus, where plantations, chiefly of coffee, have replaced the forests of bygone times, are much more productive.

CROSSROAD OF THE BIRD WORLD

We must realize that these plateaus, though often monotonous, present on the whole a rather remarkable sampling of habitats, ranging from dense forest resembling the Amazon, to marshes, stretches of desert and semidesert. It is not at all surprising, then, that birds here are numerous. A bird-collecting expedition of the American Museum of Natural History to the Mato Grosso found no less than 658 species and subspecies. These regions are a crossroads and indigenous species are rare. Among the 658 forms counted in the Mato Grosso, only 36 seem to be endemic; 372 have affinities with Amazonian species, having come from the great rain forest by way of the fingers of forest that thrust along the watercourses. The others have come from Argentina and are birds of the plains or of sparsely wooded zones.

This mixture of fauna on the Brazilian plateaus is its chief interest, for here one can observe birds from various regions living side by side, such as the nandou from the pampas of Argentina as well as tinamous *(Tinamus serratus, T. tao, Crypturellus soui, C. strigulosus)* and Cracidae *(Crax* and *Penelope)* from the Amazon. Doves are incredibly numerous, as are birds of prey, including the Everglades kite *(Rostrhamus sociabilis)*, which is found in great numbers along the rivers, where it feeds on snails. Flocks of these birds assemble toward evening and from fifty to one hundred individuals will spend the night in a tree on the shores of a river.

Elsewhere one comes upon great flocks of parrots. The ara, or macaw, is here in great variety *(Ara hyacinthinus, A. chloroptera, A. maracana)*, and parakeets of many species are even more common. The parakeet *Nandayus nenday* is also found here, mainly near cattle ranges, where it explores the wooden fences for knotholes or cracks where it can nest. Most of the Psittacidae come from the Amazon, except the gray-breasted parakeet *(Myiopsitta monachus)*, which hails from Argentina. These parrots are very numerous in forested

Iguaçu Falls, an array of cascades separated by rocky, forested islets, is most spectacular just before the waters are in spate. (Carl Frank)

areas, where their huge tenement-like nests harbor from two to one hundred pairs.

Elsewhere are the blue-crowned motmots *(Momotus momota)* with long tails that have racket-shaped tips on a bare stipe. It is not unusual to see these birds perched on a branch busily using their bills to pluck or trim the central part of their tail feathers. The common ani *(Crotophaga ani)* and the great ani *(C. major)*, with completely black plumage and a kind of excrescence on top of the beak, are abundant in most of South America. They can be easily observed, since they live near man's houses and in the shrubs on pastures; their black plumage, long-tailed silhouette and vivacity make them readily identifiable. They are among the most likable birds in South America and their nesting and reproductive habits are particularly interesting. Extremely social birds, they nest more often than not in a communal way. As many as twenty-five birds of the same flock may join in building a collective nest, where the females lay their eggs. All the birds share in hatching the eggs and in caring for the nestlings.

We still have much to learn about the habits of these and many other birds on these plateaus. We are especially ignorant about their migrations, which must be much more common than was once thought, especially in response to the rhythm of the wet and dry seasons. We are only beginning to get an inkling of some of these patterns, as, for example, in the hummingbirds, whose movements follow the cycle of the blossoming of the flowers.

THE GRANDEUR OF IGUAÇU FALLS

An uneven erosion of riverbeds explains the ruptures that produce the many falls along the edges of the Brazilian plateaus. Justly the most famous is Iguaçu Falls (from a Guarani Indian word meaning "great water") at the point where the Rio Iguaçu leaves the plateau on the frontier between Brazil and Argentina, twenty-four miles above the Iguaçu's junction with the Paraná.

There are few such spectacles of such grandeur in the world. The Swiss botanist, Robert Chodat, has eloquently described it thus: "When we stand at the foot of this world of cascades and, raising our eyes, see, 269 feet above us, the horizon filled with a line of waters, this awesome spectacle of an ocean pouring into an abyss is almost frightening. The waters of the deluge falling abruptly into the heart of the world, by divine command, in a landscape of memorable beauty, amidst an exuberant, almost tropical vegetation, the fronds of great ferns, the shafts of bamboos, the graceful trunks of palm trees, and a thousand species of trees, their crowns bending over the gulf adorned with mosses, pink begonias, golden orchids, brilliant bromeliads and lianas with trumpet flowers—all this added to the dizzying and deafening roar of waters that can be heard even at a great distance, makes an indelible impression, moving beyond words."

This description is not an exaggeration: the falls are two and half miles wide and somewhat higher than Niagara Falls. They are almost as high as the main part of Victoria Falls in Rhodesia and they are much wider. They divide into a multitude of cascades separated by rocky islands covered with dense forest. The exuberance of the vegetation, including the cedar *(Cedrella fissilis)*, the araucaria, and the lapachos, *(Tecoma ipe* and *T. ochracea)*, adds to the beauty of these roaring waters. The volume of water falling into the narrow gorges varies according to the time of year, but the average is 62,000 cubic feet per second and the maximum 450,000 cubic feet per second.

The fauna of the area is very rich but still not too well known. Mammals are represented by three varieties of deer, two of peccaries, and a tapir, a jaguar and an ocelot—to name only the largest. Birds are innumerable, ranging from the shy tinamous to gorgeous parrots.

Both the Argentines and the Brazilians have realized the value of this grand spectacle and have created national parks in the vicinity to protect the site from despoilment.

MIRACULOUS WATER PLANTS

In temperate zones, rapids and falls have little vegetation. Like the falls of humble streams, Niagara Falls shows no plant life on the beaten rocks except water weeds encrusted on the stone or mosses swollen by the spray.

But it is quite otherwise in the tropics, where a great many species of a plant family, the Podostemonaceae, have adapted to this environment. These were first discovered in the rapids of French Guiana, and have since been found in the main watercourses of the Americas. The majority are limited to the torrid zones, but some have reached as far as the United States. They have likewise been found in Africa and Asia. A particularly good place to study them is at Iguaçu Falls.

If not forewarned, an observer would probably take them for water lichens, bizarre mosses, or even algae. Yet these

Left: The giant scolopendra, which may reach a length of one foot, can give a painful and sometimes dangerous bite. (Rolf Blomberg: Full Hand) Right: Iguaçu Falls, where the Rio Paraná issues from the Brazilian plateau, is considered the most magnificent cascade in South America. (Weldon King)

plants have flowers with stamens and pistils, like other seed plants. Each species seems to show a preference for certain conditions; one type is found in the midst of the spray, another under a ledge, a third in the very path of the torrent. All of them adhere immovably to the stone, almost forming a part of it. Many have a kind of disk or sucker on the edge of which rise stems or flattened blades ending in thin feathery filaments. Others open out like funnels or fans. All are small, rarely exceeding four inches in size. In these plants the classic versions of root, stem, and leaves have disappeared and have been replaced by algae-like structures adapted to the watery environment. Aside from this, they are perfectly normal in function, assimilating carbon dioxide from the water in order to synthesize organic matter. Living one or two feet below the surface of the water, they do not get much light. Moreover, the warm tropical waters do not contain as much dissolved gas as do northern waters, but to some extent the rapid replenishment of the water compensates for this.

There still remains a major problem: reproduction. Some northern aquatic plants raise themselves above the water at certain seasons to open their flowers in the sunlight. But the Podostemonaceae seem too small to do this and the water level is uncertain because of its foaming. These plants therefore wait for the water level to lower, and at that time develop the flowering branch that contains the reproductive organs. But, unlike algae, they die when exposed for more than a day or two. So nature provides them with a flowering period of extraordinary rapidity. As soon as the rocky bed is uncovered by the receding waters, the flowers come out of their envelope and open, scattering a light pollen that will fertilize the spread pistils. In a few days the fruit is ripe and falls on a dry rock, to which it clings; as soon as the waters return, it will germinate and produce a new plant that will live for a season. Indeed, the speeding up of reproduction is so great that in some species the seed germinates while still on the mother plant, which thus becomes viviparous, or live-bearing.

A THREATENED HERITAGE

We ought now to remember that the Amazon forest occupies more than half of Brazil and other forests extend, or once extended, over the entire humid portion of the eastern coastal area. Altogether forests comprise an immense wealth for Brazil; however, there is reason to feel deep anxiety over certain parts of this rich resource.

Compared with the great forest of Africa, the Amazon forest represents a relatively unexploited area. In 1956 Brazil exported 1,500,000 cubic feet of rough timber from the Amazon forest while 83,000,000 cubic feet were exported from the forests of western Africa and the Congo. But the forests of Africa will not hold long at the present rate of exploitation, so that the possibility of immensely increased exploitation of the trees of the Amazon may not be far off. An extraordinary river system in the Amazon basin makes much of this dormant wealth easily accessible.

The situation is quite otherwise in eastern Brazil, where the tropical forests were exploited with unusual ruthlessness from the beginning of the sixteenth to the middle of the eighteenth century. In spite of certain measures taken in 1779 by the Queen of Portugal for the protection of trees bordering watercourses and in some other zones, they have almost disappeared, and what is left of them is headed for destruction. In many places there remains only a facade of forest concealing eroded stretches of land. The story of the destruction of this forest is the history of the advance of tropical agriculture—of cocoa, coffee and sugar. This agriculture, sometimes still very primitive, exploits land until it is exhausted and then moves on to new forested lands. Sugar and coffee are particularly responsible for the ruin of large wooded areas: the processing of sugar cane requires a great deal of firewood, and the "coffee front," as it moves rapidly westward, leaves behind an economy at a subsistence level.

Unfortunately, as the French botanist and forester, André Aubréville, points out, forest exploitation in Brazil is not followed by reforestation. The most obvious example of this is the araucaria forest, one of the richest of Brazil: in the one State of Pará, its area decreased from almost nineteen million acres in 1933 to less than seven million in 1953. At this rate, araucaria timber will be exhausted in from thirty to forty years. A major part of the deforested lands is reduced to second-growth forest or expanses of heath and unproductive scrub. No more dramatic example can be cited of lack of foresight in the management of forest resources.

The only countermeasure taken in eastern Brazil so far has been the massive introduction of the eucalyptus—about two billion trees, of which more than half are in the State of São Paulo alone. These artificial forests are a sound economic investment and partially protect the eroded soils. But they do not by any means contain the riches of natural forests and for the naturalist they are of very little interest. The animal life dependent upon the original vegetation has virtually disappeared.

In view of what has happened in eastern Brazil, we may feel a very great anxiety about the future of the Amazon forest. An additional threat is such roads as that which joins Belem to Brasilia, and those which will open up the Amazon basin. They will make the virgin lands bordering them accessible to exploitation, first for the forest products and then for the cultivation of the land.

The Amazon forest is one of the great natural regions of the world that is still unviolated, an immense natural boon that could be used to meet the growing need for renewable resources. A rational use can preserve the capital wealth while at the same time deriving a reasonable revenue from it. It is up to man to choose between such a rational use and a quick exploitation followed by irrevocable destruction.

Right above: The flowers of leguminous plants such as this Calliandra *often form huge pompons from which wind and insects can easily extract pollen. Among the dazzlingly colorful butterflies common in the Brazilian plateaus region are male* Epiphile *(right) from the state of Santa Catarina, and* Callicore *(far right), known as the "88" because of its pattern, from the Iguaçu Falls area. (All by Edward S. Ross)*

Water Birds, Coca Leaves and the Lungfish

From the Yungas of Bolivia to the Plains of Uruguay

9

The journey eastward from the extraordinary 12,000-foot elevation of La Paz, capital of Bolivia, via Oruro, Cochabamba, and Santa Cruz to Paraguay is like descending a grand staircase. Leaving the high tableland, the traveler starts down the side of the eastern Cordillera of the Andes and comes first to the *ceja de montana,* the "brow of the mountain forest," covering the slopes down to about the 8,000-foot level. This *ceja de montana* is a humid zone, with abundant rains and thick fogs. The vegetation, including heath plants, myrtles, bromeliads, orchids, and mosses is dense but only of moderate height.

Farther down one enters the yungas, a halfway zone extending from about eight thousand feet to about three thousand feet—a subtropical, humid, densely wooded region. Down to about seven thousand feet the vegetation is mainly imbaubas *(Cecropia)* and tree ferns; lower down the trees are taller, heralding the approach to the great forest. Among these trees are countless palms. Here too are found the thirty-eight or more species of precious *Cinchona,* which is indigenous to the eastern slope of the Andes; it is the bark of some of these species that yields quinine, the anti-malaria alkaloid. Overexploitation by the white man led to the depletion of these trees toward the middle of the nineteenth century. Today, the artificial cultivation of these trees on Java has made that island the world center of quinine production, since there is still no economical way of producing the drug synthetically.

The yungas are densely populated and covered with plantations. The plant most commonly cultivated here is coca *(Erythroxylon coca).* The leaves of this shrub, which grows to a height of about eight feet, contain the alkaloid, cocaine. For centuries the Indians who must spend their lives in the harsh climate of the High Andes have chewed the dried coca leaves and archaeologists have found much pottery from pre-Inca and Inca times showing how these leaves were used. Today there is still a heavy traffic in coca between the subtropical lowlands and the high plateaus and the leaves are sold in every shop or market even in the smallest villages. One finds that the average Indian prefers coca to a few coins as payment for a small service. Most workers, peasants, herdsmen and miners chew coca all the day round, sometimes with some powdered limestone added to liberate the alkaloid. The juices act like a local anaesthetic, allaying hunger, thirst and fatigue. They also help counteract mountain sickness. But the long-term effects are pernicious, causing a nervous depression. There is little doubt that the apathy of some Andean Indian peoples is in part caused by the excessive use of coca. Because of their power, the leaves have also assumed a magical significance and are commonly used by witch doctors in sacrifices to the native gods and demons.

Farther down on the road toward Paraguay, particularly in the valleys of the Beni, Mamoría, Iténez and Madeira rivers, the traveler comes upon dense rain forest, which at the foot of the Andes joins the Amazon forest. Extending southward into the Chaco and the plains and plateaus of Paraguay and northern Argentina, this vast region is very heterogenous. A transition zone between the west and east as well as between north and south, it is especially interesting to naturalists because very different habitats occur side by side or intermingle. Much remains to be discovered here, since on this vast tract between the tropical and temperate zones the wildlife has been able to survive in habitats that still preserve their pristine splendor.

THE CHACO

From Santa Cruz in Bolivia almost to the Salado River in Argentina and extending parallel with the Andes are plateaus that diminish rapidly in altitude as far east as the Paraná and Paraguay rivers. This region, the Chaco, has remained little known because much of it is so difficult to penetrate. The Bermejo and Pilcomayo rivers, coming down from the Andes, are its only permanent rivers; they flow sometimes across elevated areas where their banks are well defined but sometimes in low areas where they spread out into swamps. The other rivers disappear in the mud and sands at a short distance from the lower slopes of the Andes. Even the Pilcomayo vanishes underground for a part of its course. The subterranean waters that feed these rivers are for the most part saline; only in the eastern part of the Chaco, toward the Paraná River, are they more often fresh. The salt is often visible in hollows where the rivers have deposited it. On the whole, the Chaco appears to be a mosaic of dry areas alternating with swamps—the *esteros.* As the rivers pass through these swamps they are choked by aquatic vegetation that interferes with navigation. Elsewhere water accumulates in depressions, forming a maze of canals and swamps.

As one goes from east to west on the Chaco plain, the average rainfall decreases rapidly and the dry season becomes longer and more intense. At Santiago del Estero in Argentina the annual rainfall averages only twenty inches a year.

The flora reflects this variety of habitats. In the foothills of the Andes there is a transitional zone between the Bolivian rain forest and the parklands; then a dry zone with an open forest. The latter is made up of the quebracho, or "axebreaker" *(Quebracho santiqueno* and *Q. colorado),* a tree valued for

The Valley of the Moon near La Paz, Bolivia, so called because its rocks, worn bare by erosion, suggest a lunar landscape. (Robert Lawrence Pastner)

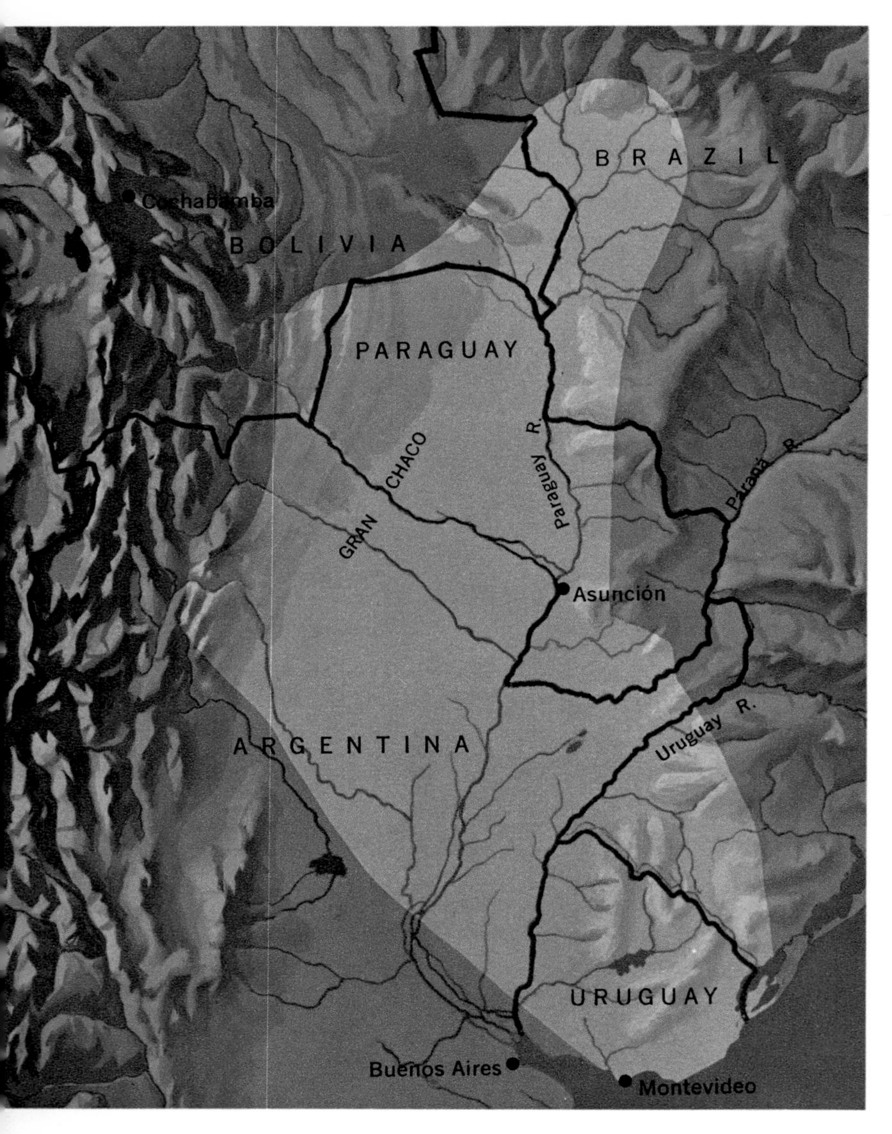

The region between the eastern foothills of the Andes and the plains of Uruguay is extremely heterogenous, including the Chaco, the marshes of Upper Paraguay and the southern rim of the Brazilian plateau.

its extremely hard wood, as well as the guayacan *(Caesalpinia melanocarpa)*, the mistol *(Ziziphus mistol)* and several kinds of palms. Toward the east the more humid climate favors a more flourishing woodland. But most widespread is a savanna formed of grasses and sedges intermingled with palms, notably the coranda *(Copernicia australis)*. These palms also form groves along the rivers.

As an area that has been invaded by species originating in a variety of bordering regions, the flora of the Chaco is rich and diverse. (But the natural resources, except for the quebrachos, are unimpressive.) It is also inhabited by a rather large variety of animals, as diverse in origins as the plants.

PLANTS AS CISTERNS

In the Chaco, as in other arid parts of South America, bromeliads form almost impenetrable thickets on the outskirts of wooded patches. All of these plants look like bouquets of large leaves, thick, hard, tapering upward, and with prickly edges. The outer leaves are a grayish-green, but the inner leaves are red, at times so bright they look fiery. From this center rises a stem covered with scales from which purple, red, or blue flowers spring. The red bracts, white scales and purple corollas of these plants gleam in the sun like flames and attract the iridescent hummingbirds. Moreover, the leaves, arranged in a rosette, act like cisterns, water accumulating in them, sometimes over a period of months. The Indians call this plant *caraguata*, meaning "a water vessel," and it can prove a godsend to travelers in the dry season. Since the water is sometimes fetid and may contain aquatic organisms, it may require filtering before it is potable.

SPANISH MOSS

Sometimes in tropical or semitropical areas one sees gray-green tufts made up of a network of fibers hanging from the branches of a tree, from a rock or, in Brazil, even from wires stretched across a balcony. At first sight, the tufts look like accumulations of mildew. They are in reality one of the strangest of plants—Spanish moss *(Tillandsia)*. A bromeliad, Spanish moss is found from North Carolina in the southern United States to as far south as Buenos Aires in Argentina, and even farther south in Chile. The story goes that Linnaeus, knowing this plant's remarkable capacity to do without water, gave it its name in a humorous allusion to one of his students, Elias Til Lands, who had a mortal fear of water.

Botanists distinguish several hundred species of Spanish moss, some of them no longer than an inch, others more than three feet long. On balconies in Brazil they become multicolored living garlands when they flower.

These plants attach themselves by mucous adhesive disks and by rootlets that twine around the support like tendrils and become like iron wires when they die. As with all epiphytes, this plant depends upon moisture in the air for the minerals and water it requires. It is easy to understand why the Indian call these plants, as well as the orchids, "daughters of the air." In dry weather the filaments and leaves of tillandsia are gray and look dried out and dead. No wonder the first observers took them to be lichens. But after a rain or a dewy night the leaves turn green, the innumerable hairs that cover them and act as minuscule pumps having become swollen with moisture. Tillandsia is so very widespread because it can not only reproduce by means of seeds, but any part of it, such as a stem or leaf, can give rise to a new plant.

THE MANED WOLF OF THE CHACO

Among the most interesting of South American carnivores is the Chaco wolf *(Chrysocyon brachyurus)*, called by the Spaniards of the region, *aguaraguazu* or *lobo crinado*, while Brazilians call it *guara*—names meaning maned wolf or maned dog. This member of the Canidae family is easily distinguished because of its unusual proportions: its height is

Beyond these barren slopes of the Eastern Cordillera of Bolivia, not far from La Paz, the tropical zone of the yungas begins. (Weldon King)

The maned wolf, here seen in Descalvados, near Bolivia, is a canine whose remarkably long limbs enable it to run down its prey. (Sasha Siemel)

greater than its length, which often reaches four feet. Its coat, rufous in color, is shaggy, especially in the middle of the back, where it forms a kind of mane; the long legs are blackish and the tail is short and white-tipped. The maned wolf is found throughout Paraguay, southern Brazil and northern Argentina, favoring open forests and bosky savannas. It is a solitary animal, except at mating time, when pairs have been observed together. Its habits are nocturnal and its howl is as sinister as its shape. Rodents, frogs and birds are its prey, and the carnivorous diet is augmented by some fruit, especially that of a shrub *Solanum grandiflorum* of the potato family so that Brazilians call the fruit of this shrub *fructa de lobo*.

The tatu or giant armadillo *(Priodontes giganteus)* is another unusual Paraguayan mammal; it sometimes attains a length of forty inches and a weight of 110 pounds. This armadillo ranges from northern Argentina to southern Brazil, but is particularly numerous in the Chaco, where it inhabits the most thickly wooded sections. In spite of its great size and clumsy appearance, it is a very agile and graceful animal, and has unusually powerful claws.

THE PANTANAL—PARADISE OF WATER BIRDS

Between the Brazilian plateau to the east and the Bolivian plateaus in the west are vast alluvial plains comprising the valley of the Rio Paraguay. Quite unlike the Rio Paraná, which is mainly within high plateaus, the Paraguay is a river of the plains, its upper part meandering across sands, silt, and gray and white clays. On both sides of its slightly raised banks extend vast marshes with lagoons drained by a complex network of streams.

These vast marshy expanses, called the Pantanal, are only a few hundred feet above sea level and are subject to annual floods. The river itself varies in depth from thirteen to sixteen feet. The waters in the plains remain low during the first two months of rain, begin to rise in December, and reach the high-water mark about May or June, that is, about a month after the end of the rains. The Pantanal is then nothing but an immense swamp, and can be crossed only in a boat. Once the waters begin to subside, great stretches of land dry out and remain dry until the next season of flood. This ebb and flow, along with the nature of the soil, prevents the growth of trees. Although the Pantanal is often regarded as part of the Mato Grosso, there is no sign of forest in it, except on its borders. Among the submerged prairies there are patches of very poor woods with a dense undergrowth of palms. The river plant called *camalote* flourishes in depressions in these watery prairies. The caranda palm is also found here and there, especially along the streams and banks of the Paraguay; although related to the carnauba *(C. cerifera),* it does not yield the wax that makes the carnauba so useful. All these plants show adaptations to the main characteristic of this curious environment—alternating periods of inundation and desiccation.

The Pantanal is a paradise of South American water birds. The rails are represented by several species. The rare finfoot *(Heliornis fulica),* related to the rail and resembling it in its shyness and its webbed feet, is found singly or in pairs all along streams edged with dense vegetation. The jacana *(Jacana jacana)* frequents ponds covered with water-lilies, moving lightly about on floating plants by means of its long, wide-spread claws. This adaptation allows the jacana to hunt insects and mollusks in an environment shut off from most other birds. Long-legged water birds are represented in even greater numbers. The roseate spoonbill *(Ajaja ajaja)* forms prosperous colonies, nesting in trees and often living side by side with the wood ibis and the egret. These birds find their food in shallow water; there they walk slowly about, swinging their heads from side to side, beak half open and submerged, sweeping the surface of the water for small crustaceans and insects. The ibis is common here. Flocks of as many as three hundred jabirus *(Jabiru mycteria)* are often seen on the shores. Although slightly resembling an African marabou stork, the jabiru, with its bald red and black head and neck, is not a carrion eater but feeds on fish, frogs, and other aquatic animals that it finds in shallow water. Jabirus build colonies of big nests in isolated trees, and parrots sometimes locate their own nests in these structures. The wood ibis *(Mycteria americana),* the most abundant marsh bird of the Pantanal may occur in colonies of as many as five hundred pairs. The great flocks of herons *(Ardea cocoi),* egrets *(Egretta alba, E. thula),* and the shy bitterns are no less numerous.

Here too it is possible to study that curious bird, the boat-bill *(Cochlearius cochlearius).* This bird, which ranges from Mexico to southern Brazil, is twenty-two inches high and has a large spoon-shaped bill three inches long and two inches wide, resembling that of no related species. Its habits are little known, for it remains hidden during the day in thickets, coming out only at night. It is said to feed on worms, crustaceans, fish, and small mammals; its odd bill seems perfectly suited to searching for prey in mud.

Ducks are also numerous, especially the Muscovy duck *(Cairina moschata),* related to our domestic—and misnamed—Barbary duck. A good fisher, it spends the hottest hours of the day perched in trees. Tree ducks *(Dendrocygna viduata* and *D. bicolor)* are found in flocks of thousands all along sand-banks uncovered by the waters. The kamichis *(Chauna torquata),* strange birds apparently belonging somewhere between the gallinaceans and the palmipeds, are very common. Their long-toed feet, barely webbed, allow them to walk with ease on the spongy surface of the swamp. Day and night they fill the air of the Pantanal with their loud but musical trumpeting. Thousands of cormorants *(Phalacrocorax olivaceus),* along with innumerable small waders, greenshanks, godwits and sandpipers, complete these communities of waterfowl, many of them coming from North America to spend the winter in this damp paradise. The birds alone are worth the arduous trip across the Mato Grosso.

When the young tapir matures, its striped fur becomes a uniformly dark color. (Sasha Siemel)

THE UNIQUE LUNGFISH

In the course of evolution, fishes have disappeared from regions in which water has gradually become only seasonal. The few species that remain are those that can survive in small pools during the dry periods. One group of fishes has become adapted in a very special way to this habitat: the lungfishes or dipnoans, fish with both lungs and gills. Most of these have disappeared, and only six species still survive, one in Australia, four in Africa and one in South America, the *Lepidosiren paradoxa.* The American representative, with a body elongated like an eel's, attains a length of thirty-two inches, and has scales beneath the skin and ribbon-like fins.

But its unique endowment is two lungs that permit it to inhale air like any land vertebrate.

When the waters are high, the lungfish lives like other fish, except that it comes periodically to the surface to breathe. When the waters recede and the swamps become expanses of mud that will soon dry and cake in the sun, it buries itself in the ground within a kind of hermetic cocoon. By placing its mouth against a narrow opening in the cocoon it inhales what little air reaches it through a tunnel from the surface. There it remains in a deep torpor, losing up to 50 per cent of its weight. Excretions, especially urine, are separated by the kidneys and stored, the water being recirculated and thus utilized to the utmost. When the rains return, the lungfish resumes active life. It is then, too, that the reproductive process begins, the female laying her eggs in a tunnel in the mud, and the male fiercely driving off any predator. The parents assure the oxygenation of the eggs by periodically agitating the water surrounding the nest. The larvae begin by breathing with the aid of gills; the functional lungs develop at the time of metamorphosis.

The lungfish is found in a good part of tropical America, but its biology is nowhere better adapted to the environment than in the Pantanal.

Amphibian fishes such as the lungfish and other dipnoans date back to the Devonian period, 300 million years ago. Although the lungfish cannot be regarded as an ancestor of amphibians, it illustrates how vertebrates have emerged from the water and evolved into land animals.

Right: Landscape in the High Bolivian plateaus south of La Paz. (Weldon King) Below: An armadillo's litter consists of two sets of identical twins from a single egg. When attacked, an armadillo curls into a kind of armor-plated ball. (Kurt Severin)

PARAGUAY—CENTER OF THE CONTINENT

Paraguay, the most nearly central country in South America, is made up essentially of the plains of the Rio Paraguay. Aside from the Pantanal, the plains are mainly covered with grassy savannas, dotted here and there with trees and palms. Since colonial times these open expanses have been the center of very prosperous stock-raising activities.

The grassy savannas stop abruptly when they reach the alluvial soil in the east. The hills of eastern Paraguay are covered with a dense forest, rather like those of the Brazilian plateaus. In the most humid localities, eastern Paraguay appears definitely tropical, mainly because of the presence of tree ferns. In drier areas, the vegetation includes cacti and mimosas, and a variety of bromeliads cover the ground in many places.

Common in these zones is a very useful plant, cultivated on a large scale: the maté tree, which yields the beverage sometimes called Paraguay tea. Although this tree grows also in southern Brazil and in Argentina, it is more abundant and more intensively cultivated in Paraguay. The *yerba maté* as the Paraguayans call the *Ilex paraguariensis,* is related to the common holly of the Northern Hemisphere, having a dense foliage of sharp-pointed and finely indented leaves about six or eight inches long. In the wild state the tree grows in dense stands, called *yerbales.* In earliest colonial times its culture was undertaken by the Jesuit missionaries (hence it is also sometimes called Jesuits' tea or Mission tea), but long before then the Indians had learned how to make maté. The leaves are gathered every two or three years, or sometimes every year, dried in ovens and reduced to a very coarse powder. The brewing of the maté is as much of a ritual as is the brewing of tea in England. The beverage is drunk through a *bombilla,* a kind of tube tipped with a sievelike ball that prevents the leaves from entering the drinker's mouth. Maté contains stimulants, mainly caffein, but in less concentration than in tea or coffee. The drink is especially popular in Argentina, and Paraguay exports the major part of the produce, estimated at seventeen million pounds a year, to that country.

THE ARGENTINE MESOPOTAMIA

Argentina possesses a strip of land almost seven hundred miles long that is enclosed, like Mesopotamia, between two important rivers: on the west by the Paraná, and on the east by the Uruguay. Its northern part, Misiones, named after the famous Jesuit missions of the seventeenth century, is a part of the Brazilian plateau. It attains an altitude of about 2,500 feet, is gashed with deep valleys and terminates in rounded hills on the Corrientes plain.

Left above: A great white heron on the wing. It is particularly abundant in the vast swamps of Upper Paraguay. Left: Red-billed whistling ducks (Dendrocygna autumnalis), *found from Texas to northern Argentina, are especially numerous in the marshes of the Chaco and the Pantanal. (Both by Rolf Blomberg: Full Hand) Right: The great white heron, one of the most widely distributed of marsh birds in South America. (Harald Schultz)*

This region is covered with a dense, distinctly tropical-looking forest. The trees, sometimes more than 130 feet high, are mostly cedars and urunday *(Astronium balansae),* which yield turpentine. Ferns, epiphytic plants and bamboos are numerous, making the forest almost impenetrable. Above two thousand feet stands of araucaria are scattered. The yerba maté is also found here and is intensively exploited.

The fauna closely resembles that of the wooded tropical districts of Brazil. Much remains to be discovered here, or perhaps rediscovered. For example, there is the story of a merganser *Mergus octosetaceus,* with a hooked bill, its plumage black, dark brown, gray, and white, and without a trace of the rusty red typical of most mergansers. Until recently this bird was known only from a few specimens in museums. It was known to have lived in the Paraná Valley but it was thought to be extinct, for it had not been seen since 1922. In 1948 some Argentine naturalists, notably W. H. Partridge, rediscovered it in the north of the State of Misiones on the Yacuy River, a small tributary of the Iguaçu, where it lives a hidden and sedentary life. Its preferred habitat is on the shores of the Paraná tributaries, wild watercourses flowing through a luxuriant tropical forest. Quite possibly it prefers this locality because the waters are free of certain carnivorous fishes, especially the dorado *(Salminus maxillosus),* one of the fiercest fish of the Paraná and a predator of the young ducks in these waters. The falls in all of these streams prevent the dorado from getting to the upper reaches where the merganser lives. In the quiet waters the duck can easily capture the fish, upon which it feeds exclusively.

To the south of Misiones begin the alluvial Corrientes plains, formed of sand and clay with vast swamps resulting from lack of drainage. Lakes alternate with some of the *esteros* (permanent swamps) and the *bañidos* (swamps that last only during the rainy season). In the center of the country, the Ibera esteros are particularly extensive and form a long string of lagoons, perhaps indicating an ancient bed of the Rio Paraná. The humid sections are marked by prairies dotted with palms and by many caranda palms, and on the sand dunes the *Cocos yatai* palms are plentiful. The zones with better drainage have scattered woodlands where the most characteristic tree is the remarkably hard nandubay tree *(Prosopis nandubay).*

At the extreme southern end of the Argentine Mesopotamia is the province of Entre Ríos, marked by sandstone plateaus topped with marl and silt, and cut by great rivers banked by steep cliffs. Elsewhere the land has been eroded into a low and monotonously undulating terrain. The landscape is mostly prairie, with vegetation characteristic of the pampas interrupted by wooded bands consisting mainly of mimosas along the rivers. Man has introduced cattle into these southern habitats and thus transformed them into a kind of pampas, but one that is more varied than those that extend beyond the Rio de la Plata.

Landscape near La Paz where erosion has deeply carved a crumbling rock. (Rolf Blomberg: Full Hand)

Black vultures taking a sunbath before returning to their scavenging activities. (Othmar Danesch)

URUGUAY—COUNTRY OF PRAIRIES

The extreme south of the ancient Brazilian plateau reaches the left bank of the Rio de la Plata and is represented, to the east of Montevideo, by a series of low granite hills with rounded domes. In the northwest the plateau resumes, covered mainly with sandstones that form low hills with gentle slopes. Elsewhere the rivers have brought down clays, silts and sands, and these deposits have filled in the depressions. Because of this, Uruguay is a country of prairies, comparable to neighboring Argentina. It is noticeably temperate in climate, the temperatures varying from 50° F in winter (July) to 71° F in summer (January–February).

As a land of prairies, much of Uruguay is covered by grasses of many kinds. The forests occupy only a small area, mainly along the rivers, and even there the trees are only about fifteen to twenty feet high. There was once a better growth of trees and shrubs on the hills but these have disappeared as a result of man's activities and have been replaced by grasses and bushes. Man has, in fact, set his stamp on Uruguay, profoundly altering the character of its vegetation. Three centuries of intensive cattle-raising has had a determining effect on the face of a country. It need hardly be added that where the face of a country has undergone such change, the animal life has suffered accordingly. Many of the most interesting animals that once inhabited this region have now disappeared. It is in fact probably too late to restore the wildlife that once flourished here.

The Prairie Sea

The Argentine Pampas

10

From the Atlantic to the foothills of the Andes and from the Rio de la Plata to the Rio Negro there stretches a flat land where nothing arrests the eye: the Argentine pampas—a word coming from the Quechua and meaning plains. The landscape is monotonous and seems perfectly level but it really rises imperceptibly toward the west, going from an altitude of sixty-six feet at Buenos Aires to 1,640 feet at Mendoza. Elsewhere it rises slightly near the occasional mountain that emerges like an island from a terrestrial ocean.

Covering almost 300,000 square miles, the true pampa is an immense accumulation of loose earth, the product of countless centuries of erosion, brought down from the Andes by mountain streams and rivers. The wind, sifting out the lighter matter, has also played a role in the distribution. These deposits, almost a thousand feet deep at Buenos Aires and much deeper at some other points, have completely buried the ancient features of the land. Thus the formation of the pampas may be explained by the play of immense natural forces moulding and remoulding the surface of the earth. In this the true pampa resembles the Indo-Ganges plain, although the conditions in southern Asia are very different.

The lack of any significant gradient does not favor the formation of a permanent river system. Rain water accumulates on the clays, collects in depressions, and forms more or less permanent lagoons. Most of the watercourses have their source in the sierras, but as they advance over the plain they spend their force, and many of them dry up not far from the foothills. The riverbeds frequently change and their floodwaters are left behind in the swampy depressions. Some of these lagoons, such as Laguna Colorada near Bahía Blanca, are below sea level, their beds having apparently been carved out by wind erosion.

The differences in climate between the western and eastern sides of the pampas explain the differences in their respective topsoils. The western and hotter part is dry and covered with a stunted vegetation, which leaves large areas bare, while the eastern part is much better watered and is covered with a dense vegetation. This distribution of climates has of course had a great influence on agriculture.

A TREELESS STEPPE

According to botanists the typical pampa is an immense grassy steppe, originally without trees. The landscape is thus completely monotonous and after a while the traveler gets the impression that he is continually passing across the same plains.

The absence of trees on the original pampas can be attributed to the fact that the ground is compact and not porous or aerated; insufficient rain during the summer may have been another cause. But man has succeeded in acclimatizing various species, such as pines, eucalypts, casuarinas, plane trees *(Platanus acerifolia)*, oaks *(Quercus pedunculata)*, elms *(Fraxinus)*, and poplars *(Populus)*. These trees have modified the pampas landscape, especially around human habitations.

The vegetation changes to the west of the pampas; from the center of the province of San Luis to the Rio Colorado it resembles that of the Chaco, which borders it to the north. In their natural state, the plains here are covered with drought-resistant vegetation, mainly thorny bushes from three to ten or more feet high, such as the jarillas *(Larrea sp.)*, various *Prosopis*, the chañar *(Gourliea spinosa)*, some *chuquiragua* and some acacias. The ground is bare on large expanses between these small trees and bushes; grasses are rare and the number of other herbaceous plants is even more restricted. Botanists consider this habitat to be completely different from the true pampa.

THE INFLUENCE OF MAN

The vegetation of the pampas has everywhere been considerably modified by man. To begin with, stock-raising has led to an improvement of pastures by the importation of various exotic plants. Thus the native *pasto duro* or *fuerte* (hard or strong pasturage) has given way to *pasto tierno*, that is, tender pasturage generally made up of a stable association of plants. Plantations have of course completely transformed other areas.

It is hard to believe that these plains remained until as recently as 1875 the domain of Indian tribes. These natives, belonging to the Araucan group, were always very few in number and, although active and nomadic, have almost completely disappeared.

For a long time the Spanish colonists contented themselves with letting their cattle roam over vast territories in a half-wild state. Toward the middle of the nineteenth century, colonization increased sharply and the whole of the pampas was settled by Argentinians of European origin. Beginning in 1857, railroads hastened the exploitation of the country, refrigerators making it possible to ship beef long distances to the coast and thence to Europe. The pampas soon became a great center of "industrial cattle-raising," with the products exported mainly to Great Britain.

Sheep-raising, first for wool, and afterward for meat, was begun in 1851. The census of 1895 showed 52,000,000 sheep in

Typical pampas, seen here between Malargüe and Laguna Llancenelo, Mendoza, is an immense treeless steppe covered with tufts of prairie grass. (Don Eckelberry)

the province of Buenos Aires alone, and sheep-raising expanded westward along with the pacification of the region. When sheep-raising began to displace cattle-ranching, the cattle-raisers started to send their herds further west. The creation of artificial pasturage and alfalfa plantations, the campaign against ticks that spread disease (especially the *garrapates*, which causes Texas fever) and above all the improvement of the stock thanks to the introduction of European breeds, soon made the pampas one of the world's great centers of beef production. Meanwhile, agriculture developed. From the end of the eighteenth century on, the pampas produced wheat, beginning around Buenos Aires and spreading as the railroads expanded.

A succession of agricultural zones can be distinguished in the humid part of the pampas. In the northwest, the area of summer rains, mainly south of Rosario, there is maize; in the west—"the colonies" of olden times—and in the southwest, where springs are rainy and summers dry, wheatfields predominate. In the drier pampas to the southeast, stock-raising, mainly of sheep, prevails, as might be expected in such a climate.

Stock-raising and agriculture are very conveniently combined in some areas, mainly in the northwest of the province of Buenos Aires and the southwest of the province of Cordoba. Here cattlemen and farmers alternate on the same land in a kind of long-term rotation. When pastureland becomes impoverished after a few years, it is turned over to the agriculturists; they till the soil for four or five years, and then restore the regenerated land sown with alfalfa.

The mara (Dolichotis), *which reaches a length of two and a half feet, owes the name Patagonian hare to its leaps and bounds. (A. Y. Owen: Life Magazine © Time, Inc.)*

The unity of Argentina was achieved around the pampas. For many years the coastal provinces and the interior provinces formed two separate worlds, the interior provinces being inhabited by people who had crossed the Andes and felt economically and culturally closer to Peru and Chile. But as the exploitation of the pampas grew, the attraction of the Buenos Aires region increased, and soon the distant provinces strengthened their bonds with the east, while relations with the Andean republics diminished to the breaking point. It was thus that a great modern nation was constituted around its prairies.

THE RIO DE LA PLATA

The southern limits of the pampas are unclear, for the plains merge progressively into the Patagonian steppes. On the other hand, the northern boundary is well defined, being marked by the shores of a vast expanse of water: the Rio de la Plata. The name implies a river, but this body of water is in fact a great gulf into which three rivers, the Rio Paraguay, the Rio Paraná and the Rio Uruguay empty. From the common mouth of these rivers flow 2,800,000 cubic feet of water per second, making the Rio de la Plata second-largest "river" in the world —after the Amazon—in terms of flow. Its width increases from west to east: thus, at the confluence of the Paraná and the Uruguay its width is nineteen miles, at Montevideo sixty-three miles, and at its mouth 140 miles.

This gulf is in fact composed of two distinct parts both geographically and biologically. The eastern part is a triangular marine bay with water that is saline, blue and clear, while in the western part—the common estuary of no less than six streams—the water is at first brackish and then definitely fresh and muddy. All the marine characteristics of the landscape and the fauna disappear west of Montevideo or, rather, after the line from Punta de Espinillo to Punta de las Piedras on the Argentine coast.

In ancient times this vast arm of the sea was much larger than it is today. It was at first reduced by an uplifting of the continental mass and then by intense sedimentation, which still continues very actively and is closely related to the formation of the pampas. The sediment has made this river mouth remarkably shallow, the depth varying between ten and twenty feet, except for a natural channel of thirty or thirty-five feet deep that must be constantly dredged to allow ships to reach the port of Buenos Aires.

There is a sharp contrast between the northern shore of the Rio de la Plata, which is steep and rocky, and the southern shore, which is flat. Sand bars extend all along the latter shore at low tide or when the wind blows away the waters that cover them in calm weather. Needless to say, these waters are particularly favorable to animal life, especially birds. There is an abundance of ducks, flamingos, and limpkins *(Aramus guarauna)*. The latter, called "crazy widows," are intermediate between cranes and rails and feed mainly upon mollusks that they dexterously extract from the shallows with their powerful beaks.

The Rio de la Plata is of great interest to the naturalist because it is a meeting place of fresh waters brought down by tropical rivers and cool or even cold salt waters. Like the Amazon, the Rio de la Plata has a cetacean all its own, the dolphin of the Plata *(Stenodelphis blainvillei)*, called *tonina*

The common rhea (Rhea americana), *a flightless bird like its relatives, the ostriches, emus and cassowaries, is common on the pampas. (Francisco Erize)*

by Argentine fishermen. It does not ascend the rivers, but lives along the coasts between 30° Lat. S and 45° Lat. S. It is a primitive animal of the Iniidae family, with a short neck and a long "beak" or rostrum. It is little more than five feet long. It feeds mainly on fish, squid and cuttlefish.

SIERRAS OF THE WESTERN PAMPAS

In spite of the depth of the alluvia deposited in the pampas, it has not managed to cover completely the mountains underneath. Isolated ranges formed of very ancient rocks emerge from the midst of the plains. They serve mainly as water towers from which rivers descend in all directions.

The most important of these sierras is formed by the Cordoba and the San Luis mountains, separated from each other by the Conlara depression. Wherever the slopes of these sierras are well watered they are covered with forest, and the most humid sections have a semitropical aspect. Above four thousand feet, the forest is restricted to the most sheltered ravines. Until the middle of the nineteenth century these sierras played a great part in the Argentine economy; their streams enabled a large population to practice cattle-raising and agriculture.

WATER BIRDS

A distinct parallel between the economic evolution of the Argentine pampas and the North American prairies will strike any student of political geography. Indeed, it will strike the ordinary traveler: as I flew over the pampas, I almost felt that I was flying from Chicago to Denver. Both are immense plains covered with grassy associations in a temperate climate.

The fauna, notably the birds, is similar in some ways to that found on the prairies. This is especially true of the water fowl abounding in countless marshes and expanses of water. Of the great variety of ducks, one, the black-headed duck *(Heteronetta atricapilla)*, found between the center of Chile and southern Brazil and between southern Brazil and Argentina, is unique among aquatic birds in being a parasite in its egg-laying habits. It resembles the teal in appearance and

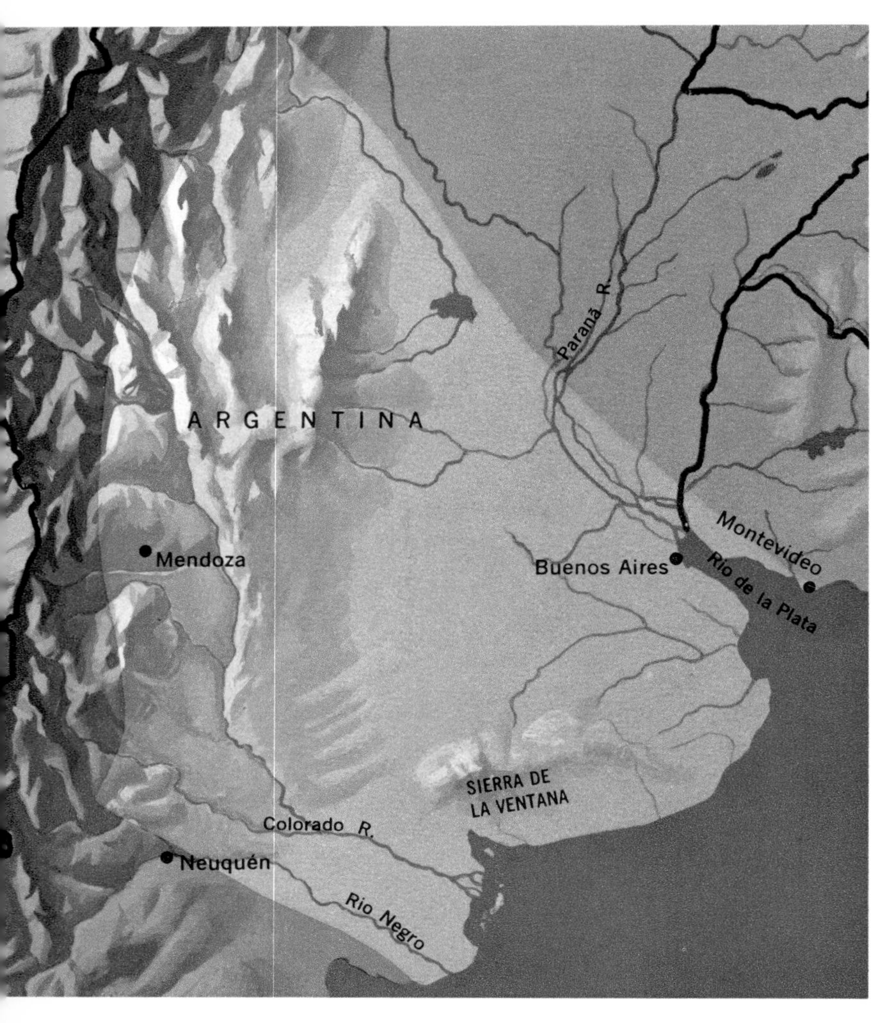

The Argentine pampas is a vast plain—the accumulation of sediments carried down from the Andes by streams and rivers.

has many characteristics in common with the stiff-tails *(Oxyura),* but instead of constructing its own nest, it lays its eggs in the nests of other ducks or of birds little related to it, such as screamers, limpkins, and gulls, or even of a bird of prey. In this parasitic habit, it of course recalls the cuckoos.

Another characteristic and very conspicuous inhabitant of the pampas is a plover, the teru-teru *(Belonopterus cayannensis)* of Argentina, which is gray with a black breast and white undersides. As soon as it senses danger, its clamor becomes almost deafeningly loud. When a traveler crosses the territory of a pair of these plovers in breeding time, both birds accompany him, soaring and circling above him and uttering piercing shrieks. The humid eastern pampas are this bird's true domain, for it likes grassy plains broken by expanses of water. The peons rifle its nests for the eggs, but the species is still incredibly numerous. In the nineteenth century a great number of these birds were killed, then salted or frozen and sent to Europe.

We should also mention the kamichis *(Chauna torquata),* aberrant representatives of the Anseriform order usually encountered in pairs on the shores of the lagoons. They let out noisy calls that sound like *cha-hah,* and these discordant cries of the *chajá,* as the bird is known locally, combined with the raucous calls of the teru-teru, provide the "music" of the pampas.

RUNNING BIRDS: THE NANDUS

The steppelike character of the true Argentine pampa is confirmed by the presence of a bird peculiar to open habitats: the nandu *(Rhea americana),* found in Argentina as far as the Rio Negro, beyond which it is replaced by a smaller species, the Darwin nandu. It is flightless and is sometimes called the ostrich of South America, although it has only a superficial resemblance to the Old World bird and is smaller, its maximum height being only a little over four feet, and its maximum weight about fifty or sixty pounds. Although now found only from the Chaco to the Rio Negro, the nandus were formerly abundant everywhere. But they were hunted by the Tobas Indians and then by the gauchos. The Indian hunter would camouflage himself to look like a bush, advance whenever the great bird lowered its head to feed, then pierce it with an arrow from a distance of only a few yards. The gauchos pursued the bird on horseback, catching it with a *boleadora,* a kind of lasso of leather thongs weighted with a round stone and flung in such a way that the thongs wrapped themselves around the bird's feet, bringing it to a stop. The nandus were hunted for sport, for their flesh (the wings and pectoral muscles were particularly prized), and for their feathers, which are less beautiful than those of the ostrich and were used only to make feather dusters. Various parts of the nandu's body were reputed, moreover, to have therapeutic properties: the forepart of the stomach, for instance, was boiled to make a cure for indigestion, an interesting empiric use of the strong digestive juices of the bird.

Agriculture and stock-raising broke up the pampas into fields or pastures fenced with barbed wire, and this contributed to the disappearance of the nandus from many areas. Fortunately the nandus are now protected by the owners of the big ranches and are managing to maintain their populations in sections of the pampas that are still wild.

The nandus live in family groups, the polygamous males gathering a harem of from five to six females, and assuming most of the domestic tasks. They dig a nest hole about a yard wide and five inches deep in an expanse of loose soil. There the females lay a pile of from twenty to thirty, or sometimes even fifty greenish-yellow eggs, each about five inches long. The male hatches them, driving away any female who approaches. When threatened, he flees, pretending to be wounded, obviously to distract the attention of the intruder. The young hatch at the end of six weeks and immediately begin to run about. The father guides them to the favored part of the pampas; and it is he who utters loud calls, while the females are silent.

STRANGE NESTS

Some birds of the pampas have extraordinary methods of nesting. One of these is the ovenbird *(Furnarius rufus);* this

Western Argentina consists of a series of plateaus terminating in eroded cliffs, such as Quebrada Canyon in the province of Salta. (Weldon King)

Furnariidae is not to be confused with a bird of the same name in the United States—a Parulidae, *Seiurus auricapillus*. This bird, about eight inches long and with a rusty-red plumage above and white and beige beneath, is one of the commonest in Argentina. It is also one of the most familiar, for it likes trees near human habitations, and especially around *estancias*. It carefully constructs a large nest of dried mud in full view on a tree branch, house cornice, rock, or fence post. Hundreds of these nests can be seen on the pampas. The nest, which is sometimes globe-shaped and sometimes oval, measures at least twelve by eight inches. The bird establishes a foundation of earth, then raises walls an inch thick with a round dome and an opening in the side. Like an Eskimo igloo, a wall inside the entrance creates a kind of vestibule; beyond that is the breeding chamber. Since the bird mixes straw and vegetable fibers with the mud, the result is a reinforced concrete that affords protection from all kinds of weather, lasts for more than a year and may be used again the following year, especially by the swallows. It is this nest, resembling an old-fashioned baker's oven, that has, of course, earned the bird its name—ovenbird in English, *hornero* in Spanish and *fournier* in French. The bird is so characteristic of the pampas that the ornithological society of Argentina has called its magazine *El Hornero*.

The pampas are also inhabited by a member of the parrot family, the monk parakeet *(Myiopsitta monachus)*, of sober plumage—green above, the head, throat and breast gray, and the undersides greenish yellow. This parakeet, like its counterparts elsewhere, lives in large flocks and nests in colonies. The nests are suspended side by side from the tips of tree branches, forming a thick tangle. Such a collection of nests sometimes measures more than six feet in diameter and weighs a quarter of a ton, its volume amounting to an average wagonload. Even when a large tree holds as many as eight such collections of nests, each pair has its own nest, repairing it throughout the year. Monk parakeet flocks, sometimes composed of several thousand individuals, can devastate a plantation, especially of maize, thus recalling the Carolina parakeet, which was eventually exterminated by man.

MIGRANT VISITORS

The Argentine pampas are the winter quarters of many North American birds, attracted no doubt by an environment similar to that of some parts of North America. These birds carry out amazing migrations across almost the whole of the New World. One of the most astonishing of all is the golden plover *(Pluvialis dominica)*. These plovers nest in the tundra of Canada and Alaska; then, at the beginning of autumn, they assemble in Labrador and fly in a direct line over 2,400 miles of the Atlantic Ocean, before barely touching down at the Bermudas and the Antilles en route to the Brazilian coast. After spending the winter in the more humid parts of the pampas, they start north in the spring. In their return flight, they pass over the center of South America and over Central

Guanacos, the original form of the llama and still found in the wild, gather in a band under the eyes of an adult male. (A. Y. Owen: Life Magazine © Time, Inc.)

The long-haired armadillo (Zaedus pichyi) *is found on the plains from northern Argentina to the Rio Santa Cruz. (Jose M. Cei)*

America, covering a distance of eight thousand miles to reach their nesting territories. Thus the plovers describe an enormous ellipse across the New World, a stupendous roundabout journey that has yet to be explained.

Many shore birds from the north migrate in winter to the Argentine pampas: godwits, redshanks and sandpipers take advantage of the water habitats so plentiful in this part of South America precisely when the available food reaches a maximum.

During the winter of the Southern Hemisphere, when the subarctic migrators have departed to nest in the Northern Hemisphere, they are partly replaced by migrants from Patagonia, driven by the severe winter of the southernmost part of South America. Among these is a plover, *Charadrius falcklandicus,* and a seed snipe, *Thinocorus rumicivorus.* Thus the pampas play an important part in the biology of New World migrants, being visited alternately by birds from the north and from the south.

THE MAMMALS OF THE PAMPAS

The North American plains were once inhabited by herds of large mammals that fed on the grassy ground cover. Similarly, in Africa antelopes indigenous to the grasslands are most abundant. On the other hand, there are few such big animals on the South American pampas, a clear instance of the lack of recent mammalian types in a Neotropical region.

The animal best adapted to the grassy regions is the guanaco *(Lama guanicoe),* found from the province of Buenos Aires to Patagonia, in northwest Argentina, and in a part of the Andean region. We will return to this subject in our chapter on Patagonia.

The pampas is also inhabited by a beautiful species of Cervidae, the pampas deer *(Ozateceros bezoarticus).* Its distribution widely overflows this zone since it is to be found from central Brazil southward; it has not penetrated Patagonia, or beyond Rio Negro, which here again acts as a biogeographical limit. This deer is now rather rare on the pampas but is still well represented in the Mato Grosso and a few districts of Paraguay. Hunting is partly responsible for its reduced numbers. This deer and the guanaco are the only large mammals found on the grassy pampas, despite the fact that this environment could surely sustain many more such animals.

This scarcity of ungulates seems to be balanced, in obedience to a common biological law, by the great number of rodents on the pampas. These small animals make most use of the ground cover. Probably the most interesting of these is the plains viscacha, of the genus *Lagostomus,* which to a certain extent occupies the same kind of ecological niche that the prairie dog fills in North America. The pampas species is a much heavier-looking animal than its relative in the Andes, with a massive head, a length of as much as twenty inches, and short, very soft gray fur. Unlike the viscacha of the Andes, the viscacha of the plains is purely nocturnal; by day it remains out of sight in family groups in vast underground burrows with many openings.

The mara *(Dolichotis patagonum)* is a strong-looking rodent that attains a length of about thirty inches. Called the Patagonian hare, it is unrelated to the true hares but superficially resembles them because of its highly developed hind quarters and ears that are sometimes as much as four inches long. At the same time its eyes, very large and with long lashes, give it a gentle look, rare among rodents. It thus gives the strange impression of being a kind of composite. Related to the agouti and the capybara, it is native to the pampas between the province of Cordoba and Patagonia. It lives in groups of from three to six individuals and one can sometimes see them sleeping in the sun, their legs outstretched. At the least sound they sit up and seem literally to fly away, moving at a rapid run interrupted by gigantic leaps. It has disappeared from populated zones.

We also must not forget that the southern part of South America is the land of the fur-bearing nutria *(Myocastor coypus),* which attains a length of about twenty inches and has a tail sixteen inches long. With its webbed feet this rodent is aquatic and is found near streams and lakes, living somewhat like the beavers and muskrats of the Northern Hemisphere. The commercial value of its fur has caused it to be bred in semicaptivity. Introduced into North America and Europe, it is now acclimatized in the wilds on these continents.

It is only natural that the pampas, with its expanses of loose alluvial soil, should attract burrowing rodents, with habits similar to those of the voles. And in fact this area, as well as Patagonia and all the open habitats of southern Brazil and Bolivia is the domain of the tucutucos or *Ctenomys,* their common name deriving from the cry with which they communicate underground. These native South American rodents are sometimes eight inches long, with a short tail, massive head and body, short ears and powerful incisors. Their toes are provided with silky hairs in the form of a comb; hence their scientific name, meaning comblike. The tucutucos live

Nutrias (Myocastor coypu), *large rodents native to Chile and Argentina, are raised in captivity for their valuable fur. (Paul Almasy: Bavaria Verlag)*

about two feet underground in vast burrows with many galleries and outlets and with a main nesting-room and store-room about ten inches in diameter. Since these rodents live in colonies, they end up by completely undermining the ground, so that cattle and horses often crash into the burrows and break their legs. The tucutucos stay in their burrows throughout the day, venturing out at night but remaining close to an entrance to their dwellings. They feed on plants, fruits, and grain.

Of the many types of carnivores on the pampas, skunks *(Conepatus)* are among the most numerous, for these animals, protected by their evil-smelling secretions, show a marked preference for open ground. They spend the day in natural cavities or in burrows other animals have dug, coming out to hunt at night. They feed mainly on insects, especially beetles and centipedes, as well as spiders, some rodents, and the eggs of land birds. The *hurón* or *huroncito,* as the Argentinians call a ferret-like animal *(Lyncodon patagonicus),* is a Mustelidae that is characteristic of the pampas and is distributed from La Rioja in northwest Argentina to the Rio Chubut in Patagonia. The small size of this animal, no longer than twelve inches, and its nocturnal habits explain why it is one of the less-known South American carnivores.

Among the Canidae, the most common here is *el zorro de la pampa,* the gray fox *(Pseudolopex gymnocercus),* about thirty inches long with a fourteen-inch tail, an animal native to open habitats and more especially to grassy steppes, where it leads a nocturnal existence, traveling alone or in pairs. It feeds principally upon rodents, but also takes land birds and will not disdain the smallest prey. Its numbers have declined sharply as a result of being hunted by man, and this has led to the rapid increase in rodents.

Numerous armadillos also make their home on the pampas. At least two species are native to the area: the seven-banded armadillo *(Dasypus septemcinctus)* and the peludo *(Chaetophractus cinctus),* which is partially covered with stiff hairs and is known for its extremely irritable temper. It is especially active at night, spending the day rolled up into a ball or else underground in a burrow.

THE SEA LIONS OF THE LOBOS ISLANDS

Near the mouth of the Rio de la Plata is a small archipelago, the Islas de Lobos, which takes its name from the flippered sea mammals that inhabit it. The presence of these marine carnivores testifies to the wealth of fish in the locality and to the coldness of the waters brought from the south by the currents. The Lobos group, located seven miles off the coast of Uruguay, consists of a low main island, 1,000 yards long by 500 yards wide, flanked by lower islets and numerous masses of rocks. The islands are formed of rugged granite ledges, boulders and cliffs, and by volcanic activity that has left traces in the form of lava flows. The stunted vegetation is mainly harsh brake and minuscule cactus. The shores are steep cliffs, and sand beaches are rare. Countless sharks infest the waters, some large enough to prey upon the sea lions.

Two species of pinnipeds frequent these islands. A third, the elephant seal *(Mirounga leonina),* which here reached its northernmost distribution, has disappeared as a result of the ruthless hunting to which it was subjected. The southern fur seal *(Arctocephalus australis)* is still present but it has been considerably reduced by hunting, barely managing to survive in the southernmost districts, notably Tierra del Fuego. If rationally exploited instead of being massacred, this animal, with its fur, could have been a continuing source of wealth.

The other species, *Otaria flavescens,* is much more abundant. Distributed all along the southern Atlantic and Pacific coasts of South America, its colonies often flourish. One of them is located on the Lobos Islands. Generally arriving in December, the males, huge beasts, are the first to come ashore, choosing a territory on the beach or on the plateau, and defending it against their fellows; then the females arrive and, after violent clashes among the males, are grouped by the males in harems. The colony sometimes includes as many as two thousand individuals, and the beaches swarm with animals, the largest males sometimes more than nine feet long. The threatening roar of a male resembles the bellowing of a bull, and the barking of the females and the young fills the air, rising above the sound of the waves and the cries of the gulls that come to gorge themselves on the leftovers of the seals. The males must constantly mount guard to keep their females from running away or from being captured by other males. Towering above the crowd, their noses pointing upward and the skin of their necks falling in thick greasy folds, the bulls survey their surroundings, ready to suppress the least movement of flight or to challenge a threatening neighbor. The combat between the males is often restricted to threats, but at times it is violent and deep scars on the adults testify to the ferocity of these encounters. Then the colony settles down, the females submissively grouped around their lord; the beach now assumes something of the aspect of one of our beaches on a summer Sunday.

The young sea lions are born in January. The females bring them up, teach them to swim, and see to it that they don't do the foolish things natural to children. The pups are very playful and as awkward and blundering as puppy dogs. They assemble in small nurseries, facilitating surveillance by the mothers; each mother, however, knows her own offspring, and she alone nurses it. Soon the pups are old enough to begin their sea existence and the colony disperses, leaving the beaches deserted until the next breeding season.

These pinnipeds, feeding solely on fish—they consume as a rule thirty to fifty pounds a day, and sometimes up to one hundred pounds—have only a few natural enemies. The adult males are pursued only by the killer whale but many of the young and the females become the prey of sharks. Their major enemy is man, who hunts them for their oil. An animal of medium size yields from twenty to thirty-five quarts of oil. Man has therefore carried out an unrestrained hunt for these animals and the colonies would be entirely depleted by now had not legislation begun to offer them some protection.

The high plateaus of Argentina have a cold dry climate against which many of the cactus plants are protected with a thick coat of brushlike hairs. (Don Eckelberry)

Volcanos and Hummingbirds

The Andes of Colombia and Ecuador

11

In 1735, three French scientists, Louis Godin, Pierre Bouguer, and Charles-Marie de la Condamine, were sent to Ecuador to verify the shape of the earth and to prove that our planet is "a spheroid slightly flattened at the poles." There was a good reason for these illustrious scientists to choose this section of the world in which to make precise measurements. Elsewhere along the Equator the land is covered with dense forests that make geodesic and astronomical measurements problematical and inexact. A few regions, particularly Africa, were still completely cut off from the outside world. The exceptional physiography of this part of South America—open country that could be easily crossed, though close to impenetrable forests—is caused by the Andes, which have modified the natural conditions in Ecuador and in Colombia.

It is worth adding that La Condamine left his colleagues after the measurements were completed and did not return to Europe until 1745, after he had made the first scientific exploration of the Amazon, and crossed Brazil and the Guiana region.

The most complex part of the Andes is in Colombia. Near that country's southwestern frontier the two ranges that constitute the Andes form a single grand mountain mass, the *Nudo de Pasto,* and a short distance to the north, the Central Andes form what is called *Macizo Colombiano.* From this point the Eastern Andes branch out—completing in this way three distinct massifs. The valley of the Rio Magdalena, located between the eastern and the central ranges, is six hundred miles long and from nine to forty-five miles wide. The valley of the Rio Cauca, between the central and the western range, is smaller in overall size. Both valleys were created by a caving in of the earth's crust, and are in fact colossal rifts resembling the Rift Valley in eastern Africa. It is this circumstance that accounts for the presence of low tropical plains in the very heart of the Andes Mountains. Thus, an overall view of the Colombian Andes shows a succession of high ranges with a cold or temperate climate, and lowlands with a hot climate. This alternation occurs three times within relatively short distances and has a profound effect on the distribution of animal life.

Located in the torrid zone, Colombia should have a very hot and humid climate and should be covered with a dense tropical growth, but because of the three Andean ranges that cross it from one end to the other, it is a mosaic of intersecting zones of vegetation. A book by Luis Maria Murillo, a biologist, is entitled *Colombia, Biological Archipelago,* and nothing could be more descriptive. The splitting up of the Andes into isolated mountains in the midst of areas with very different ecological conditions has not only caused a differentiation of species in each of the mountain ranges but has also affected the human population. Over a long period of time it has led to the division of the population into small groups; to this day there is no one principal city in Colombia but several metropolitan centers.

The Eastern Cordillera encompasses a large area of cold lands, extending 170 miles between the Rio Magdalena and the low eastern regions; the latter are dense jungles, for the most part unexplored. The northern sections form llanos covered with grasses that are alternately inundated and arid, and cut by large rivers bordered by gallery forests. South of the Guaviare River, these eastern llanos give way to the jungles of the Amazon. Although extending over two thirds of Colombia, this eastern region is inhabited by only two per cent of the population, and has for this reason remained in a very wild state. The Eastern Cordillera includes some very high ranges, among them the Sierra Nevada de Cocuy, which rises to 17,852 feet. But very close to these are somewhat lower stretches such as Sabana de Bogota (8,661 feet), flat highlands that have a very pleasant temperate climate with abundant rains.

The Central Cordillera is a long ridge covered with volcanic ash and capped at intervals by some of the most beautiful snow-capped volcanos in the Andes, including Nevada del Ruiz (18,340 feet), Santa Isabel (18,200 feet), Tolima (18,425 feet) and Nevada del Huila (18,701 feet), second-highest peak in Colombia. In the south are found the volcanic chain of Puracé and Coconucos—which reaches its highest point at Pan de Azúcar (16,400 feet)—and the Sotará volcano. Ruiz and Huila show some volcanic activity; Puracé periodically erupted until 1960 and still sends out smoke through a fissure near the main crater. To the north, this cordillera spreads out to form the plateau of Antioquia, whose foothills merge into the low valley of the Rio Magdalena. This worn-down plain contains deposits of gold-bearing sediments brought down by the Cauca and Nechí rivers especially near Pato and Zaragoza, where they are exploited.

The Andes of Colombia are bordered on the north by wide plains oriented toward the Caribbean Sea. These plains are mainly the delta of the Rio Magdalena, the river spreading out into lagoons and marshes. This valley includes vast stretches, the *cienagas,* that are permanently or periodically inundated and where the direction of the rivers reverses as a result of the rise and fall of the water level.

Because of the trade winds, rainfall is scarce in northeastern Colombia, and the region is therefore covered with a drought-resistant vegetation, small trees and shrubs with

The region around Cerro de la Teta, near La Guajira, Colombia, is one of the dryest in South America although it borders on one of the most humid areas. (Guillermo Molano)

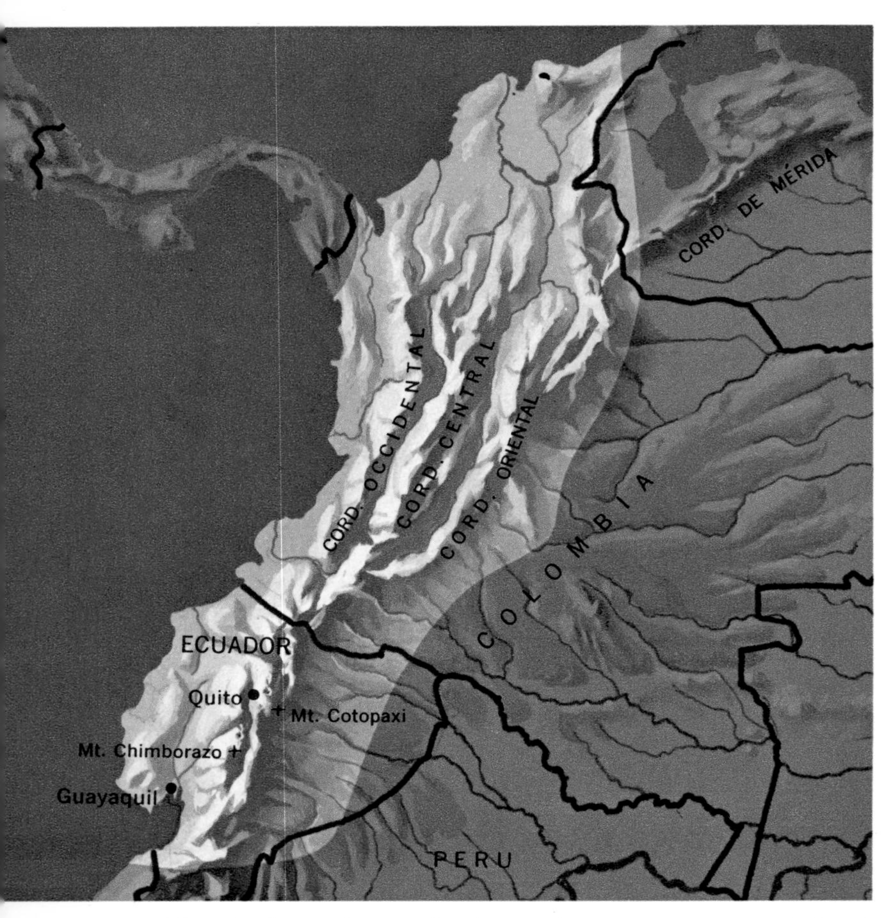

The Andean chains dominate the western part of South America. Topographically, the most complex part of these mountains is in Colombia. In Ecuador, extensive volcanic activity has remodeled the original mountain structure.

tough evergreen leaves, thorn trees and bushes, and numerous succulents. Cacti such as the *Lemaireocereus* and *Acanthocereus,* with huge candelabra, abound in some places.

On the other hand, the Pacific coast and northwestern Colombia is one of the most watered zones in the world. Throughout these areas there is at least two hundred inches of rainfall a year, and at certain points much more: near Buenaventura as much as 365 inches of rain has fallen in a single year, and some places have rain on more than three hundred days a year. The forest here is therefore of a rare luxuriance, with trees from 100 to 120 feet tall, burdened with lianas and epiphytic plants. The size and aspect of these trees is like that of their counterparts in the Amazon, and many of them are buttressed. Wherever enough sunlight reaches the ground, the undergrowth, composed of palms, ferns, and even of herbaceous plants, is thick.

This low-altitude forest gives way, at about six thousand feet, to a subtropical forest and then, higher up, to a temperate-zone growth. The humidity, maintained by frequent fogs from the condensation of vapor in warm air rising from the valleys, supports a lush vegetation. The rain forest recalls that of the lowlands, but the species of plants are different and the trees with prop roots occupy less space. The undergrowth of bamboos, tree ferns and shrubs is very dense, and the trees are covered with orchids and mosses. Unfortunately this forest has been greatly damaged by men, some of the land having been put under cultivation, mainly for grazing and for coffee. Colombia is one of the world's great coffee producers and coffee comprises three quarters of its exports. Still higher, at eight thousand feet, the trees begin to diminish in size, but the forest remains dense. Approaching 11,500 feet especially in the Sierra Nevada de Cocuy, the vegetation becomes typical of the paramos. Above that begins the strange vegetation of the High Andes.

ECUADOR: LAND OF ERUPTIONS

Ecuador is one of the most interesting countries in South America because everywhere, except on the exterior slopes, the primitive architecture of the Andes has been almost entirely masked by gigantic volcanic formations. A country profoundly marked by vulcanism, Ecuador has no less than twenty active volcanos between Mount Sangay and the Colombian frontier.

One of the effects of the volcanic eruptions has been to deposit an enormous mass of loose fragments in the valleys and hollows. The lower slopes of the volcanos themselves frequently disappear beneath these accumulations, giving them soft rounded forms in strong contrast with the sharp peaks that dominate the landscape.

Vulcanism has also piled up strings of huge volcanic cones on the Andean summits, making them giants. In the western range the Pichincha (15,763 feet) overlooking Quito, the Iliniza (17,240 feet) and the colossal Chimborazo (20,702 feet), the highest point in Ecuador, are only the most famous. The Eastern Cordillera includes Cayambe (18,980 feet) and Cotopaxi (19,498 feet). Sangay (17,464 feet) is farther east. Although some of these occur in the middle of the inter-Andean furrow, most of them are on the axis of the mountain summits, adding to their great height.

Although some of these volcanos are ancient and extinct, as for example Chimborazo, which has no crater, many others, such as Cotopaxi and Sangay, are still very much alive. Earthquakes are frequent and often destructive, such as the one in 1949 that ravaged the center of Ecuador and destroyed half the town of Ambato, and are a constant threat.

In addition, the volcanic outline of the mountains was long ago remoulded by glaciers. In ancient times these glaciers extended much lower than they do today, as can be seen in the traces left in moraines and hollowed-out cirques. Clinging glaciers still cover many volcanos.

The upward thrust of mountains, the fire spouting from the center of the earth, the cold of the extremely high altitudes, and the tropical sun have thus leagued together to make Ecuador one of the countries with the greatest extremes in natural habitats in the world.

QUITO

I had just landed in Quito, the capital of Ecuador, a city I had long wanted to visit. The day was hot but the heat was

View from the southern tip of the Cordillera Macarena, showing the Rio Guayabero in Colombia. (Harriet Barclay)

quite endurable, and mists hid the surrounding mountains. I was not disappointed at not getting an immediate glimpse of the celebrated environs of the city for I knew that at noon the mountaintops, especially the summits of the great volcanos, vanish behind mist and clouds.

Next morning I rose before dawn to get out of the city and observe the landscape before the sun and the heat caused the fogs to form. By six o'clock I was on the lower slopes of the Pichincha, and a awesome view was spread before me.

Quito, the oldest of the capitals of colonial South America and one of the most beautiful, is situated on a spur of the Pichincha volcano between two deep ravines carved out by mountain torrents. From where I stood, the entire geological history of this region was there beneath my eyes, far easier to read than on any map.

At my feet was the city backed by the mountain and surrounded by a vast terrace. This terrace, about 9,000 feet high, is in a temperate zone, the result of the filling up of an Andean valley by volcanic ash from nearby craters. To the east of Quito, quite near the city, is an abrupt escarpment, plunging 1,800 feet to the bottom of the valley. When I looked down, this was already filled with a fleecy mist that was slowly rising to envelope the Quito plateau. It is probable that this entire valley was filled with volcanic debris until mountain streams and rain water began their work of erosion, carving out a deep valley, bordered by steep cliffs, and now occupied by the Rio Guaillabamba. At the latitude of Quito this river flows only at about 7,500 feet above sea level and, due to this low elevation, constitutes a warmer zone where tropical plants still manage to flourish.

My first glimpse of this fabulous landscape that early morning recalled pictures of volcanos in the textbooks of my boyhood, for there rising out of the mists was a perfect cone, snow-capped and dazzling in the level sunshine. It was Cotopaxi, the "ideal volcano," as the great mountain climber, Edward Whymper, described it. The vegetation that covers its lower slopes was lost in blue shadow. Toward the north, above streamers of fog, loomed another volcano, the Cayambe, a great white mass against the blue sky. The tropics were still new enough to me so that I could marvel at eternal snows and glaciers capping volcanos almost directly on the Equator.

Painfully, then, I began to climb the Pichincha, whose two yawning craters of black rock tower above the city of Quito. The climb was arduous, for I was not yet used to the altitude. This volcano last erupted in 1666 and is probably extinct. The vegetation on its sides is mainly tough grasses and sedges. In the ravines, however, some shrubs and ground bromeliads form a more pleasant environment that attracts birds; even some hummingbirds come here to plunder the flowers and capture insects.

By evening, the weather cleared, but the clouds still clung to the peaks of the volcanos. As I had been told, it is only at dawn that they reveal themselves.

It is worth mentioning that Whymper, who crossed the equatorial Andes in 1879–1880, was perhaps the first to bring back to Europe etchings of these mountains and valuable information, mainly concerning the effects of altitude on human and animal life. His book on his travels in Ecuador is still one of the best on the subject, for it describes the charm of things that have now disappeared and revives an epoch when such a journey was not arranged by a travel agency.

THE LANDSCAPES OF ECUADOR

No other country in South America accommodates such a large variety of plant communities as Ecuador.

Left: The brown booby (Sula leucogaster), *found in all warm, tropical seas, nests on sandy beaches of the Pacific coast of Colombia. (López M. Nereo) Right: This tropical forest along the Upper Puyo River in eastern Ecuador continues as far as the Amazon basin. (Paul Schauenberg)*

Overleaf: The vast grassy steppe typical of the Andes above 12,000 feet, with the 17,240-foot Iliniza Mountain of Ecuador in the distance. (Gottfried Hirtz)

As far as Cabo Pasado, a little below the Equator, the lower slopes on the Pacific Andes are covered with a dense rain forest, an extension of similar regions in Colombia. This soon gives way to xerophytic brush, heralding the approach to the Peruvian deserts. The southern coast of Ecuador is touched by the Humboldt Current, the chill of which causes a sharp reduction in rainfall.

The few thorny or xerophytic trees are intermingled with a great many cacti and *Croton*. Perhaps the most celebrated tree of this region is the *palo de balsa (Ochroma lagopus* or related species), of the family of Bombacaceae. Found in the Rio Guayas Valley and on the lower slopes of the Andes, exactly as in northern Peru, this tree yields the lightest wood in the world, weighing no more than from six to eight pounds per cubic foot, which makes it twice as buoyant as cork. It is therefore not at all surprising that the Indians should have used it for their light boats—the Spanish word *balsa* means raft—and that it is useful nowadays as shock absorbing material and insulation against cold or heat. But probably the most famous single instance of its use was in the raft *Kon-Tiki* in which the Norwegian ethnographer Thor Heyerdahl floated 4,300 miles with the prevailing winds and currents from Peru to the Polynesian islands. As every reader of Heyerdahl's book knows, he believed the raft had to be made of balsa logs.

In this district, too, one finds a plant that looks like a palm, the *Cardulovica palmata* or bombonaje, of the Cyclantaceae family; its fibers are used in the fabrication of the famous "Panama hats," the center of this industry being in Ecuador and northern Peru.

One of the most interesting trips by rail in South America is the one between Guayaquil and Quito. Leaving Guayaquil, one takes a boat across the Rio Guayas, where the train waits beside the muddy river. At first the route crosses the arid coastal plain, where irrigation alone permits the cultivation of the land. Soon the train climbs to the forested level, passing through little stations where peddlers offer the traveler the products of the country as well as food cooked on small stoves or fires beside the station platforms. Then the cars go up a dizzyingly steep slope—a disquieting experience, for they stagger and sway over the rough roadbed. And instead of following curves which are perhaps impossible on such a steep slope, the train climbs by a zigzag route, going forward up one segment and then backing up the next—quite disturbing to the traveler who has not been forewarned.

The steep climb takes us rapidly from one natural environment to another. From the rain forest around Naranjapata at 1,500 feet we go to Huigra, at 3,700 feet, where the vegetation is mainly shrubs and bushes *(Piquiera peruviana, Helianthus lehmanni),* aloe with floral spikes from six to eight feet tall, cactus, and patches of forest. Around 9,000 feet up, the train enters the High Andes, where herbaceous plants, especially grasses, predominate.

The train then enters the inter-Andean trough. Here the native flora has undergone a considerable regression, the land having been under cultivation since ancient times. The acclimatized eucalyptus is a new element and is not without charm; these trees are now such an integral part of the flora at this altitude that they have almost become characteristic.

Beyond the Eastern Cordillera, after a transitional forest of trees from thirty to forty feet high, the tropical flora begins, and extends over the entire eastern equatorial region in continuation with the Amazon basin.

The abundance of cacti in the High Andes bears witness to the aridity of the climate. (Rolf Blomberg: Full Hand)

In the foreground is a puya, a gigantic bromeliad, on the High Andean plateaus of Ecuador. After about ten years the plant develops a floral stalk, bears fruit and then dies. (Rolf Blomberg: Full Hand)

HUMMINGBIRDS

In about the year 1838, a Frenchman in Bogota began to collect birds and send them to Paris, where women had taken to ornamenting their hats with the most brilliant bird feathers. Thus began one of the most gigantic commercial exploitations of birds. Because of this, millions of unfortunate birds perished.

Interest was also aroused in the birds of Ecuador, but many decades were to pass before reliable information about the birds of Ecuador and Colombia became available. The delay

can be explained not only by the inaccessibility of some areas but also by their incomparable wealth of avifauna. According to a list drawn up by Frank M. Chapman, Ecuador has no less than 1,357 species and 151 subspecies of birds. A recent work by the American ornithologist R. Meyer de Schauensee on the birds of Colombia includes 1,556 species, divided into 2,640 subspecies, or 56 per cent of all the species found in South America. In comparison, there are only 691 species of birds on the 7,200,000 square miles of North America from the Rio Grande to the Arctic Circle.

This great diversity of species is unquestionably the product of the variety of natural habitat. Innumerable birds native to the tropics—parrots, toucans, trogons—may be found not far from birds that have come north from Patagonia. Ecuador and Colombia are, therefore, privileged regions for ornithologists.

There is no more interesting group of birds in these countries than the hummingbirds, a family with marked morphological and biological peculiarities. Strictly indigenous to the New World and distributed from Alaska to Tierra del Fuego, they are found in the most diverse environments. However, the hot and humid regions shelter the largest number of species, and the greatest concentration is undoubtedly in Ecuador and Colombia, with at least 120 different species in Ecuador alone. One of my most interesting experiences as a naturalist was exploring Ecuador in a search for hummingbirds.

Southwestern Ecuador, where the arid climate is like that of the Peruvian deserts, is inhabited by a small number of species, one of which, the *Myrmia micrura,* is distinguished by the very short tail feathers of the male. The more northern and humid zones are inhabited by a great many more species. The *Phaetornis,* generally of dull brown or gray plumage, are abundant, along with the white-collared hummingbird *(Florisuga mellivora).* The subtropical forests of the Andean slopes are richer still. There one can observe the *Androdon aequatorialis,* its mandibles indented like a saw, and the rare *Eugenia imperatrix,* named in honor of the Empress Eugénie. At a higher altitude are even more beautiful species, notably the *Cyanolesbia,* with a long forked tail and showing every tone of blue and green, and the magnificent *Diphlogena* with its flame-colored head. The *Eriocnemis* can be recognized by the downy white bands like garters around their feet, while the *Heliangelus* can be identified by their iridescent throat.

This profusion of species allows the biologist to study the remarkable specialization of these tiny creatures. The first peculiarity that strikes the observer is the speed and ease of their flight. They look as though they were surrounded by a halo, exactly like the hawk moth of European gardens. This is caused by the high frequency of their wing beats, usually fifty per second, and up to even two hundred per second in the smallest species. It is therefore a true vibratory flight, the wing tip tracing an elongated figure "8" in space. This unique flight explains the insect-like humming sound the birds make when in motion. These birds can also change direction almost instantaneously, hover like bumblebees and, unlike any other bird, even fly backward.

Hot gas and steam often issue from vents in the crater of 19,498-foot Cotopaxi, highest active volcano in the world. (Gottfried Hirtz)

This flight is perfectly adapted to the birds' method of feeding. A good part of their diet is nectar, the sweet liquid secreted by certain flowers. The hummingbirds use their long tongues with their curled-up edges as a supple tube to suck in the nectar. As the birds do this they become powdered with grains of pollen that they then transport to other flowers, thus carrying on the work of fertilization.

Hummingbirds also feed on many insects, sometimes seizing them on the wing. They overtake insects easily since they can fly at from fifty-five to sixty miles an hour, and sometimes up to a hundred miles an hour. They seize their prey on the tip of the tongue, a feat which would be impossible were it not for the remarkable precision of their flight. They describe graceful arabesques in space, flying zigzag with an ease unequaled in the bird kingdom.

We sometimes say of a person who lacks appetite that he eats like a bird. But in truth, no animal needs as much food as a bird. And hummingbirds are among the biggest eaters, for their expenditure of energy is very great. It is estimated that hummingbirds consume each day more than twice their weight in nectar and insects, whereas other birds consume from only ten to twenty-five per cent of their weight. Relatively speaking, a hummingbird that weighs 3 grams consumes 150 times more calories than a laborer weighing 150 pounds.

The males and females live apart, the females doing all the nest-building. Before mating, the male claims a kind of territory, and it is generally toward this territory that he will attract the females. He sometimes does this with a kind of weak cheeping—song is not the hummingbird's strong point—but more often by a nuptial flight. He describes arabesques in the air, halts, starts in another direction, seems to hesitate, and then returns to his point of departure.

In some species the male will not tolerate the approach of other males, while in other species the males assemble in small flocks. The *Phaetornis,* for instance, assemble within a limited area in flocks of about twenty very noisy individuals, each one occupying a portion of the area and continuously cheeping. These assemblies are a typical example of a collective nuptial parade and are much more widespread among hummingbirds than was first thought. Once the females are attracted to a perch the males circle around them, humming like insects, or lure them into an aerial display, the birds pairing off and describing complex yet perfectly parallel patterns. Reaching a climax of excitement, the pairs indulge in a dazzling aerial dance, and then mate.

The female has already begun to build a nest; now she rapidly completes it. Most hummingbird nests are small masterpieces, about two inches in diameter, shaped like a cup and bound to a branch. They consist mainly of vegetable fibers, bits of leaves or seeds bound together with spiderwebs, cotton and other fibers, and ornamented with mosses, lichens and fragments of plants, while the inside is lined with downy material.

The hummingbird lays two pure white eggs. At hatching, the nestlings are truly minuscule, naked except for some down filaments on the back. The beak is short, like that of a small passerine. Their beaks gradually grow longer, and their down becomes feathers. They then take flight under the surveillance of their mother. But it is only after the moult, sometimes several moults, that they will acquire the plumage with its countless sparkling colors that is the glory of these

creatures, undoubtedly the most beautiful birds of the New World.

PARAMOS—GRASSLANDS OF THE HIGH ANDES

Whereas the High Andes or *altiplano* of Peru are dry, the High Andes of Venezuela, Colombia and Ecuador, called paramos, are cool and damp. Temperatures are always low, but the variation within twenty-four hours is large, the mercury dropping from 54° F during the daytime to 28° F at night. The humidity is very high, because of abundant rainfall distributed throughout a good part of the year. The cloud formations are dense, thick fog clings to the mountain slopes, and the sun breaks through only for short periods. The characteristic weather of the paramos is a penetrating drizzle, sometimes turning into snow, amidst a fog that leaves everything dripping wet. The black acid soil is often deep, and this combined with the moisture has encouraged a peculiar vegetation. The extreme humidity throughout the year is clearly a beneficial factor lacking in the High Andes of southern Peru.

I had wanted to visit these strange mountain landscapes, so like the high habitats of tropical Africa, ever since I had seen photographs of them as a child—but it was not until 1958 that a voyage to Ecuador gave me the chance to do so. I was in no way disappointed when after a long ride out of Quito, we came to a paramo.

The grasses that carpet the ground are of species belonging to the *Calamagrostis* and *Festuca,* growing in tufts and mingling with many herbaceous plants, often with bright-colored flowers. *Bomarea* with elegant red and yellow blooms, purple gentians, *Geranium, Cerastium* with their woolly covering of whitish hairs, and lupins *(Lupinus alopecuroides)* with yard-high spikes of flowers, are but a few of these. The composites, such as the *Erigeron* and the *Senecio,* are also very numerous. The *Azorella* of the umbellifers form cushions, exactly like the *Distichia,* a Juncaceae native to the High Andes environment.

This herbaceous ground is surmounted by taller plants, sometimes more than six feet high, with small hard leaves, sometimes overlapping, making them look like conifers. These plants belong to many different families, ranging from the Rosaceae, such as *Spiraea,* to the Gutifereae *(Hypericum)* and the Myrtaceae.

The most typical plants of the paramos are, however, the *Espeletia,* or frailejones; they alone justify a trip to the paramos. Aside from a number of technical characteristics, these plants are distinguished by leaves in the form of a tight rosette. At first the plant looks like a bouquet of leaves resting on the ground or perched on a very short stem. As the stem

Left above: A Sobralia *orchid, a characteristic flower of the humid tropical areas of Ecuador. (Edward S. Ross)* *Left:* Heliconia, *a genus of the Musaceae, has vividly colored flowers and huge showy leaves. (Gottfried Hirtz)*

Right: In northwestern Colombia, one of the most humid areas in the world, the rivers, such as the Santa Isabel above, widen into marshes as a result of heavy rainfall throughout the year. (Robert Lawrence Pastner)

develops and carries the leaf bouquet higher and higher, the leaves dry out one by one and die, forming, as they hang down, a kind of muff or sleeve surrounding the trunk as if to protect it from the cold. The espeletias when fully grown are good-sized plants, reaching heights of from fifteen to more than twenty feet, with a trunk surmounted by an enormous bouquet of long lanceolate leaves covered with hairs that give them a whitish or pale yellow-green look. At the time of flowering, the espeletias acquire a covering of groups of flower heads that sometimes rise much higher than the leaves.

Every mountain range seems to have its own species of each family of plants. Certain espeletias, such as the *E. Weddellii* of Venezuela and the *E. Caldasii* of Colombia, are ordinary-sized herbaceous plants. Most of the others, however, are gigantic. Many have leaves with a covering of down that is used by the people of the region in making mattresses and pillows; and the Indians sometimes line their clothes with these downy leaves as protection against the cold. Other espeletias such as *E. argentea* and *E. phaneractis* have smooth silvery leaves. A very few have a branching trunk, and one in the wooded regions of Colombia, *E. nerifolia,* is virtually a tree.

Inevitably, one compares these plants with the senecios of the high mountains of eastern Africa, Kenya, Kilimanjaro, and Ruwenzori among others. These African plants are also members of the compositae family, revealing important differences only to botanists who examine them closely. This is a singular instance of parallel evolution, surely the result of analogous environments. The African senecios grow in the cold and humid climate of an alpine belt of tropical mountains. As on the paramos, water oozes everywhere, and fogs maintain a humidity that is only rarely dissipated by the sun.

ANIMALS OF THE PARAMOS

Among the few mammals of the paramos, by far the most interesting is the woolly or mountain tapir *(Tapirus pinchaque* or *T. roulini),* an animal with a heavy and chunky body and a long and woolly black pelt. It is not strictly limited to the paramos, of course, since it has been found at altitudes between 6,500 and 14,300 feet, probably migrating from one level to another according to the season, and coming to lower altitudes when the weather forces it down. Its food consists mainly of ferns and bamboo shoots *(Chusquea),* and on the paramos it feeds on grasses, espeletia and puya fruits. The same holds true of a small deer with short velvety ears, the *Pudella mephistophelis*—its coat dark reddish-brown in Ecuador and golden black in Colombia—which is, alas, the least well known of all the South American members of the Cervidae family.

Among the other mammals that have inhabited the paramos is the spectacled bear *(Tremarctos ornatus)* called *ucumari* by the Indians, the only South American member of the Ursidae. This medium-sized bear has a black coat except, in some cases, for white rings around the eye, which account for its name. It is found at various altitudes from western Venezuela to Bolivia. Its diet is mostly vegetarian—fruits and roots. At certain periods, especially when the maize is ripe, it unhesitatingly descends to the bottoms of the valleys and does serious damage to plantations, and when hungry it has been known to kill young cattle. It sleeps at night in a kind of nest made of leaves and branches.

Like most bears, it is a confirmed vagabond; a traveler can expect to encounter it only by the merest accident. For long days we searched for it on the eastern foothills of the Peruvian Andes between 8,125 and 9,800 feet above sea level, in an environment rather like that of the paramos. A fine rain fell ceaselessly and fog shrouded the landscape, rendering the atmosphere almost unreal and the shrubbery as wet as a soaked sponge. But there was nowhere a sign of *tata ucumari*—Papa Bear. Because of the rarity and nomadic habits of these carnivores—and also, according to the Indians, because we failed to engage in the magic ceremonies that ought to precede the hunting of any animal such as man and bear—we saw no bears.

Antisana Peak (18,874 feet) in the Western Cordillera of Ecuador was visited in 1740 by two Frenchmen, La Condamine and Bouguer, and in 1802 by a German, Humboldt, and scaled by an Englishman, Edward Whymper, in 1880. (Rolf Blomberg: Full Hand)

In Colombia's humid forests a bromeliad develops leaves that can funnel rain to the heart of the plant. (Othmar Danesch)

In many places the High Andean plateaus are clad in a steppe of grass which grows in bristling tufts dried by the sun. (Herbert Wilhelmy)

Birds are relatively numerous on the paramos, although none is truly native to this zone. All have come here from the southernmost part of South America, where they live at low altitudes. Such is the case with the Furnariidae *Cinclodes fuscus* and *Upucerthia* and the ground tyrant *Muscisaxicola alpina*. It is likewise true of the condor, which is seen in all the higher zones of Colombia and Ecuador, and never on the coast—quite the contrary of the situation in Peru. Among the other birds are a thrush, *Turdus fuscater,* two species of wrens and several finches; even a few tanagers have spread to the lower parts of the paramos.

A few hummingbirds must be classed among the most typical birds of the paramos even though one cannot help but be amazed to find birds as seemingly frail as these in a cold and hostile environment. Yet their presence is no more surprising here than it is in the Peruvian puna, an arid area with less dense ground cover. The *Oxypogon* is still commonly found up to 15,600 feet, hunting insects among the flowers and leaves of the espeletias. The tiny *Metallura tyrianthina,* the commonest species at this altitude, found from Bolivia to the Caribbean Sea, has adapted particularly well to the humidity of the environment. Its soft plumage constitutes no doubt an adaptation against the damp cold, and is quite unlike the rigid plumage of the *Oreotrochilus* of the puna. This hummingbird frequents bushes and low plants; we are told that it can hang from the underside of branches like a titmouse. The *Metallura williami atrigularis* lives in the Sangay Mountains, in a climate of unequaled humidity. It nests in wild ravines carved by water in deposits of volcanic ash. The traveler and ornithologist, Robert T. Moore, has well described how astonishing it is to see a nest among the plants hanging only two or three feet above a mountain torrent. The rain that had come down almost without stopping for eleven days had not prevented the female from completing her nest and laying two eggs in a construction like a wet sponge.

Higher still on Mount Sangay, braving the cold and the snow, a female of another species, *Chalcostigma stanleyi,* had set its nest in a narrow ravine less than 650 feet below the permanent fields of ice covering the cone of the volcano. The same species is to be found in the crater of Pichincha between heights of 14,600 and 15,600 feet.

The high altitudes are not a favorable habitat for cold-blooded animals because of the low temperatures. Reptiles and batrachians are thus rare, although not completely absent. The salamander *Oedipus adspersus* is found occasionally in the paramos up to 11,400 feet, and the toad *Atelopus carrikeri* to an altitude of 15,600 feet in the Andes of Santa Marta, a record for a batrachian. The lizard *Phenacosaurus heterodermus* is found in the temperate and lower levels of the paramos up to 11,400 feet. And one species of serpent has made its way into this environment, the *Leimadophis bimaculatus;* this species displays a remarkable adaptability, being found at all levels between 750 and 10,500 feet above sea level. The paramos have thus been inhabited by a fauna which is sparse but of great interest to the naturalist.

At about 14,000 feet altitude, the vegetation becomes very thin, and above 15,000 feet only a few isolated plants, recalling those of the Alps or subarctic lands, persist. A dozen flowering plants have been collected at 15,300 feet on the Antisana, and three at 16,900 feet on the northwest slope of Chimborazo. A few mosses and lichens have been noted on rocks free of ice between 17,900 and 18,700 feet on the latter volcanic mountain. They are thus pioneers of the vegetable world in the region of eternal snows.

WHERE TROPICAL FOREST AND MOUNTAINS MERGE

The division of the Andes into three distinct chains in Colombia has therefore resulted in a mosaic of biological zones. Immense expanses of rain forest have penetrated far into the interior of the cordillera, climbing along the slopes, then giving way to prairies or to the paramos.

The juxtaposition of these very different zones has had a profound influence on the human beings as well as the fauna of these regions. The proximity of hot regions and more temperate plateaus has allowed man to establish plantations of the most varied kind. Since the Spanish conquest the plain of Bogota has one of the most populated areas of Colombia. The Chibcha Indians founded a powerful nation here, better organized than the societies of the Nutabe and the Tahami Indians of the Antioquia region. Movement was easy and the resources many. The Spaniards followed this example and have maintained a well-balanced economy, making use of the resources of both tropical and temperate areas. This is also why in Colombia the naturalist finds treasures even more precious than the emeralds of which this country is the world's major producer. And Ecuador is in no way less interesting, for it constitutes a remarkable synthesis of the extremes of South American habitats.

The paca, one of the world's largest rodents, here seen near Tenguel in Ecuador, sometimes grows to a length of over two feet. (Paul Schauenberg)

Icy Land Beneath a Tropical Sun

The Peruvian Highlands

12

It hardly seems possible that within a single day's ride by train one could see a desert as grim as Death Valley, a landscape as icy as Greenland and a dank tropical forest alive with multicolored birds. And yet nature has achieved this combination in the Peruvian Andes.

A one-hundred-mile ride inland from Lima—which is only a few miles from the Pacific coast and stands like an oasis amidst barren stony desert—brings one to Galera at an altitude of 15,681 feet. It is perhaps a tiring excursion but it gives one a glimpse of all the natural regions of Peru. It also brings the traveler to one of the highest inhabited areas on the globe. When crossing Ticlio Pass, one travels on the world's highest standard-gauge railroad. There the traveler is rewarded with a view of wild and dramatic splendor. The spectacle of sculptured peaks and polar-like tundra combined with the rarefied atmosphere leaves the traveler almost dizzy. And yet, just about a hundred miles away lie the steaming jungles of the Amazon.

IMMENSE MOUNTAIN BARRIERS

The Cordillera of the Andes may be thought of as a gigantic backbone passing down through the South American continent, with its widest and most complex sections in Peru, Bolivia and northern Chile. Here, the mighty chains of mountains constitute a formidable barrier, although some of the loftiest peaks are actually located farther to the south. No other mountains of the world can rival this continuous solid wall. Nowhere except in Tibet can one find such extensive plateaus at such a height—an average altitude of thirteen thousand feet.

Lake Yahuacocha, Peru, in the northern reaches of the Cordillera de Huayhuash, a section of the Western Cordillera of the Andes. (George Bell)

The Andes might be described as made up of two parallel cordilleras, one along the Pacific coast and the other to the east. Stretching four thousand miles from Chile to Colombia, the Western Cordillera is a mighty rampart almost perpetually veiled by cloud and mist. It is within the circle of volcanos bordering the Pacific known as the "ring of fire" and is thus partly volcanic. In the distant past it was a chain composed mainly of limestones, and vestiges of these ancient rocks remain up to an altitude of four thousand feet. The original rocks were then submerged beneath a succession of lava flows surging up from the depths of the earth. As many as one hundred distinct flows can be distinguished on the seven-thousand-foot wall of the Cotahuasi Canyon. Fresh volcanos were continuously formed on these volcanic plateaus, their topmost craters sometimes towering to a height of eighteen thousand feet.

Several very lofty peaks are to be found in the Western Cordillera, particularly north of Lima where the chain is almost cut in two by the Rio Santa Valley. The Cordillera Negra—the Black Cordillera—so named because of the lack of the perennial snow, rises to the west of the valley to a height of 14,764 feet. The Pato Canyon crosses it, and the river, carving a channel through its precipitous slopes, has opened the way for rail and auto routes that often seem frighteningly perilous.

The Cordillera Blanca rises to the east of the valley and constitutes the watershed between the Atlantic and Pacific sides of the Andes. The steep valley of the Marañón River extends along its lower eastern ridges; the river, which has its source in a tiny lake, eventually becomes the mighty Amazon. This one-hundred-mile chain, oriented from north-northwest to south-southeast, is without doubt the mightiest mountain mass in the tropics. It takes its name partly from its snow-blanketed peaks but also from the pale-colored rocks, mainly diorites, that compose it. Among its many impressive peaks are the Huascarán, at 22,205 feet the highest point in Peru and only about one thousand feet lower than Aconcagua, the highest summit in South America. The glaciers are relatively short as a result of the steepness of the slopes and the limited basins of accumulation. They extend downward toward the lateral valleys, often terminating in glacial lakes. These are hemmed in by frontal moraines, vast masses of boulders, sand and clay left after the retreat of the glaciers. Often, these natural dams cannot withstand the great pressure of the water, which then plunges out toward the valley in an overwhelming cataract, mercilessly carrying everything in its path. In 1962 such a catastrophe destroyed several villages in the Rio Santa Valley and claimed thousands of lives.

The Eastern Cordillera is also made up of a series of chains but not quite as high as those of the Western Cordillera. Impressive mountains are nevertheless to be seen in the Cordillera Real on the eastern shores of Lake Titicaca, and in the Cordillera Vilcapampa, with the rugged Salcantay Massif rising to 20,575 feet. Beyond their steep slopes, deep valleys lead off into the Amazon basin.

Left: Composed of two distinct cordilleras, the Andes are separated by extremely lofty and complex plateaus—one of the great rooftops of the world. Right: At about 12,000 feet, the High Andean plateaus are a steppe with scattered clumps of grass known as puna. *(Baldomero Pestana)*

The vast complex of the High Andean plateaus, called the *altiplano* by the Peruvians, spans the area between these two cordilleras. A maze of valleys, hills, and vast expanses framed by mountain barriers characterizes these plateaus. Where mountain chains intersect amidst this complex topography, water accumulates in basins to form lakes and marshes. The average altitude of this lengthy corridor of plateaus, sometimes as much as 125 miles in breadth, is between 12,250 feet and 14,000 feet. These geographical features have had a profound influence on the climate, creating a natural region that rises like an island between the coastal deserts bordering the Pacific and the emerald seas of the Amazonian forests.

And yet, to describe these high plateaus as if they were suspended between two mighty cordilleras is an oversimplification. There are, in fact, not just two but a whole series of more or less parallel cordilleras; some, like those bordering the basin of Lake Titicaca on the north, are transverse. It might be more accurate to think of the Peruvian Andes as a vast group of complex chains, with the loftiest at its eastern and western boundaries.

There has been much speculation about the geological origin of these plateaus. The Andean folds date back to the Late Cretaceous Epoch and continued during the Tertiary period. Violent horizontal compression of the earth's crust resulted in these folds, although they did not form, as in the Alps, the great overlapping flat sheets known as overthrust masses. But vertical movement also played an important role in the cordilleras; this can be seen in the almost horizontal strata, embedded with plant fossils dating back to the Miocene, found as high as thirteen thousand feet. A combination of crustal movements uplifted these ancient deposits thousands of feet above their original altitude.

Three other processes were also involved in making these mountains. Glaciation played an important part. The terminal moraines that mark the maximum extent of a glacier can be seen at quite a low level on the eastern slopes of the Peruvian and Bolivian Andes—several thousand feet below the limit of the forest. The cordilleras were also deeply eroded by watercourses fed by these mountains. The Marañón, Huallaga, Apurimac and Urubamba rivers all vigorously carved the Andes before cutting spectacular gorges and canyons down the eastern slopes. Some of the less vigorous waterways worked on a smaller scale, eroding the Amazonian slopes into an intricate maze. Finally, let us not overlook volcanic activity. The entire length of the cordilleras is studded with volcanos. Earthquakes are frequent and almost every Andean city has at one time been totally demolished. Indeed, the Andean folds frequently went hand in hand with the eruption of intrusive rocks. Some geologists view the cordilleras as a gaping scar in the earth's crust, a scar unhealed since the Jurassic period. Rocks erupting and flowing from this wound added to the effects wrought by crustal movements .

Such then is the complex structure of the awe-inspiring ranges that greeted the Spanish conquerors. This vast domain, uplifted to great altitudes by the mysterious forces of the earth's crust, with a severe climate in spite of its tropical latitude, is one of the most fascinating on the continent. The traveler is lured by the scenic splendor of snow-blanketed mountains looming above tropical forests. The naturalist is kindled by the desire to discover how flora and fauna adapt to life at such high altitudes. The archaeologist may study the traces of the great civilizations that once flourished in perfect harmony with a harsh habitat. The insights he gains may well guide the ecologist; after all, man, like all other living creatures, must cope with his environment.

EXTREMES OF HOT AND COLD

As we have noted, the Peruvian altiplano boasts of extremely low average temperatures for its tropical latitude. For example, at Vincocaya, a small village some seventy five miles from Lake Titicaca, the average temperature is only 35° F. November is the warmest month of the year with an average temperature of 41° F, while the coldest month, July, has an average of 28° F. This alone illustrates how much altitude reduces temperatures. But such statistics fail to convey the extreme variations of the temperature in the High Andes, particularly during the dry season when there is no cloud screen to check a sudden loss of heat. At altitudes of about thirteen thousand feet, there may be a daily maximum of 68° F dropping to a nocturnal minimum of 5° F, in other words a range of 63° F within a single day—a great strain on all living creatures, including man.

Moreover, temperatures such as these are recorded in the shade so that they give no impression of the extraordinary intensity of the sun's rays. A passing cloud may lower temperatures by twenty degrees in the space of just five minutes. On the shady side of city streets the ice never melts, and yet the heat of the midday sun is almost unbearable. But once this sun disappears, a mantle of ice blankets the ground. Of course, this kind of climate prevails in all the higher regions of the globe and every skier has had a taste of it. But it is particularly pronounced in the High Andes and has a great influence on plants and animals since their rhythm of activity is adjusted to the daily temperature. Moreover, rock heats most rapidly and thus acts as a reservoir of warmth, or, better still, a "thermic fly-wheel."

As is usually the case in an intertropical zone, it is not variations in temperature but in rainfall that determine the seasons. The period of highest rainfall in the altiplano occurs during the austral summer, just the opposite of the situation on the coast. Beginning in November and ending in March or April, this rainy season is called *invierno* or winter by the Peruvians even though it is actually their summer. The extent of annual precipitation varies roughly from about 24 to 55 inches, depending upon the local conditions. There seems to be a gradient of decreasing humidity from north to south. There are also great variations in rainfall from one year to the next. Thus in Morococha, a central Peruvian village near the Western Cordillera at an altitude of about thirteen thousand feet, the average rainfall is fourty-one inches but the range varies from twenty-five to forty-five inches. Needless to say, such variations have a profound effect both on vegetation and local crops. The slightest drought brings lower temperatures and night frosts since no cloud layer insulates the daytime warmth. Such periods spell famine on the high plateaus.

During the rainy season scarcely a day passes without a

The snow-clad summit of the Nevado Chacraraju in the Cordillera Blanca of central Peru. (George Bell)

rainstorm. One wakes to find a sparkling sun in an intense blue sky, but it starts getting cloudy at about eleven o'clock and once the storm bursts it usually lasts most of the afternoon and into the night. Often the rain is mixed with snow and hail, especially at altitudes above thirteen thousand feet. In spite of this summer rainy season, the altiplano is still a very arid region because the rest of the year is so very dry. Another striking feature of the altiplano is the constant and often unusually violent wind, further accentuating the coldness and dryness of the climate. Such then are the hardships of life in this icy land beneath a tropical sun.

STUNTED VEGETATION

It is not surprising that such harsh conditions have strongly influenced the flora. With low temperatures and arid soil, plants tend to grow close to the ground, and there is a notable sparsity of arboreal vegetation. Like the alpine plants of European or North American mountains, many of the stunted growths look a little like hemispherical cushions. This is particularly true of the umbelliferous *Azorella,* called *yareta* by the Indians, which grows in such dense convex-shaped masses that it would be difficult to wedge a knife between them. The natives gather and dry them for fuel. Most other plants are perennial grasses.

The only trees on the altiplano are arborescent Rosaceae called *queñoas* by the Peruvians and *Polylepis* by the botanists. They may be considered the "highest" trees of South America since they are found at altitudes up to 14,500 feet. Their tortuous trunks and rich mahogany-colored branches are covered by a thick parchment-like bark—a protective cover against the cold. Queñoas grow only in the more sheltered places, especially at the base of steep-sided valleys where, out of the reach of icy winds, they form veritable forest galleries. Unfortunately, they disappear rather rapidly in the vicinity of inhabited areas where the Indians have used them for firewood.

Elsewhere, especially in the great Andean pampas, the vegetative cover is stubby and sparse. Above a certain altitude, usually around sixteen thousand feet, but varying according to the area, the landscape is oppressively barren and the rocky slopes maintain the last vestige of vegetation. Botanists have described the stony area and rocks at the extremes of vegetation as being oases of warmth in an icy wasteland.

LIFE AT HIGH ALTITUDES

Such are the conditions that meet the hardy creatures that venture onto the high plateaus. Such creatures have made both physiological adaptations directly related to altitude and ecological adaptations to climate caused by the altitude.

The higher one goes, the lower the barometric pressure and the partial pressure of oxygen. At eighteen thousand feet there is only half as much oxygen as at sea level. At such heights, living creatures are nearly asphyxiated and normal physiological functions are almost paralyzed, particularly in the nerve centers. The whole metabolism of the body is thrown off balance.

Although there is very little information about the reactions of animals, much was learned about the effects on man even before the age of aviation, when this aspect of physiopathology became crucial. Indeed, with such a large portion of the population and natural wealth at an altitude of thirteen thousand feet, there was good reason for physiologists in the Andean countries to make thorough studies of the problem.

Travelers often experience certain unpleasant symptoms at such heights. One of these, mountain-sickness, known as *soroche* in the Andes, is a feeling of suffocation; causing poor circulation, it also affects the blood vessels, the pulse beating faster and the extremities turning blue. But the effects on the nervous system are the most unpleasant: an overwhelming drowsiness, headaches, and in some cases a lethargy that is almost a coma. Some individuals are overwhelmed by anxiety, sometimes verging on delirium. But such reactions are exceptional, and millions of tourists visit Puno, the charming provincial capital on Lake Titicaca, without experiencing any more ill effects than they do in other high places.

During a brief sojourn at high altitudes the body does make a short-term adjustment: the heart pumps blood more rapidly; the lungs work harder to oxygenate the blood, the number of red blood corpuscles increases from four and a half million to between seven and eight million per cubic millimeter of blood. But only after a prolonged stay do more permanent physiological changes take place. The highlander may have a greater number of red blood corpuscles and a more rapid rate of respiration than the plainsman, and other significant modifications occur in the tissues and the blood.

Natives of the High Andean plateaus have had generations to acclimate themselves and many of their racial characteristics may be a response to the environment. Thus Indians of the Peruvian cordilleras have an almost cylindrical rib cage—sometimes exceeding 730 cubic inches—to accommodate their great lung capacity. The heart of a European is quite different from that of a dweller in the Andes; indeed, a physician seeing his first Andean patient might diagnose him as a heart case.

Settlers of European origin colonizing the Andes after the Spanish conquest made similar adaptations—not without great hardship, as we know from the records of the times. Colonization of the High Andes was thus a very trying period for the Spanish settlers. It was not until 1598, fifty-three years after the establishment of Potosí, a Bolivian city at an altitude of thirteen thousand feet, that a child born of Spanish parents survived infancy. Antonio de la Calancha notes that the event was considered a miracle. Domestic animals suffered the same hardships as their owners. Cats in particular had difficulty in making the adjustment. The animals we meet on these High Andean plateaus seem to live and breed as easily as related species at lower altitudes; but the little we know about their physiological functions shows that the modifications in them, particularly in the circulatory system, are as deep-seated as those in man. The llama has more than twelve million red corpuscles per cubic millimeter of blood, the vicuña more than fourteen million, and the viscacha over seven million; animals of the plains equivalent in weight and form have far fewer. The heart of a High Andean animal is also much more developed, increasing the rate of blood flow

View below Puente del Inca in the Argentine Cordillera. The many hot springs bear witness to the volcanic origins of these barren mountains. (Weldon King)

The condor, largest of all long-flight birds, is a characteristic inhabitant of the High Andes. Nesting on high rocky ledges, it soars over the pampas in search of carrion. (O. P. Pearson)

and the amount of oxygen carried to the tissues. But one cannot generalize on the basis of the few observations that have been made; as demonstrated by migratory birds, adaptation can be instantaneous. Ducks, waders, and even little passerines have been observed flying at such altitudes as 20,000 or even 22,000 feet, soon after taking off from sea level. And they do so with perfect ease in spite of the seemingly incredible effort needed just to fly. But it must be remembered that this is a momentary feat whereas the animals of the High Andes must endure rarefied air permanently.

The climate resulting from high altitude has profoundly influenced inhabitants of the Andes. "Candidates" for colonization coming from much milder regions must have great adaptability in order to adjust to the harsh conditions. Few have succeeded, and this explains the limited fauna, in contrast to some of the world's richest wildlife districts in the lower regions bordering the Eastern Cordillera. Many of the animals on the heights are definitely visitors from these neighboring lower regions; others have come northward from Patagonia to take advantage of the altitude. Strangely enough, these cold mountains in the tropics offer these animals a habitat similar to the one they are accustomed to at much lower latitudes or at sea level. Some of the Patagonian fauna thus spread to the north, sometimes as far as Colombia and Venezuela. Such is the case of the Andean goose, a species peculiar to high altitudes in Chile, Argentina, southern Peru and Bolivia, where it nests from twelve thousand feet to the snowline. Strolling about on the Patagonian plains and nearby icy shores is its close cousin, the Magellan goose.

The settlement of the High Andes has thus been influenced

far more by ecological factors than by the actual altitude. The latter has never, by itself, prevented a species from moving into the higher regions. But the inability to find food in an exposed, arid habitat, among such sparse vegetation, and to resist the wintery clime, has been a most effective deterrent. Birds and mammals are to be found at sixteen thousand feet, and, conditions permitting, even higher. Invertebrates can stand even loftier places, but where the phanerogams, or seed plants, wane, all animal life ceases. Then only lichens are to be seen. The record in altitude is held by certain highly specialized algae, capable of living in freezing water and even in ice, which they tinge red. Above this, there is no sign of life except in the skies, where a few birds—such as the condor, "King of the Andes"—soar above the ice-capped peaks.

The Andean flicker (Colaptes rupicola) *nests in galleries that it hollows out in loose soil, especially along steep river banks. (Jean Dorst)*

WIND, COLD AND RAREFIED AIR

The route from Lima to the central Andes via the Rio Chillon Valley winds through a series of mountain passes flanked by naked mountain masses. The broad layers and the strata of rocks tell of successive volcanic deposits. Many of the peaks are like gigantic heaps of stony blocks and conglomerates, gracefully sculptured by erosion. Rock falls are frequent, as are avalanches of mud and loose soil whenever the rains penetrate to the deepest beds.

As we go higher, the slopes take on a covering of cactus, particularly torch thistle, and at about five thousand feet an increasingly dense undergrowth of steppelike vegetation. Unlike the arid coastal plains, rain falls upon these subtropical or temperate zones during the austral summer; constant moisture is maintained throughout the year by the fog. In some places there are even small patches of forest; these are of particular interest because they are the last remnants of the temperate-zone forests so extensive in Ecuador. This forest level has long been densely populated and cultivated by man. Eucalyptus trees, introduced with great success in all the temperate areas of the Andes, are by now an integral part of the landscape.

Beyond this zone the road winds upward in hairpin bends to regions covered by a thick carpet of grassy vegetation. At last the road opens into what geologists call a hanging valley—that is, a valley whose lower end is notably higher than the level of the valley to which it leads—with a dark lake on its floor. As the road emerges from the pass it goes downhill and then winds through a maze of hilly masses intersected by valleys. We are now on the High Andean plateaus. The traveler is struck by the grandeur of the view, for everything is on the vastest scale. Somber volcanic mountains occasionally loom in the distance but in most places great hilly masses, etched by a network of torrential streams, roll out to an unbroken horizon. Course, scrubby grasses grow upon these slopes and the terrain is treeless, bearing at best a scattering of stunted bushes.

Traveling through these high plateaus can prove quite monotonous; each valley and slope is so much like the last one that one moves forward without the feeling of making any headway. This is not the rough hewn land one finds in the wilderness of Africa or Asia but rather a lifeless place suspended somewhere between heaven and earth. The wind, the cold and the rareness of the air seem to have reduced life to a state of slow motion. It is not surprising that such harsh circumstances have left their imprint on the temperament of the Andean Indians.

MAN AND THE CORDILLERAS

Although a hostile region, the High Andean plateaus, particularly the Lake Titicaca basin, have been the cradle of great civilizations and mighty empires extending from Colombia to Argentina. Even today the cordilleras, or at least the temperate zone, are highly populated and there are even instances of overpopulation. As a result, the Andean republics have expanded their economic plans to include the development of the Amazon zone and the still unexploited eastern slopes of the Andes. But such human migrations are easier planned than carried out. Transplanting the Indians from the high plateaus to the warmer and unwholesome lower regions creates a whole series of problems that even the Incan sovereigns recognized in their own time. Modern health and medicine, housing and land development may have changed the situation, but habit and tradition continue to exert a powerful influence over our lives.

The concentration of population on the high plateaus is largely due to the ease of travel across the vast pampas of the Andean corridor; the coastal plains are too dry and the Amazon forest so difficult to penetrate that to this day they shelter only nomadic communities still at the food-gathering level. Then too, the temperate zones of the high plateaus are fertile; using specialized techniques the Indians have been able to farm at altitudes up to 13,500 feet. Since time immemorial it has been possible to cultivate the entire Lake Titicaca basin because of its relatively mild climate; like the sea, the waters of the lake have a moderating influence. Crops have been chosen by the natives to suit the soil. The potato, for example, originated in the Andes. The Indians preserve them by freezing and then drying, which yields a black and white specialty called *chuño*. Among their other crops are plants of the family Chenopodiaceae: *quiñoa (Chenopodium quinoa)* and *cañahua (Ch. canihua)* eaten in the form of a gruel. Tubers such as *oca (Oxalis tuberosa)* complete the range of plants. Corn, requiring much warmer temperatures, has not penetrated these cold, high plateaus.

Indian cooking hardly appeals to travelers. A dish of *chuño*, that is frozen potatoes, with a side dish of *charqui*, pieces of mutton or llama meat dried in the sun and then soaked in water, with the look and taste of rancid leather, is at best a trying experience.

Although crop-growing is somewhat limited, the high plateaus lend themselves very well to grazing. The grassy pampas that stretch across a great portion of the altiplano furnish the finest pasture for stock-farming. To exploit this wealth, the Indians have since ancient times domesticated the llama and the alpaca. Related to the vicuña and the guanaco, none of the domesticated species remain in the wild state. Although they are a valuable source of meat and wool, in early times they were mainly exploited as beasts of burden, rather than as mounts or even as a source of milk—a product not exploited by pre-Colombian Indians.

Introduced by the Spaniards, sheep are today the chief source of wealth, supplying both meat and wool. Horses and cattle flourish only in the most humid valleys, and the absence of goats on these high plateaus is hardly to be regretted, considering the damage they inflict on land and vegetal cover.

Another natural resource that has long brought men to the Andes is its mines. Peru's gold lured the Spanish conquerors, and their caravels sailed home heaped with a precious bounty. There is also a profusion of other metals still more precious today. Central Peru, particularly the region of Cerro de Pasco, La Oroya and Huaron, ranks among the richest areas of the globe for its ores. Many centuries of mining have left their scar upon the landscape; as early as the pre-Colombian era, the Indians had begun to riddle the mountains with mining galleries. Practically every gully slicing the plateaus hides the traces of an old, abandoned furnace. Silver ores, at one time extremely popular, were smelted in primitive furnaces using llama dung as fuel. Then toward the end of the eighteenth century the exhaustion of oxidized ores forced a change to pyrites and with it the use of new refining methods.

Silver and gold extracted from alluvial deposits are today only the showpieces of the mineral wealth of the plateaus. With the new techniques and improved communication and transport of the twentieth century, the most important metal has come to be copper. At least a dozen others, including bismuth, zinc, lead and vanadium, are also exploited. The complex of mines from Cerro de Pasco to La Oroya has an annual yield of some fifteen thousand tons of copper and nine thousand tons of lead, not to speak of zinc, silver and many other rarer metals in ever-increasing demand by modern industry. These desolate cordilleras, a great source of mineral wealth during Incan times, still hide a fabulous treasure in terms of the present world economy.

PUNA: THE VAST GRASSY STEPPE

Predominating in the high plateaus are the grassy steppes that the Peruvians call *pajonal de puna*, or simply *puna*—a name sometimes applied to the entire region. Such vegetation stretches across all flat expanses, valley beds, plateaus and even up some of the abrupt slopes. Formed of coarse tufts of harsh plants, the overall color is a straw yellow because the dead outer leaves droop over and hide the live core. These grasses, sometimes reaching a height of two feet, are all indiscriminately called *ichu* by the Indians although they belong to various species of the genera *Festuca* and *Calamagrostis*. Between their tufted stems grow a variety of herbaceous plants.

There is little shelter for bird life on these open plains and only very specialized species are found here. As we make our way through the pampas we meet the tinamou most often; several species have established themselves on the high plateaus. Similar in habit and coloring to the partridges, their beige or coffee coloring and mottled patterns make them almost invisible. The nest, resting against the tufts which shade it from the sun, contains as many as nine richly colored eggs. Somehow, the chick embryos have a great resistance to the cold—a form of adaptation to the Andean climate. The male plays such an active role during incubation and especially in raising the young that, according to some observers, the maternal instinct of the female tinamou has completely waned.

Although passerines do not abound in these parts, several species of the grain-eating species are regularly found on the steppes. The most common of all is the Peruvian song-sparrow *(Zonotrichia capensis)*, a bird found throughout most of the continent. A cousin of the North American sparrows, it nests on the ground, where a canopy of grassy tufts shelters the eggs from the intense rays of the sun.

One of the most characteristic birds of the pampas is almost a replica of the wheatear of the Old World but actually is a common miner, *Geositta cunicularia*, belonging to a very distinct family peculiar to the Americas: the Furnariidae or ovenbirds. There is almost a perfect duplication in the coloring of these two widely separated birds: a beige-colored plumage on the upper parts turning to off-white on the underparts, with a very light patch on the rump and at the tip of a dark tail. The ovenbird is also much like the wheatear in habit

In the Valley of the Rio Checayani in southern Peru, at about 12,000 feet up, erosion has sculptured sandstone terraces flanked by cliffs. (Jean Dorst)

and even in its call. It keeps to the ground with its tail in a constant flutter as it probes the soil for insects and larvae. It would seem as though similar habitats and ways of life have cast two birds from the same mold although they issue from very different stock.

Making our way further through the grassy pampa, we suddenly notice a rustling noise beneath the tufts. If we keep perfectly still we may catch sight of a tiny rodent, *Akodon boliviensis,* its brown coat specked with black. Found in great numbers on the altiplano, it is of the size and demeanor of a meadow mouse, with the same short tail. Here again, nature seems to have repeated itself, probably because of related habitats. It makes its home in extensive thirty-to-fifty-foot underground passages which it digs more than a foot below the surface with several alternative entrances camouflaged beneath grassy clumps. Active by day, it escapes the nightly chills in this elaborate shelter.

GUINEA PIGS AND GIANT CONDORS

Living near rivers and in damp prairies are colonies of wild Guinea pigs, a creature that has long been domesticated by the Indians for its meat, much in the same way that some people raise rabbits. Their fur, a brownish olive color, never has the variegated coloring characteristic of the domestic variety. This array of rodents lures predators. The jackal-like, long-legged Andean fox *(Cerdocyon)* comes to hunt in the pampas before retiring to its lair in rocky caverns. Numerous too are birds of prey. The pampas are the feeding ground for vultures attracted by the remains of domesticated animals. The urubu, a lesser lord with black plumage, is common throughout tropical America although less so than along the coast. Giant of the flying land birds is the condor, with a wingspan of as much as ten feet. They are sometimes seen in troops of about fifteen birds, slowly lifting their great bodies into the air and gliding in vast majestic circles. The great size, prowess and stately bearing of this bird has won it special renown since ancient times.

At times, the Indians still hunt the condor according to ancient ritual. They dig a hole in the ground big enough to hide a man, cover the opening with a lattice of branches, and lay a dead animal on it. When the condor, lured by the bait, settles down on it, the hunter is rewarded for his long vigil in the putrid atmosphere: he seizes the giant creature by its feet.

GUANACOS AND VICUNAS

The pampas are also the home of the wild members of the Camelidae family, the guanaco and the vicuña. Vicuñas are peculiar to the altiplano of central Peru north of Argentina, but guanacos are found at lower altitude in Patagonia as well. No other animal of the Andes is quite as handsome and graceful as the vicuña. It resembles the llama but has much finer proportions and its downy fleece is incomparably soft and silky.

At altitudes of between 12,000 and 16,000 feet, and especially above 14,000 feet, vicuñas still abound, living in families made up of an adult male with a harem of from four to eighteen females as well as the young. There are also roving bands of immature males. Each troop occupies an area varying from twenty to one hundred acres, depending upon the terrain and the quality of the pasture. This territory, protected by the male from outside intruders, sustains the troop in all its activities throughout the year.

Females calve in January and February when all is in bloom after the rains. Like most herbivorous animals, the young are extremely precocious. They can stand a quarter of an hour after birth; a half hour later they are walking, and a day-old vicuña is fit to follow the troop.

In the eyes of the Indians of the high plateaus the vicuña possesses an almost mystical attraction. To eat the raw liver and spleen is to gain both physical and spiritual well-being and to drink the blood, preferably when still warm, is assurance of longevity and prowess. During Incan times the fur was worn exclusively by kings and royalty and thousands of their subjects were mobilized for the great hunts. Today, vicuñas are protected by law but poaching continues on a large scale. Ranchers, moreover, have transformed the plateaus by fencing off pastures so that the herds of vicuñas can no longer wander across vast unbroken spaces. Here as elsewhere the world grows too small for freedom-loving creatures.

CAVE-DWELLING BIRDS

With scarcely a tree to offer shelter to nests, suitable sites for nest-building are rare on the high plateaus. Although a few passerines find shelter beneath the coarser grasses, they cannot escape the icy nocturnal chill or the penetrating rains. Many Andean birds have thus chosen to make their home beneath the ground or under rocks, or they hide in rocky debris. Anyone who visits the area with a flashlight at night will surely come upon little groups of birds, particularly grain-eating passerines, all huddled together beneath blocks of stone. At times, these communal dormitories accommodate quite a number of guests. On Mount Chacaltaya in Bolivia at an altitude of 16,300 feet, the German ornithologist Günther Niethammer observed a dormitory of the white-winged *Diuca* finch *(Diuca speculigera)* with no less than two hundred birds crowded in a glacial declivity. Such gregarious habits have served these birds well; certainly they diminish the individual heat loss.

Needless to say, the young are much more susceptible to the cold and inclement weather. For this reason many birds on the Andes have adopted an underground way of life and nest in deep passageways hollowed out of loose ground. Wherever running water has eroded embankments, we may find these banks riddled with countless holes. If we watch these during the breeding season we soon catch sight of the owner—usually a passerine of the Furnariidae family. Such nesting habits are very popular among the *Geositta* and *Upucerthia,* which explains their Peruvian name *mineros,* or miners. Ground tyrants such as the *Muscisaxicola* have also adopted these ways.

All of these birds are capable of digging their own burrows; the beak serves as a pickaxe and they scoop away the earth with their claws. But they are also clever enough to utilize the labor of others by remodeling and repairing the same nest from one year to the next. In some cases these living quarters seem overly spacious, compared to the size of the owner. This is especially true of the earth-creeper *(Upucerthia),* a bird the

Puyas, giant bromeliads of the High Andean plateaus, are armed with thorns but the leaves shelter many birds. (Jean Dorst)

size of a sturdy finch, with plumage a henna-brown on the outerparts, fawn-colored on the underparts and with a characteristic scythe-shaped beak. These passerines construct their nests at the foot of tiny embankments, at times no more than seven feet high. They hollow out a straight passageway from two to three inches wide, four or five inches high, and as much as three feet long, terminating in an incubation chamber which is covered with an ample mattress composed of straw and grain husks.

Still further architectural perfection can be observed among the ground tyrants. These, too, hollow out burrows at least three feet in length with an incubation chamber about ten inches in diameter. Within this cavity a nest very similar to that of our warblers is built. Composed of fine branches delicately woven together and lined with bits of sheep or vicuña down, it is a cozy little shelter for the brood. In such nests the birds are well able to scorn the elements; neither burning sun nor icy chill can reach them. Although temperatures outside may vary by as much as 55° F, within the burrow they are almost constant. Moreover, such underground living quarters also protect the birds from storms and predators, especially foxes who particularly relish young chicks.

Of course, the birds of the Andes can hardly claim a monopoly of such underground nests; they are also found among such other birds as the sand martins, the bee-eaters of the Old World, and the kingfishers—all living in milder climates. But the fact that the nests assume such a highly developed form in the High Andes might well be considered a response to the hostile climate. At the price of such elaborate adaptations, Andean birds have been able to flourish in a seemingly hostile habitat.

AN UNUSUAL WOODPECKER

Traveling through the pampas one may suddenly hear a strange call, almost like a baying sound: *ou-ay, ou-ay,* sometimes fading out into a kind of tremor: *ou-a-a-a-a.* The name *yaco-yaco,* resembling the call itself, has been bestowed by the Aymaras Indians upon this woodpecker, the rock flicker *(Colaptes rupicola),* a close cousin of the United States flicker *(Colaptes auratus).* This type of bird is found throughout the

American continent except in wooded tropical regions. Most other members of this family live in trees, but groundliving habits have permitted these woodpeckers to penetrate the High Andes. Just about every activity of this species is carried out on the ground. The open grassy steppe of the pampas, especially near a river, is its favorite habitat, but it is just as much at home upon some rocky crag.

The rock flicker lives in colonies and is almost always found in small troops, even when hunting for food. Its menu consists of worms, insect larvae, and the insects themselves—all found by a careful search of the ground. With a long, conical-shaped beak and an extensible tongue ending in horny, toothlike projections, it is specially equipped to dig for its prey. Although their noisy calls are part of the High Andes chorus throughout the year, the flicker's performance is especially tumultuous during the courtship season. The nuptial displays include frenzied and ecstatic gestures, each partner facing the other and mimicking it. Each bird constantly displays the colored stripe on its jaw that distinguishes its sex—red and black on the male and black on the female.

Once a mate has been found, the flickers choose a home, usually on a cliff overlooking a river, although they sometimes settle for lower embankments. Here they dig tunnels using their beaks as a pick to loosen the soil while the claws do a very rapid clearing job. The nesting colonies of these sociable creatures may include about ten pairs of birds. The tunnels, which are long and roomy, lead to a large incubation chamber; here the birds lay their eggs and raise their young.

Like much of the birdlife of the High Andes, the flicker benefits greatly by his underground nesting habits. A biological comparison with the North American flicker reveals the extent to which this bird has adapted both to climate and to a habitat without trees, so necessary to most members of the Picidae family.

PUYAS: REFUGE AND DEADLY SNARE

Normally, plants of the bromeliad or pineapple family, with their short stems and large decorative leaves, grow clinging to a rock or on a tree. But the High Andes, where nature sets its own patterns, are the range of a special arborescent variety: puyas *(Puya raimondii),* found in the central Andes (the Cordillera Blanca), the southern Andes of Peru, and in Bolivia. Huge in size, they are somewhat similar to palms and seem like trees with a cluster of tough leaves growing from the trunk. Each leaf is edged with sharp thorns, the points crooked like fish hooks and just as dangerous. The oldest leaves shrivel and die, hanging parallel to the trunk. When the plant reaches full maturity at fifteen or twenty feet, it blooms at the summit and the plant attains its maximum height of about thirty feet. With a stretch of the imagination, this strange plant may recall the espeletias of the paramos in Columbia and Ecuador, or the giant lobelias of the high alpine zones of East Africa.

With such a "housing" shortage in the High Andes, it is not surprising that birds should flock to what must seem a heaven-sent home. A few come back nightly, including the bare-faced dove *(Gymnopelia ceciliae);* as many as thirty of this species may perch side by side on a single puya. These plants are especially noteworthy as nesting places for turtledoves, hummingbirds, several species of the sparrow family, and various other small passerines.

At the bottom of some well-protected gully among a clump of puyas, one may also catch sight of an elaborate nest almost two feet in height. This is occupied not by some huge bird of prey but by a passerine about the size of a sparrow, the black-winged spinetail *(Asthenes d'orbignyi),* whose plumage is chestnut-colored above and whitish below, with a bold russet patch on the rump. Because of the basketlike effect of the woven branches of the nest, the bird has been dubbed *canastero* in Spanish, from *canasta,* the word for basket.

Puyas may be a haven for some birds of the High Andes but they are the ruination of many others. A too hasty take-off and the bird may find itself caught on the spiky hooks of the leaves. The more the bird struggles to free itself, the deeper into feather and flesh the spines pierce. The bodies of as many as ten unfortunate creatures may be found on a single plant—usually turtledoves, but passerines as well, and sometimes even the larger birds of prey who were probably pursuing their small prey back to its refuge. Refuge and deadly snare: nothing is simple in the world of nature, where some drawback lurks behind each blessing.

Left: The viscacha spends its morning sunbathing on ledges but takes refuge in rock piles at night. (O. P. Pearson) Right: Sunrise on natural rock formations in the High Andes near Huancavelica, Peru. (Robert Lawrence Pastner)

STAGS AND SQUIRREL-LIKE RABBITS

At the foot of the steeper slopes, protected from icy winds, the grassy vegetation gives way to scrub. Cactus is also seen here—an indication of the aridity of the soil. Some of the cacti are clothed in a mantle of pale down, no doubt protection against low temperatures, especially nocturnal frosts.

These slopes are often littered with great heaps of rocky debris; and torrents rushing from higher altitudes have carved out deep gullies and cliffs which are clad in dense vegetation. A milder climate and more abundant food supply make this one of the rich zones of animal life in the high plateaus. It is here that we meet the guemal *(Hippocamelus antisiensis),* a deer about the size of a Virginian deer. It is found as high as sixteen thousand feet on the small lushly carpeted prairies of sheltered slopes.

Rodents also find this zone to their liking and many species take shelter beneath the rocks. The viscacha, found at higher mountain levels from northern Peru to Patagonia, is by far the most characteristic. With long, wiggly ears, it resembles a rabbit, but has the bushy tail of a large squirrel. Its thick, fluffy coat, silky to the touch, is a pearl-gray mixed with black on the back; the belly is a lighter color, often brightened by a cream or russet hue. When the viscacha stands watch on a rock, its body erect and its ears held high, it reminds one of a rabbit but in motion it seems more like a squirrel or even a small kangaroo, for it uses its well-developed hindlegs to make strong leaps and bounds. Supple and elastic pads cushion the paws.

Viscachas are gregarious creatures, and family groups live together in colonies of as many as a hundred individuals. Entirely diurnal, they spend the night in some rocky crevice; their feet are ill-equipped to dig in soil and they never build burrows. At the break of day they emerge and take up a position in the sunlight where they stand guard for hours, eyes half closed but all their senses keenly alert. At the slightest sign or sound of danger, one of these little sentries promptly gives warning to his fellows with sharp, repeated whistles like those of the marmot, and they all scurry to safety in the rocks.

After hours of basking in the sun, the viscacha goes in search of food but never wanders very far off. Even the spiniest plant satisfies its appetite and after breakfasting for a good part of the morning, it is ready for more sun bathing. Weather permitting, it also takes a copious afternoon meal but it carefully avoids the rain lest it find itself shivering beneath its drenched fur.

In former times, the viscacha was accompanied in this way of life by the chinchilla. A rodent of the same family, the latter was distinguished by shorter and rounder ears but principally by the luxuriance of its plush gray fur—one of the most precious of all skins and the cause of its ruin. Prized as early as pre-Colombian times, chinchillas were in even greater demand as soon as they were discovered by Europeans. During the last century, however, they were still plentiful, and in 1905 as many as 18,153 dozen skins were traded at the Chilean center of Coquimbo. This figure was cut to half in 1907, halved once again in the following year, and by 1909 only 2,328 dozen were sold. Today, the source of supply is gone.

In Chile the chinchilla has probably disappeared, while in Bolivia and Peru it is nearly extinct. Preserved in captivity, the chinchilla is a sad example of how intensive trapping can wipe out a species.

COLD-BLOODED ANIMALS

Few reptiles are to be found in this cold region; in fact the Peruvian altiplano can boast of only two species: a nonvenomous snake and a lizard of the iguana group, *Liolaemus multiformis,* exhibiting an incredible polymorphism in color and pattern.

The very harshest of habitats is not shunned by this creature, although it prefers to make its home upon slopes with favorable exposures, often as high as sixteen thousand feet. Here it either digs burrows or occupies a small depression. Tiny leaves and buds, butterflies, spiders, and flies compose its menu. A largely vegetarian diet tides these lizards over the dry season when insects are rare.

Low temperature is the main problem confronting these Andean lizards, and they meet it by taking maximum advantage of solar radiation—intense but lasting only a few hours of the day. They emerge at daybreak, stretch out on a rock or, better still, on some grassy patch, and rapidly absorb the sun's warmth. It has been found that while outside temperatures were still at 23° F the body temperature of the lizard had already risen to 66° F. Yet even at its lowest body temperature this lizard is capable of coordinated movements, and this is perhaps its greatest asset. With its body temperature at 35° F it is still able to move about, sluggishly but satisfactorily, whereas other reptiles in this state would be overwhelmingly torpid. The fact that a group so generally lacking in adaptability as the reptiles is represented on the high plateaus is a demonstration of the flexibility of the animal world.

HUMMINGBIRDS

Another interesting inhabitant of the High Andes can be found on the sunnier slopes. Here our attention is soon caught by a small bird darting by with a humming sound, its breast casting flashes of light. Our first impulse is to call it a hummingbird but this seems like a wild guess in such an unlikely habitat. And yet these parts of the High Andes are indeed the haunt of a creature often associated with much warmer regions.

A remarkable facility for adaptation has permitted several species of this group of tiny birds to colonize the plateaus as high as sixteen thousand feet. Besides the giant of the group, *Patagona gigas,* usually found in temperate zones, the most common are the hill stars or *Oreotrochilus,* a name itself signifying "mountain hummingbird." Despite their wide distribution on the high plateaus, these birds shun the cold open pampas and seek instead those slopes where sunshine prevails or sheltered gullies with bushy vegetation.

As a group, hummingbirds are known to have a mixed diet of insects and the nectar of various blossoms. They are particularly fond of *Loasa,* thick tufts of herbaceous plants armored with stinging nettles and producing a scarlet-red flower laden with nectar. But on the high plateaus, where flowers are rare, the hummingbird's diet consists almost exclusively of insects. The choice of a nesting site is perhaps the best example of how the *Oreotrochilus* has adjusted to its habitat. Rather than

Vicuñas frequent barren plateaus at altitudes of about 15,000 feet like those around the Ubinas volcano in southern Peru. They generally live in small troupes led by an adult male. (O. P. Pearson)

hide the nest among plants, the female, who undertakes the nest-building, chooses the eastern face of rocky cliffs so as to take advantage of the sun's warmth as soon as day breaks. No less than 75 per cent of the nests are placed at the edge of these cliffs, while the remainder are set in shrubs at their base. But some birds also shelter their nests in veritable caves and even in abandoned mining galleries where temperatures are even all the day round.

The nests are surprisingly large, considering the small size of the bird, sometimes five inches wide by four inches deep, whereas in warmer climates the hummers usually build the tiniest of structures with scarcely enough room for the female and the young. Composed of a variety of materials—bits of leaves and fern fronds, vegetable fibers, tufted fruits, feathers, wool and spider's webs—these elaborate nests are excellent protection against the cold. They are also thought by the Indians to possess special powers to heal sheep diseases. The sick animals are shut up in a sealed hut and a bonfire is made of the nests, the smoke serving to disinfect and fumigate the enclosure. The Indians base this belief on the fact that the hummingbird collects a unique combination of medicinal plants for its nest.

The female lays just two eggs with an incubation period of twenty or twenty-one days as compared to only fourteen or eleven days for species living in warmer climates. The climate slows down development before birth as well as after the young are hatched. Fledglings cannot take flight for thirty to thirty-eight days whereas tropical species can fly after twenty days.

For hummingbirds of the high plateaus, the cold is by far the most formidable challenge, but as long as they are able to feed themselves, the low temperatures are no great threat to their survival. During the freezing nights, however, when temperatures drop below the danger point, the bird is not able to hunt for food to compensate for its loss of energy; it withdraws to its nest or a crevice of a rock where it sinks into

a state of lethargy. The normal body temperature of between 98° F and 102° F may then drop to about 58° F, which is approximately the temperature within the shelter. The bird then remains totally inert, its metabolism slowing down to such a point that it requires only a minimum of food. Although this trait may also be observed in other hummingbirds, particularly those of North America, it is a very useful habit for the Andean species. This venturing to colonize a habitat where survival would seem almost impossible indicates how extremely robust and adaptable the bird is.

A WEALTH OF LAKES

If the High Andes are on the whole rather poor in flora and fauna, their lakes are unbelievably rich and they constitute an important feature of the Peruvian and Bolivian plateaus. The complex topography of these chains has created many closed basins and no other region of Peru can boast such a wealth of lakes. Along the Pacific coast such waters are a rarity while on the Amazon slopes neither the topography nor the flow of watercourses lend themselves to the formation of true lakes.

Some of these bodies of water are merely seasonal, depending, as do the pampas, on each rainy season to bring fresh inundations. At such times, grassy tufts thrust above very shallow waters where snipes, ducks and rails with their multicolored bills can be seen wading about. Such wet places are also the winter quarters for a multitude of waders migrating from North America.

There are, on the other hand, many permanent lakes, although they vary in area according to the season. Some of these are quite large, the largest being Lake Titicaca, at an altitude of almost 12,400 feet. Measuring 110 by 35 miles, it is more like an inland sea. The vast flat plains stretching beyond its northern shore were doubtless the bottom of an even larger lake in the not too remote geological past. Lakes Junín, in central Peru, and Sarococha, between Puno and Arequipa, along with Bolivia's Lake Poopo at thirteen thousand feet, are also among the larger Andean lakes.

These large lakes offer uniform physical conditions throughout the year in terms of temperature and the percentage of dissolved gases. This is especially true of Lake Titicaca, whose waters are always between 50° and 55° F. Even when temperatures drop steeply during the dry season, the larger lakes up to an altitude of sixteen thousand feet never freeze over and their waters are rich in oxygen. In the case of Titicaca, the surrounding shores are actually temperate. The level and shallow shores of most of these lakes are often fringed by bulrushes, known as *totoras,* the most characteristic vegetation of the Andean lakes. Occasionally, they form virtual thickets, as on the north shore of Lake Titicaca. These rushes harbor a variety of aquatic creatures and even provide a refuge

Left above: A llama near Cuzco, Peru, a species domesticated so long ago that its wild ancestor has now disappeared. Left: While the llama is valuable as a beast of burden, the alpaca, also one of the Camelidae of the High Andes, furnishes a wool finer than that of the best breed of sheep. (Both by Robert Lawrence Pastner) Right: Alpacas such as these near Puna, Peru, were, along with llamas, the only domesticated animals of the Indians of the High Andes. (D. Hecker: Bavaria Verlag)

for men: the Uru tribe, threatened by more advanced peoples, has retreated to these rushes, and their entire life takes place on floating islands made up of the plant. The rushes are also utilized for their dwellings, clothing and boats; even the sail of their famous *balsas de totoras* is made from the plant. Feeding upon fish and upon the animals and birds sheltered by these islands, the Urus have developed what might be called a "rush culture." These primitive tribes are rapidly disappearing as they mingle with other Indians and abandon their unique lake habitats.

The Andean lakes provide an interesting study for the zoologist because the indigenous fishes, though few in number, include a rather wide variety of fascinating species, all coming from quite a limited original stock. Although a well-defined group normally keeps to one characteristic diet, in these lakes one species may have carnivorous habits while another member of the same family may be vegetarian. The student is thus able to trace the evolution of Andean fishes in relation to the habitat and the availability of food. Unfortunately, man has upset the delicate balance of nature in these waters by trying to draw profit from them. Several North American salmon species have been introduced and these carnivorous creatures have gobbled up the indigenous species. Ironically, the salmon has not always proved its worth in terms of gain for the fisherman. The Andean lakes will continue to be of much value as natural laboratories for the zoologist only if some of them are preserved in their original state.

The guemal deer finds both pasture and shelter on small grassy terraces of steep mountain slopes. (O. P. Pearson)

THE AMPHIBIANS RETURN TO WATER

It is significant that although amphibians long ago abandoned the water to live on land, they still seem to hesitate between the two ways of life. They breed in water and remain there through the larva stage. After metamorphosis, some, particularly frogs and toads, move out into land but never stray too far from water because their skin cannot prevent an excessive loss of body fluids.

The Andean habitat, with its low temperatures and dry climate is thus far from satisfactory for these amphibians. On the other hand, the presence of so many lakes has apparently induced them to adjust their habits. Some Andean toads have, for instance, developed a tough skin reinforced by a horny armor. The most efficient adaptation, however, has been simply to return to the water, where temperatures are favorable throughout the year; many Andean amphibians, such as the huge toads in Lake Titicaca, have thus become totally aquatic creatures.

Several curious anatomical modifications have resulted from this new way of life. Adapted to underwater vision, the eyes of these amphibians, for example, look almost like those of fish. Some of the amphibians are blown up like a balloon when they are caught, the skin then shriveling in folds about the body when they die. This is a way of increasing the surface of the skin, through which all respiration takes place—the lungs being relegated to the condition of vestigial organs. Thanks to well-developed web feet they also swim with remarkable ease. By means of such modifications the toads are able to spend their entire lives in the water. Andean amphibians have thus returned to the primordial way of life of their most remote ancestors.

The Urubamba River Valley is typical of steep slopes along the eastern spurs of the Andes that have been deeply carved by rivers flowing toward the Amazon basin. (Carl Frank)

TINY GREBES AND GREAT FLAMINGOS

The Andean lakes are particularly noteworthy as a haven for birdlife. Indeed, there is often such a grand display of birds that some stretches of water seem like the well-stocked pond of a zoological garden. Grebes abound, especially the tiniest member of the family, *Podiceps rolland,* its ruby-red eye glinting from a chestnut-brown plumage. It makes its home near the shore, where the waters teem with plant life. These zones are also the haunt of one of the most interesting birds of the Andes, the giant coot *(Fulica gigantea).* About the size of a small goose and weighing about seven pounds, it is a lake inhabitant of the high plateaus in Peru, Bolivia and northern Chile. Its coal-black cloak is brightened by a bright yellow-and-white patch above a red beak, while the feet are a vivid coral color. Muscular lower limbs make up for rather stunted wings. Giant coots live where the waters hide the densest tangle of plants, building their nests on veritable floating rafts. These rafts, which they use year after year, measure about twelve feet in diameter and are strong enough to support a man. They are made of the plentiful underwater plants that are also the mainstay of the coot's diet; indeed, it is not unusual to see a coot hungrily nibbling away at its own nest.

This Andean toad (Pleurodema cinerea) *develops a large throat pouch during the breeding season and uses it to utter loud, melodious calls. (Jean Dorst)*

As the basements of these floating houseboats sink and rot away, the coot keeps adding fresh material to the upper stories.

Cormorants are also found here, their range thus extending from the seashore and the lowland lakes to the high upland lakes. Whereas in the lower areas they nest in trees, here they place their nests on the ground or amidst the floating islands. Just as unexpected at thirteen thousand feet is the Andean gull, *Larus serranus,* which resembles a gull found in the lofty lakes of Tibet, in many ways comparable to the Andean lake zones.

The vast profusion of ducks, both in number and in species, is another striking feature of the bird population. Swimming between the dense clumps of bulrushes or in open expanses of water are ducks with a blue bill and jet-black crown, the puna teals *(Anas puna),* yellow-billed teals *(Anas flavirostris),* one of the commonest of Andean web-footed birds, and perhaps a crested duck, *Lophonetta specularioides,* easily recognized by its prominent profile and an iridescent garnet red patch, or speculum, on the wing. The Andean pintail, with its long silhouette, is another common waterfowl in this zone.

The waters of some of the Andean lakes are saturated with mineral salts; they form shallow sheets of water encircled by stretches of bare mud with a glinting crust of crystallized salt. In some cases the lakes may be exploited by industry for their salts, as in the Salinas lake of southern Peru. Naturally, only a highly specialized fauna would be able to subsist in such briny water or in the still more saline mud, but these are made to order for the flamingo and are quite similar to its haunts in the coastal lagoons. Of the three Andean species, all peculiar to the locale, the most common is the Chilean flamingo; it is comparable in size to those nesting in the Caribbean zone and in southern Europe. The James flamingo is by far the rarest and was even thought for a time to be totally extinct. It nests in some of the highly saline lakes of the Bolivian Andes and it was only recently that their colonies were discovered in the midst of a strange, Dantesque landscape, among banks of icy mud encrusted with jagged salt crystals, surrounding an expanse of murky reddish waters. Here the birds have established nests shaped like a flattened cone; and in these the female lays a single egg.

Naturalists have long been fascinated by the flamingo's preference for habitats much too saline for almost all other birds. But the Andean flamingo is perhaps the most curious of all, for the altitude, freezing clime and hostile conditions all make for an environment at the very limits of the habitable.

The High Andean plateaus of Peru, Bolivia and northern Chile, one of the highest regions to shelter life, thus harbor a unique flora and fauna: stunted plants, huddling close to the ground and anchored against the winds by powerful root systems; giant plants like the puyas; condors with a mightier wingspan than any other land bird; vicuñas and chinchillas with their precious fur; birds nesting underground to protect their young; others, such as the hummingbird, dwelling in rocks or caves; gulls and flamingos at unusual heights; lizards undaunted by cold; and amphibians harkening back to the ways of their ancestors. Severe and mournful is the landscape, leaving its stamp on the native Indians; yet in grandeur it is unsurpassed by any other region in the Americas. The adaptation of life to this lofty no-man's-land bears testimony to the amazing versatility of the inhabitants and is in a sense a victory over the stern laws of nature.

Totora reeds (Scirpus totora) *cover the shallow margins of Titicaca, the highest lake in the world. Seen in flight is a yellow-shouldered marsh bird* (Agelaius thilius), *a characteristic passerine of the reedbeds. (Robert Lawrence Pastner)*

Arid Coasts and Teeming Seas

The Deserts of Chile and Peru

13

Everyone has heard of the great deserts of Africa, Asia, North America and Australia, but few realize that South America has deserts, too. Indeed, a continent would scarcely seem complete without a desert.

But first let us try to define a desert. The word usually suggests a gravelly expanse or great drifts of sand bare of the least tuft of vegetation or animal life. Yet such utterly lifeless expanses are rare; living creatures with their great capacity to spread out and adapt themselves have settled zones that seem uninhabitable. Geographers think of deserts as any areas with very sparse vegetation and a limited number of animals. This is vague and makes it difficult to draw the line. The result is that the term desert is used to cover a whole gamut of areas ranging from the purely mineral desert to a kind of arid steppe.

The South American continent has its share of deserts. Indeed, one of the strangest and most paradoxical of the arid zones of the world is to be found along its Pacific coasts between about 3° Lat. S. and 30° Lat. S. Along this stretch of about 2,200 miles can be found "absolute" deserts seemingly without any trace of life. These vast, arid, stony and sandy expanses may be relieved only by an occasional islet of verdure: an oasis, the bed of a torrent flowing from the Andes or perhaps stunted growths of drought-resistant (xerophytic) plants and cactus. The lower foothills of the sierras are no less stark. They form a network of dead, gullied valleys framed by naked mountains, either in the form of great eroded cliffs or vast heaps of stony debris.

The narrow coastal plains of Peru and northern Chile form a lengthy north-south corridor pressed between the seacoast and the great wall of the Andean chain. This chain reaches a height of almost twenty thousand feet, dropping somewhat only in northern Peru. The narrow coastal band, sometimes a mere forty to sixty miles wide, is a zone with a tumultuous geological past. During the Tertiary and Quaternary epochs, there were faults along the entire present coast. An immense fissure has submerged some of the coastal lands beneath the Pacific while a corresponding uplift progressively acted upon the peaks of the cordilleras until very recent times.

These tectonic movements have not yet ceased. Chili and Peru are within the "ring of fire" circling the Pacific and are thus studded with a series of craters. Their volcanic activity may not be great, but numerous earthquakes along the lines of fault indicate a general instability. An average of two hundred seismic shocks is annually recorded in Lima. Some are barely noticeable but others leave catastrophe in their wake. The Peruvian capital has repeatedly been destroyed by quakes in the course of its history and each of her churches has undergone many reconstructions and restorations. The same is true of Arequipa, at the foot of the mighty El Misti, and of many other cities of the coasts and the cordilleras. It is not surprising that the cathedral at Cuzco shelters *Nuestro Señor de los Terremotos*—Our Lord of the Earthquakes—who is invoked solely as divine protection against these frequent cataclysms.

Most of the waterways cutting through these coastal plains (some forty in Peru) were at one time arrested in their course by the submerging of the plains and the uplifting of the sierras. Studies of the sea depths reveal the contours of submerged valleys several hundred miles off shore.

Many of these waterways are in the youthful stages of the erosion cycle. The origin of some of these predates the last Andean folds. Thus, their courses must have been altered as they were compelled to cut their way across chains raised to a higher level. An example of this is the Rio Santa, whose upper course runs parallel to the axis of the cordilleras before its waters drain to the Pacific in an almost vertical canyon cut into startlingly abrupt mountain ranges.

A STRANGE CLIMATE

Travelers have long been intrigued by the strange climate of the Chilean and Peruvian coasts. As early as the mid-1500's, the Spanish historian, Cieza de Leon, recorded that beyond 4° Lat. S. there was a pronounced aridity of climate. It was centuries before the complex set of conditions producing this anomaly could be explained. The main features of the climate are relative coolness and a lack of rainfall combined with a high degree of humidity. Temperatures throughout the year are unusually constant, hovering around 68° F—abnormally low for an intertropical zone. Lima on the Pacific coast is on the same latitude as Salvador on the Atlantic coast; yet the average temperature of its warmest month is seven degrees less than that of Salvador and the average of the coldest month is twelve degrees less—a significant difference to a climatologist.

The temperature is influenced by the neighboring sea, which is abnormally cold for such latitudes. The Chilean and Peruvian coasts are bathed by the Humboldt Current, bearing northward the waters from the southern zone of the great Westerlies, rather than from the Antarctic as was formerly believed. Somewhat like a river in the midst of the sea, the Humboldt Current rises at about 38° Lat. S., is often only about one hundred nautical miles wide, and flows at rates of from three to six miles per hour. It moves due north along

Some deserts along the Peruvian coast are made up of sand swept by the wind into graceful dunes. (Swiss-Foto, Lima)

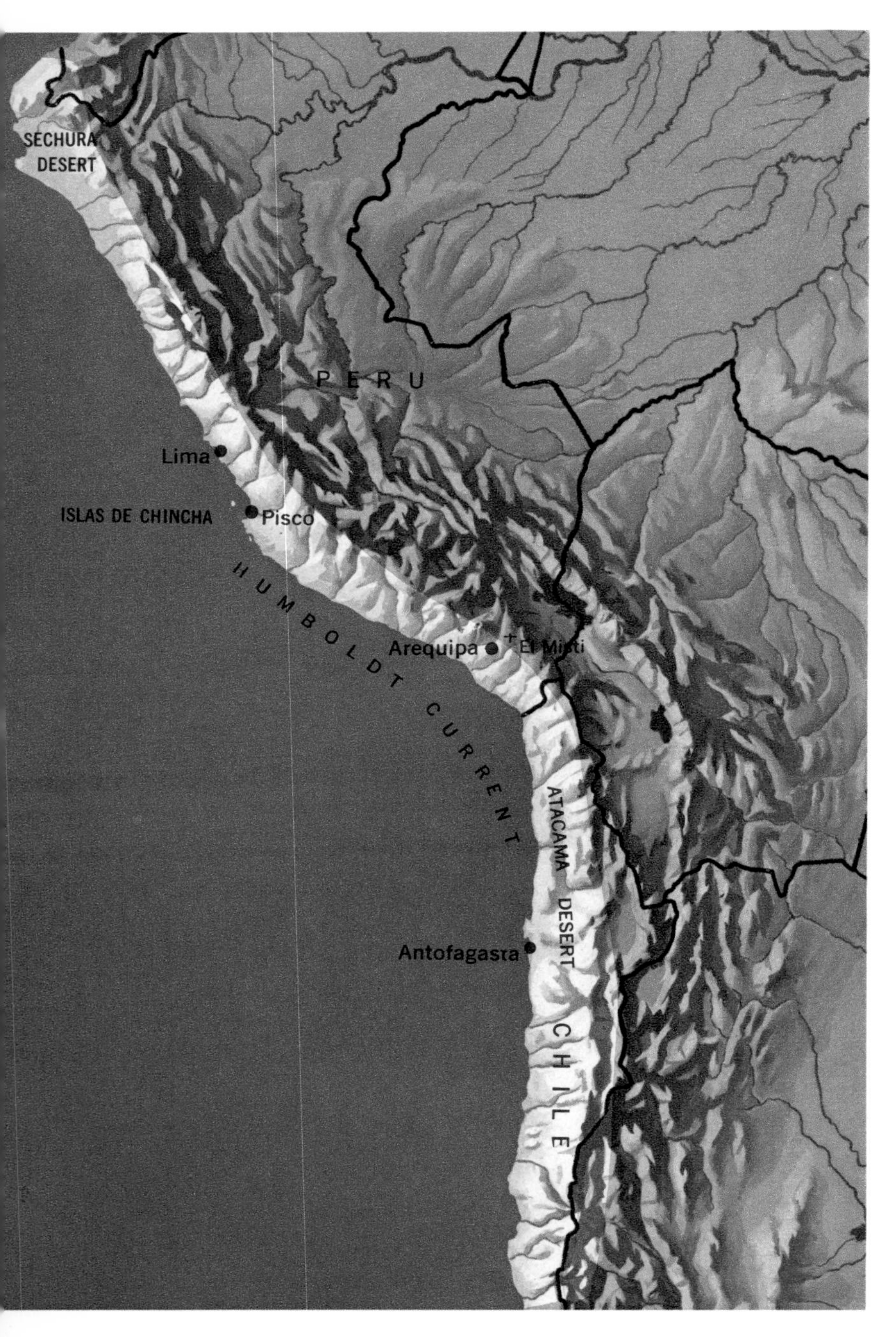

Flanked by the Andes, narrow coastal plains of uninterrupted desert extend between Ecuador and central Chile.

the South American coast to Cape Blanco (4° 27″ Lat. S.) and then veers toward the northwest and the Galapagos after encountering the Niño, a warm current from the Gulf of Panama. Its waters are cold and strongly saline. Surface waters off the coast of Peru range from 58° F to 64° F, as much as eighteen degrees less than the temperatures that one would theoretically expect in these latitudes. Due to upwelling of deeper waters, many other anomalies can be found in the temperatures at different points of this sector of the Pacific. For example, during the southern summer, the waters off Callao are about six degrees colder than at Antofagasta, a city more than six hundred miles to the south. The waters of the Humboldt constitute a unique marine habitat, rich in dissolved salts, relatively cold, and remarkably constant except for exceptional circumstances to be discussed later on.

This cold current explains the inversion of normal atmospheric temperatures. Air in contact with the water cools more rapidly than the air at higher altitudes, forming a thick layer of cold air beneath higher layers of warmer air—the exact opposite of normal conditions. The result is a cloud layer not more than thirteen hundred feet in thickness at an altitude varying from one thousand to three thousand feet that blots out the sun and prevents the warming of the air close to the ground. Temperatures are more than 75° F above the cloud layer, while those at sea level range from 56° F to 61° F. The coast of central Peru is thus the cloudiest desert area of the world along about 300 miles of its length. And yet it never rains except under abnormal circumstances. Precipitation is never truly rain but merely the condensation of the overhanging mists. Life in the coastal settlements is well adapted to this peculiar climatic condition; the primitive huts have roofs made of dried earth that would literally dissolve in rain.

Without sunshine for at least six months of the year, this is a strange, arid zone. Gray skies hover over the countryside obscuring and distorting its contours with a veil of mists called *garuas* by the Peruvians. These mists give way to intense sunshine only during the summer months.

In the extreme north and south of Peru these conditions are less marked. Here the sun seems to assert itself, for the clouds disappear during a good part of the year and there is considerable evaporation—almost as much as in the arid steppes of Australia or the deserts of Upper Egypt.

Thus a strange combination of conditions prevail on the Peruvian coast: cold seas rich in marine life; desert lands without a drop of rainfall, yet for half of the year screened from the sun's rays by a thick blanket of clouds and with air so humid that a dank mustiness permeates everything indoors. An anomaly of nature has created this paradoxical land—tropical coasts within the influence of the circumpacific "ring of fire" bathed in a current of cool waters originating in the cold south.

DESERTS

There is considerable variation within these dismal expanses of coastal desert. Some are sandy—vast accumulations of shifting dunes. Often the sand has been borne inland from the beaches by the winds, and lies like a blanket over the buried features of the terrain. This is the case in the Ocoña region of southern Peru where the winds have patiently amassed mountain-like dunes. The road connecting Lima with the south cuts right across these dunes; bulldozers must be constantly on hand to clear this vital traffic artery. In other regions, particularly in northern Peru, these sandy plains seem strangely like land that has emerged from the depths of the sea and been reshaped by wind action.

Such sandy deserts are much like those in the Sahara and central Asia. Scattered throughout is the characteristic dune or *barkhan*. These dunes take on the shape of a crescent

A vast expanse of rocky coastal desert near Paracas, Peru. (Bernard Villaret)

closing in on itself because the incessant winds meet with more resistance at the center than at the edges of the dune. Xerophytic shrubs are strewn all over the sands; the tangle of their roots takes hold in the drifting sand, thus bracing them against the erosive action of the winds. This makes possible the formation of the kind of plant-covered mounds characteristic of the Sahara. These tiny hills are an attractive haven for rodents and they come to dig cool passageways as escape from the killing heat and dryness, as do the jirds or sand rats *(Meriones)* in the deserts of the Old World.

Another resemblance to the sandy deserts of the Sahara is the date palm introduced long ago by the Spaniards and now growing freely in many places. The camel, introduced at the same time as a beast of burden, has now disappeared, although for a while small troops of them survived in a wild state.

Other than the xerophytic plants already discussed, vegetation is rare in these zones. The only plants characteristic of these sandy expanses are bromeliads of the genus *Tillandsia,* clumps of firm gray leaves about a foot in diameter. Their roots are too sparse to take a firm hold in the sand but they lie like a thick carpet on the slopes of those dunes and on sandy stretches exposed to southeasterly winds. Except for a few lichen, no other plant life can survive here. Nourishment is provided exclusively by the atmosphere; along with moisture, the leaves absorb mineral substances carried by the wind. The soil thus provides a support but no nutrients.

The fauna of this habitat is understandably limited. The few scorpions and insects are the prey of lizards *(Tropidurus)* and of a miner, a small passerine of the genus *Geositta,* one of the rare visitors to this hostile land, along with an occasional bird of prey or vultures lured by the carrion of domestic animals.

There are also stony deserts—the result of the disintegration of rocky masses on the lower Andean slopes. As in other parts of the world, the alternation of scorching days and cold nights, along with variations in humidity have acted to split up these rocks. Wind erosion has also helped transform the terrain, although to a lesser degree because winds here are relatively moderate. The topography still bears the traces of watercourses that once cut through mountains, carved valleys and canyons, and spread gravel deposits in their drainage basins. Now a dead and almost fossilized terrain is the only evidence of the waterways that once shaped it.

Plant and animal life are very scarce in these stony deserts. The growth of a few scattered shrubs and herbaceous plants such as lichens enables certain specialized insects and poisonous spiders to colonize these deserts. A few stray birds, such as the miner mentioned above, are the rare signs of life on these vast wastelands, doubtless one of the grimmest expanses in the world.

LOMAS

In the midst of these nearly absolute deserts, the traveler may suddenly stumble upon a verdant area, although there is no water in sight. The explanation is that the winter mists bring these carpets of vegetation, which recede at the beginning of summer. Called *lomas* by the Peruvians, they thrive only in areas with eight to twelve inches of annual precipitation in the form of mists during the winter. The mists prevent a rapid evaporation of moisture; indeed the evaporation in October is eighteen times lower than in January, thus permitting a specialized flora to flourish temporarily. These climatic peculiarities were utilized by man as early as the pre-Incan civilizations; evidence exists, notably at Arequipa, that some of these lomas were cultivated long ago by means of a kind of dry-farming.

The specialized flora consists mainly of annual plants that tide themselves over in summer in the form of seed, and of plants with underground bulbs or rhizomes. Cactus occurs but is rare and there are few perennials. Algae make their showing with the first condensations of the mists. They are soon replaced by bulbous plants, notably the *amancay,* an Amaryllidaceae *(Hymenocallis amancaes),* whose blossoms cover the scene with patches of bright yellow. A great number of herbaceous plants thrive, although few are grasses. These plants blossom at staggered intervals. Lomas dry up at the beginning of summer when moisture is no longer available from the mists and when evaporation by the sun becomes too intense. Vegetation disappears and the area is transformed into a kind of steppe or even desert, retaining only shrivelled vestiges of the ephemeral vegetation.

Desert dunes and rocky expanses stretch for hundreds of miles along the Peruvian coast. (Johannes Hartmann: Bavaria Verlag)

Terrestrial bromeliads in the Peruvian desert grip the ground by means of withered fibers but these do not serve as roots; as with epyphites, the air provides the plants with water and mineral substances. (Edward S. Ross)

The animal life colonizing these scattered areas has adapted its annual cycle to the seasonal rhythm of the vegetation. Insects spend the hot dry season in a pupa or chrysalis stage and hatch at the beginning of winter. Several birds, such as the Peruvian song-sparrow *(Zonotrichia capensis)* and the Pacific blue-black grassquit *(Volatinia jacarina),* visit the lomas at this time; they come to nest and naturally take advantage of the relative profusion of animal life and vegetation. They raise their young during the summer season and then retire to more humid haunts. Once they are gone the doves move in, attracted by the fallen seeds awaiting germination.

The lomas in bloom are also visited by hummingbirds and I remember my surprise at discovering the male of one of the most beautiful, *Rhodopis vesper,* in a small barren valley not far from Lima. This tiny bird, the breast glinting with a purplish-blue iridescence, seemed utterly incongruous in the midst of an almost flowerless desert, yet several species are found in the deserts of Chile and Peru. The ripe flowers and fruit of the cactus provide the mainstay of the hummingbirds' diet here; when pierced by birds and insects the cactus yields a thick, syrupy liquid.

Lomas are thus an odd kind of haven, flourishing in winter and permitting a relatively abundant fauna to prosper—a reversal of the norm perhaps, but actually in harmony with the cycle of the plants upon which animals depend for their survival.

VERDANT ZONES

In certain areas, a more abundant vegetation is able to flourish. Here and there groups of cacti are reminiscent of areas on the lower slopes of the cordilleras. Some are found down to the very edge of the sea; others are almost hidden in small valleys where a more plentiful vegetation is maintained almost secretly by underground waters. These cacti are principally torch thistle, for example, *Cereus macrostibas,* which branches out at the base and holds long candelabra as high as thirteen feet from the ground, and the *cardo (C. Cartwrightianus)* of the Peruvians, similar in size but branching out only near the top. Although these cacti growths shelter few animals, some birds, particularly hummingbirds, come to plunder the rich nectar of the flowers or to pursue insects nestling in the notches of the branches.

As a result of considerable underground water and intermittent summer rains, the climate in northern Peru and southern Ecuador is far more favorable to animal life than are areas farther south. Particularly characteristic is an open forest consisting of trees with roots powerful enough to draw up water from great depths. Since this water is available throughout the year, the trees are never leafless. Most frequent is a species of the Leguminosae family, *Prosopis juliflora;* Peruvians in central Peru call it *huarango* while in the north it is called *algarrobo,* a name given to it by the Spaniards because of its resemblance to the true *algarrobo* so frequent in the Mediterranean. The dominant species of these forests, it has rather short thorns and when in bloom is covered with clusters of pale yellow flowers. It is accompanied by other species like the yellow-flowered arborescent Leguminosae known as the faigue *(Acadia macracantha),* and several *Capparis,* one of which is the sapote *(C. angulata).* These cactus and brush forests vary in density depending on the amount of water available and the orientation of the slope. Cactus predominates in certain areas, particularly in the southern regions of Ecuador.

Forests of this kind have penetrated beyond the Andes in the northern part of Peru, following valleys along the lower slopes of the cordilleras. They are found notably in the Marañón Valley, at an altitude of about 1,400 feet, in what is called *la cuenca de Bellavista.* This basin ends at the Pongo de Rentema, a passageway through which the river flows before emptying into the Amazon plains. In spite of the summer rains the climate is remarkably dry and the basin is thus covered with drought-resistant vegetation, particularly huge arborescent cacti.

These open woods are more favorable habitats for animal life. Insects abound, and these in turn attract a multitude of birds. Flycatchers are numerous and systematically exploit the stock of insects, each species specializing in a particular form of feeding. The Elaenia flycatcher *(Elaenia modesta),* named fio-fio by the Peruvians for its call, hunts by methodically exploring the foliage while other species wait to pounce on their prey as it flies out into the open. Among the latter is one of the handsomest birds in this area, the scarlet flycatcher *(Pyrocephalus rubinus).* It is about the size of a warbler and the head and breast of the male are a vivid scarlet. It is easily observed because it likes to perch on an exposed branch and dive on passing insects. The long-tailed mockingbird *(Mimus longicaudatus)* is also characteristic of this zone, and because of its liveliness it too is easily observed.

The distinctive fauna that has thus evolved along this arid coast sometimes reveals rather strange distributions; for example, the Peruvian white-winged dove *(Zenaida asiatica meloda)* is found here but it is also found in the arid regions of Central America and parts of the Antilles—lands that lie beyond the intervening forest expanses of Colombia and Venezuela. A likely explanation of this distribution is that the bird favors the open spaces and shuns dense, humid forests.

The open forests are far from being continuous; occurring only in the more humid areas, they are interrupted by vast desert expanses. These deserts extend right up to the city of Tumbes and the transition to the zone of denser equatorial vegetation begins only very gradually in the north.

RIVERS AND HUMID VALLEYS

Rivers from the western Andes flow across the coastal plains and empty into the sea. Once they leave the Andes, their lower valleys are not very long and few convey any large quantities of water. Many might almost better be described as torrents, for the bulk of the rainfall on the Andes flows across the Amazon basin toward the Atlantic. These rivers are from fifty to two hundred miles long—meager in comparison with other rivers in South America.

Some of these rivers flow strongly only during the short rainy season from January to March, but others carry down a

Rocks bizarrely carved by wind and rain at Santo Domingo, near San Antonio, Chile. (Bob Borowicz)

goodly quantity of water throughout the year. Among the latter, the Rio Santa is fed during the dry season by glaciers of the Cordillera Blanca, while the Rio Majes in southern Peru is fed by the meltwater of the Nevados Huarancante, Mismi, Coropuna and Sabancaya, besides the overflow from the numerous lagoons of its upper basin. Seasonal variations are considerable. The Rio Santa has a maximum flow of 98,000 gallons per second in March, and a minimum of 13,000 gallons in August and September. However, the rate of flow is high in relation to the surface of the basin.

The steep pitch and violent flow of the Andean watercourses has a great effect on the lower basins. During sudden freshets they sweep hundreds of acres of fertile soil seaward. They also detach a good deal of sediment from their upper basins, bear it for great distances and then deposit it on the plains. Such vast accumulations can sometimes force a river to change its course.

An abundant vegetation flourishes along these watercourses. True gallery forests thrive along the banks, combining broad-trunked trees with dense underbrush and numerous herbaceous plants. Willows are found, occasionally algarrobos if the soil is relatively dry, and a composite shrub, *Tesaria integrifolia,* the *pajaro bobo* of the Peruvians.

The most characteristic tree found in these riverside galleries is an Anacardiaceae, the pepper tree *(Schinus molle).* Its graceful evergreen pinnate leaves and greenish flowers cast delicate patterns in the sunlight, and the leaves, containing volatile oils used for medicinal purposes by the Peruvians, give off a very pleasant aroma.

It is quite likely that at one time the forests typical of northern Peru covered the entire plains and extended right up to the foothills. But most of these disappeared ages ago, for man's presence in this area dates to the most ancient times. Even before the Inca era, the arid coast of Peru was the seat of flourishing civilizations. The Indians had developed irrigation and farming techniques as effective as those that transformed Mesopotamia into a fertile agricultural land. Thanks to a highly perfected technique of exploiting arid zones, the Nazca and Mochica civilizations were able to flourish as early as the beginning of the Christian Era. And still earlier, the Chicama Indians of around 2500 B. C. and the Indians of the Viru Valley in the first millenium utilized subterranean waters to create a network of irrigation canals, some of which are still in use today.

When sufficient water is available the soil becomes quite productive, and cultivation in these regions is now proving profitable. Of Peru's total exports, sugar, rice, and cotton comprise 51 per cent, whereas metals and minerals, important as they are, amount to only 43 per cent. The coastal region constitutes almost a third of the country's cultivated land. The government fosters agriculture by encouraging very large projects for diverting watercourses and for irrigation in the north (the Rio Quiroz area) and in central Peru (the Rio Ica area). The Rio Quiroz projects irrigated the fertile but often arid valley of the Rio Piura, thus increasing tenfold the production of cotton.

Seen from the air, the first chains of the Western Cordillera appear as barren and stark, showing the drainage patterns of dried-up watercourses. (Weldon King)

The burrowing owl (Speotyto cunicularia) *finds the Peruvian deserts suitable to its nesting habits and builds burrows to shelter its young. (Edward S. Ross)*

MOUNTAINTOP OASIS

A discussion of the arid Peruvian zone would be incomplete without noticing the Arequipa region in the south. The road leading there from the coast winds through a series of desert plateaus, their rocky masses a blend of white, rust and ochre hues; gradually it rises across a series of low, almost imperceptible hills, and leads finally through a narrow winding pass into a vast basin enclosed within mountain heights. The fertile patch in the middle of the basin is at an altitude of 7,550 feet. This oasis is the city of Arequipa, second largest in Peru and the true southern capital. The city is dominated by one of the most famous volcanos of Peru and indeed in the world—El Misti, a peak almost perfectly conical in shape. Often covered with snow, El Misti reaches a height of 19,166 feet. Rivaling it on its left is the gigantic Chachani, rising to a height of 19,931 feet. The successive eruptions of these two giants that dominate the Arequipa basin have vitally affected the topography of the region. The terrain is banded with lava flows; and entire plains are covered with volcanic dust and debris. Most characteristic is the white tufa, a stone extensively used for construction because it is so light and so easy to handle. It is used in monuments and in churches with richly sculptured porches and its white brilliance lights up even the humblest of dwellings. It is easy to understand why Arequipa is called *la ciudad blanca*—the white city.

Arequipa's inhabitants have lived in constant fear of their volcanos since the city's origin in 1540. Eruptions have long since ceased but earthquakes are frequent and have brutally destroyed the city several times. As recently as 1960, a powerful quake brought down the church towers and wrought havoc. Numerous thermal and mineral baths (such as those at Yura and Socosani) are other signs of the volcanic character of the area.

But here, as elsewhere in the world, volcanic activity has also led to great fertility. A host of tropical and temperate plants flourish in the combination of a warm climate and a fairly high altitude. Water is never lacking, either by irrigation from the Rio Chili or the same summer rainfall that drenches the sierras. It is no wonder that the Arequipa region, with a wheat yield as high as sixty bushels per acre, is one of the most productive of Peru.

This is just another example of how a desert can be transformed into the seat of a flourishing civilization.

THE TEEMING MARGINS OF THE SEA

In contrast to the arid inland zones—except where man and nature have transformed them—the seas abound with animal life. This richness can first be observed on the sandy beaches, where a vast profusion of marine invertebrates attracts a multitude of birds, especially gulls. As many as five thousand of these birds have been counted along four miles of shoreline, a world record for density. Some of these are local species; for example, the gray gull *(Larus modestus),* typical of sandy beaches, nests along these coasts, living here in the company of waders. The gray gull seems to feed exclusively on the sand bug, or hippa *(Emerita analoga),* a tiny shellfish that is about one inch long and is a typical sand-dweller. Other birds are migrants from North America during the northern winter. Among these, the Franklin gull *(Larus pipixcan)* comes in great flocks to these shores bathed by the food-rich Humboldt Current. It is joined in its travels by several kinds of waders.

The amount of debris and dead creatures washed ashore is naturally in direct proportion to the amount of living matter in the sea itself. This debris provides nourishment for a host of scavengers, ranging from crabs to birds, which are the most active garbage removers. Among these are seagulls, black vultures *(Coragyps atratus)* and turkey vultures *(Cathartes aura).* And those eager to see condors *(Vultur gryphus)* should most certainly visit the beaches of Peru, notably in the south where the mountains extend closest to the coast. This king of terrestrial birds will not disdain even the smaller carcasses swept in by the tide; one of the attractions of these beaches is the sight of these huge birds engaged in this incongruous hunt.

The rich marine life in these regions is still more apparent in the heart of the seas themselves. The zones bathed by the Humboldt Current constitute an exceptional physical habitat. According to oceanographers, such cold waters rich in salts are ideal for biological prosperity. A truly benevolent cycle of interdependence of life occurs: mineral elements are supplied by great quantities of diatoma and microscopic algae; these serve as food for small animals, which in turn are fed upon by other animals.

There is an extremely high proportion of species within each zoological group. Quite a few of the local species, including the bird life, are peculiar to the Humboldt Current itself. But the number of individuals is even more astonishing; the waters are so laden with pelagic invertebrates that oceanographers often describe them as having the consistency of a thick soup. An unbelievable profusion of tiny crustaceans flourishes upon the algae: copepods, schizopods and others, as well as medusas and salps. These and their larvae constitute the plankton that gives the water its dark, soupy quality. Sailing through the eastern Pacific, from Chile to Easter Island, for example, there is an astonishing contrast as soon as one leaves the Humboldt Current for warmer waters. The density of animal life ceases so abruptly that it is almost like suddenly coming across a desert.

The microscopic animals make possible the survival of larger ones, particularly microphagous fish. An anchovy *(Engraulis ringens)* may be one of the smallest of this group but it is the very foundation of these marine communities: the number of individuals in this species is believed to be as high as ten thousand billion; tiny creatures though they are, this still represents a mass of about twenty million tons. In their turn these fish provide nourishment for others with a carnivorous diet, notably the abundant bonitos. Fisheries along the coastal areas bathed by the Humboldt rank among the richest of the world.

Strips of pebbly beach are visited by small colonies of sea lions, who, along with large whales, also feed upon this abundance of marine life. The coast of Peru is a well-known haunt of the sperm whale, and the whaling industry in this area is well established and quite lucrative.

But the bounty of marine life is enjoyed chiefly by birds, and they are numerous both in species and in individuals. Among them are albatrosses, shearwaters, petrels, storm petrels, pelicans, boobies, cormorants, gulls and terns. Some of these are endemic and peculiar to the Humboldt Current, as for example the Inca tern *(Larosterna inca),* with its slate-gray plumage accentuated by a bright, coral-red bill and feet, and with moustache-like tufts of white feathers projecting from the angle of the mouth. They nest in vast colonies along rocky shores, often not very far from sea lions, the two seeking different levels of quite similar habitats.

Peruvian penguins *(Spheniscus humboldti)* are also found in this company of sea birds. They are closely related to species characteristic of colder Antarctic regions and their presence can only be explained by the waters of the Humboldt Current and the paradoxical climate that it brings. In the Galapagos Islands we shall come across penguins that have evolved in another way and have been able to wander farther north and mingle with tropical birds.

THE GOLD CALLED GUANO

Toward the end of November, 1954, I set out from Lima, driving south to the tiny port of La Puntilla, where, as the guest of *la Compania del Guano,* I was to take a small tug boat

Brown pelicans and gulls along the coast of Peru. (Pierre A. Pittet)

headed for the Islas de Chincha. These islands, about two and one half hours off the Peruvian coast, are the site of an unbelievable congregation of sea birds, most of them guano-producers. The next morning we embarked under a gray sky with great veils of cloud and mist shrouding the waves. As we approached the island, thousands of cormorants invaded the skies, flying in long, winding bands, each containing about a hundred birds. The closer we came to the islands the denser these flocks grew, so that by the time we set foot on the rocky coast they swirled about us like a dark storm. At the foot of the coastal cliffs we were welcomed by a colony of Inca terns beneath a sky streaked with cormorants, boobies and some large and graceful pelicans. A roaring filled the air—the clatter of hundreds of thousands of birds on the island. Soon the stale, nauseating stench of guano filled our nostrils and permeated our clothing; we were seized with sneezing fits from all the down floating like a fine powder in the atmosphere. As if these discomforts were not enough, a rain of droppings from the flying birds fell on us constantly.

Once I had climbed to the summit of the cliff, an unbelievable spectacle greeted my eyes. The entire island was literally covered with birds, like a vast black-and-white carpet spread over the ground. I was gazing at one of the most prosperous colonies of sea birds in the world.

For many, the name Peru evokes memories of the golden treasures of the Incas once sought by Spanish galleys. But today, one of the principal sources of the wealth of Peru lies in guano, the highly exploitable layers of the droppings of a few sea birds. The name guano signifies excrement in Quechua, the most widespread Indian language; but the word is now widely used for the commercial product, particularly valuable as fertilizer because of its high proportion of nitrogen.

Of course, Peru is not unique in having accumulations of guano. Besides those on the Pacific coasts of South America, deposits of guano can be found in Lower California, the coasts and offshore islands of South-West Africa, as well as on the numerous islands dotting the Pacific and the seas bordering the Asian continent and the Indian Ocean. Peru's stock, however, is still the most important.

In order for such a sizeable accumulation to build up in a given place, certain biological and geophysical conditions must be fulfilled. There must first be a sufficient number of birds and, moreover, birds of a gregarious nature. Such a concentration of bird life could only thrive in a habitat providing them with abundant nourishment. Moreover, it would be useless if the birds dispersed their droppings in the sea, instead of on land. Also, the area cannot be one of high rainfall; the rains would wash away the accumulations and hasten chemical disintegration, particularly of ammonia nitrates. Finally, the bird colonies must be established on flat terrain, otherwise the accumulations of droppings would gradually slide into the sea.

All these conditions are amply fulfilled in Peru. As we have noted, the waters bathing the Peruvian and Chilean coasts surpass all others in their density of marine life, and they

The most famous of the tiny islands fringing the Peruvian coast are the Islas de Chincha. The boobies in the foreground are one of the major guano birds on these islands. (Rolf Blomberg: Full Hand)

have little rainfall. The Peruvian coast also happens to be flanked by numerous tiny islands, some separated from the mainland only by a few miles. These islands, bordered by steep cliffs, have table-like expanses that are most attractive to sea birds. Here they are sheltered far from man and carnivorous creatures, particularly the small foxes abounding on the mainland. The only enemy to be feared here is the urubu, common everywhere, and occasionally the condor because of his keen liking for young birds in their nests.

Among the rich birdlife of the Peruvian coast, three of the pelecaniformes play the leading role: the Peruvian or guanay cormorant *(Phalacrocorax bougainvillii)*, the variegated booby *(Sula variegata)* and the brown pelican *(Pelecanus occidentalis)*. These three species currently represent the largest producers of guano. (Others may contribute, as for example, the blue-footed booby *[Sula nebouxii]*, nesting in offshore islands off the northernmost coasts of Peru, but their economic importance is negligible.) These birds meet all the conditions essential to producing guano. Their populations are great: recent counts show a world figure of fifteen million birds for the three species. Instinctively gregarious, they assemble in huge colonies. And like all pelecaniformes they leave their droppings at their nesting or resting places, as opposed to those fish-eating birds who scatter their droppings in flight. Indeed, these birds may be considered efficient machines for the conversion of fish into guano.

The Peruvian cormorant surpasses the other two as a guano producer because of the vast populations in its colonies.

Right: Rocks and sand alternate along the coast of Peru, near Lima. (Tony La Tona) Below: Although some cormorants have diminished wings and are almost flightless, the guanay cormorant is an agile flyer and cruises far when fishing. (Ivan Csillag)

The Peruvian or guanay cormorant does not build a nest but its droppings accumulate around the egg-laying site and form a hardened cone of guano. These cones are ground up for commercial fertilizer. (Paul Almasy: Bavaria Verlag)

Known as the most useful bird in the world, this cormorant resembles the penguin in silhouette and in the brilliant contrast of its white underparts with the metallic blue-black of its outer plumage. A red ring about the eye and an orange carbuncle or knob, developed during the mating season, add a final splash of color to its plumage. Unlike other cormorants, it is an excellent and agile flyer, able to wander great distances from its nesting place in search of food.

In the Islas de Chincha alone, the colonies of these birds are made up of four to five million individuals. During the nesting period it has been estimated that there are about three nests per square yard. Since a cormorant pair raises an average of about two chicks, this brings the density to the astonishing figure of twelve birds per square yard! At first, the nest is a simple formation made up of a few feathers and pebbles. But by the time the young leave the nest it has become a thick cone of guano deposits hardened by the sun.

Amidst such a dense population one wonders how the parents are able to find their own nest. The slightest error leads to squabbles that spread like the wind across this constantly agitated mass. It is quite probable that the birds recognize their own by ear, identifying each other by voice sounds, as do the penguins of the Antarctic.

The variegated booby usually nests in colonies not quite so dense and owes its name to the mottled brown and white of the wings and outerparts, contrasting with the solid white of the head and underparts. There are certain islands where it abounds, especially north of the latitude of Lima, where colonies can be found both upon flat expanses as well as along cliffs falling steeply to the sea. Like all boobies, it has

the habit of making a swift, vertical dive into the water and making a great splash. Because of these reckless plunges it has been called *piquero* in Spanish.

The indolent pelican, with its cumbersome and disproportionately large beak, is the largest of the guano-producing birds although the colonies are no longer quite as numerous as they were. And yet some, for example at Lobos de Afuera off the northernmost coast of Peru, contain as many as fifty thousand pairs. The population density of a bird of this size is understandably smaller and is limited to about two nests per square yard.

The nesting season of these various species continues throughout a good part of the year, beginning in October and lasting well into the austral summer. Of three guano producers, the Peruvian cormorant is responsible for 85 per cent of the current guano stock, while the booby can be counted upon for only 10 per cent, and the pelican 5 per cent—understandable differences in view of their respective populations.

It is not surprising that these birds consume huge quantities of fish. According to rough estimates, a colony of cormorants can eat more than one thousand tons daily. Altogether, the sea birds on this coast consume about 5.5 million tons of fish yearly, the bulk of it anchovies. But dinner is always on the table for these birds. They fish in enormous flocks led to the shoals of fish by scouts. The pelicans, who are skillful divers in spite of their size, dive headlong for their prey, as do the boobies. Cormorants drift with the waves in flocks often as large as those found on land; their hunting is a community affair and each shares in this miraculous draught of fishes.

The great quantities of guano produced by the birds are a result of this abundance of food. According to studies, each bird produces an average of 1.5 ounces of "commercial" guano daily, or approximately 35 pounds each season. Efforts have been made to establish the "efficiency" of guano-producing birds, in other words, the relationship between fish consumed and guano produced. It is believed that each ton of guano requires the consumption of about fifteen tons of fish and it is supposed that two thirds of all droppings fall on land. Even the remaining third is not a total loss because it enriches the sea; microscopic vegetation thus flourishes and, with it, the entire cycle of organic life. Nothing is wasted in nature. Current figures put the quantity of guano produced annually in Peru at 350,000 tons. In Peru it is utilized in the cultivation of the rich soil in tropical areas.

The exploitation of guano is hardly new and was certainly practiced well before colonization by the Spaniards. In his *Royal Commentary or History of the Incas,* in 1604, Garcilasso de la Vega, the famous historian of the Inca civilization, reports the following: "Along the entire coast from Arequipa to Tarapaca, a distance of more than two hundred leagues, the only manure used comes from bird droppings, and the birds of the Peruvian coast are so numerous that the sight of their great flying flocks is indeed astonishing. They nest on the deserted islands of this coast and leave them so whitened that from afar they seem like snow-covered mountains."

The countless archaeological artifacts embedded in "fossilized" guano layers, sometimes at a depth of sixty feet, are ample proof that exploitation dates to ancient times. Some of the artifacts belong to the Mochican civilization, thus harking back to the third century B. C.

Of course, in those times and even during the early Spanish colonial period, guano was used only on a very small scale. Thus, over the course of thousands of years, vast layers were able to accumulate undisturbed. When travelers first came across these deposits—sometimes 130 feet in depth—they were so astonished that they truly believed they had found the fossilized droppings of antediluvian creatures.

During the second half of the last century, a race to exploit guano began in North America and Europe—the two continents vying for its possession. The exceptional fertilizing potential of substances rich in nitrogen was realized in the 1840's. Intensive industrial exploitation began. Entire fleets set out for the distant lands of Peru and returned via the interminable route of the Straits of Magellan. They brought back cargos amounting to millions of tons in order to revive the exhausted soil of the Northern Hemisphere. Armies of coolies were transported from Asia to dig in open mines of guano. It is estimated that between 1851 and 1872, ten million tons were taken from the Islas de Chincha alone, although the entire initial stock was probably not more than thirteen million tons. Within forty years the islands were raked clean.

In the general scramble no thought was given to the birds, although they were the true productive source. With mining operations on a year-round basis, nesting was greatly hindered. Besides, the birds were sought for food by the workers. The men also took the greatest pleasure in hunting and slaughtering for fun. At the same time, hundreds of barrels of the eggs were exported for various industrial uses.

All this rapidly led to the exhaustion of the initial stock and, what was worse, without replenishment. The "harvest" of 1909–1910 realized a mere 23,000 tons, a modest figure in comparison with earlier years. With one of the very foundations of Peru's economy threatened, the government was forced to take firm measures and in 1909 the Compania Administradora del Guano was created. With full authority in its domain, the bureau's first laws were aimed at the preservation of all nesting grounds. The islands were declared off-limits for all ships—and eventually planes. Protecting the birds themselves was hardly an innovation; the Incas had already recognized their potential. De la Vega wrote: "At the time of the Incan Kings, these birds were zealously protected and during the nesting season it was considered a mortal crime to visit the islands, lest the birds be frightened and leave their nests. The same punishment applied to anyone killing one of these birds, inside or outside the limits of the islands." This is proof enough that Incan rulers were highly enlightened in the realm of conservation.

Research also played an important role in the new conservation program; thorough investigations were made of ocean zones and currents, as well as of the life cycle of sea birds, giving man an understanding, if not control, of the birds.

It was not long before the birds returned to their former mating grounds and colonies flourished. There were, however, curious changes in the balance of the various productive species. The cormorants multiplied at a startling rate, whereas the pelican and booby colonies were never able to reach their former size. According to counts made around 1856 by the Peruvian naturalist Raimondi, the Islas de Chincha—particularly in the interior—were heavily populated by the booby, while the cormorant played only a lesser role in guano production. The entire southern island was covered with colonies of the Inca tern, and the guano stock owed much at that time to penguins and several species of petrels.

It is not difficult to discern the reasons for this upset in the balance of species. The more timid species, namely the pelican and booby, reacted most acutely to man's drastic interference, whereas the cormorant made a better adjustment to it. Once preserves were established, the cormorant moved into them more vigorously than more sluggish competitors. It thus took the lead and left the others, particularly the pelican, far behind. In general, the colonies multiplied so rapidly that a surplus of birds came over to the mainland to inhabit some of the higher rocky points. Walls were built around these promontories on the mainland to protect the new colonies from the ravages of carnivorous creatures and restraints were placed upon man's devastation. The overflow on the mainland quickly rivalled the island colonies in abundance.

It was soon possible to resume collecting operations, respecting, of course, the mating season of the birds and following a schedule of rotation from one island to the next. The guano accumulations were no longer as great as formerly, fresh layers of three to four and sometimes as much as five inches in thickness being deposited each year on cleared ground. Because of topographical irregularities, machines can probably never be used and a good deal of manual labor is required to gather the guano. The work is done with pickaxe and shovel; the soil is then carefully raked to gather every last particle. Once pulverized and homogenized, the guano is ready for use.

The story of the sea birds in Peru vividly illustrates how man in all parts of the world began by destroying natural riches in his blind desire for immediate gain. But the enlightened methods now used are a good example of how the protection of wildlife is wholly reconcilable with the utilization of a natural resource.

IRREGULARITIES IN THE HUMBOLDT CURRENT

There is never perfect stability in any oceanographic situation. Not only can the equilibrium of such forces be thrown off, but the norm itself may undergo drastic transformations. The Humboldt Current is not exempt from such fluctuations.

Annually along the northern coast of Peru this marine river encounters the warm Niño Current from the north, causing variations in the two currents. During the austral summer the warmer current thrusts farther south, bathing the Peruvian coast in much warmer waters. Occurring around Christmas, it is called "the current of the Holy Child."

In what seems to be a seven-year cycle, this phenomenon is accentuated in the extreme. The meteorological equator—which divides northern weather areas from southern—is dislocated in the eastern Pacific and low pressure areas reach unusually far southward, bringing violent winds of monsoon intensity. Warm waters, low in saline content, are pushed to the south and replace, or overlie, the cold, more saline waters along the Peruvian coasts. The most memorable instance of this occurred in 1925 when the Humboldt Current shifted as far south as the latitude of Arica in Chile. This disturbance had the most immediate effect on land, drastically altering the climate. The deserts of Peru were practically inundated by the rains; precipitation in Lima reached a high of sixty inches, compared to an annual average of only two inches. Paradoxical as it may seem, the heavy rainfall brought disaster to the agriculture of this arid zone.

But the consequences of such upsets have much wider repercussions in the seas themselves. Cold-water fauna cannot survive the rise in temperature and the decrease in salinity. The plankton perishes *en masse* and the waters are poisoned and polluted by the myriads of dead organisms and the proliferation of bacteria. Creatures dependent on plankton for food, particularly fish, go hungry and die. The whole complex life cycle is thus disrupted and the only recourse for those thriving on the riches of the seas is to seek nutriment elsewhere. Such is the fate of the bird life, particularly the guano birds, and their colonies disperse in utter confusion. Some emigrate southward in the hope of finding sustenance along the coasts of Chile. Others travel to the north and even inland; in either case it is not long before they perish. Observers have described the tragic sight of hordes of famished cormorants wandering aimlessly through pastures amidst grazing cattle—searching for a substitute for their favorite fish. The helpless birds fall prey to anemia, epizootics, and parasites. During such disasters, millions of dead victims are washed ashore along the Peruvian coasts; about ten million birds may succumb within a few months.

As a rule, the cormorant suffers more severely than the pelican or the booby because of its habit of fishing in surface waters more deeply affected by the invasion of warmer waters, whereas the others dive for their prey into depths which are not so drastically disturbed.

The situation along the Peruvian coasts well illustrates the delicate balance of nature's forces. The slightest disturbance may lead to the most serious disorder, sometimes at the expense of prosperous species that are highly useful to man. This is another reason for man to insure their safety.

DESERTS AND NITRATES

The northern part of Chile, beginning at about 30° Lat. S., can lay claim to a climate almost more arid than that of the Peruvian coast. Water is very rare here and one may travel many hundreds of miles without crossing a single watercourse. Waters coming off by the nearby cordilleras simply disappear into the sandy and pebbly expanses, except for sudden freshets, which create disastrous floods in the lower regions. The average annual rainfall at Iquique over a period of twenty-one years is a mere 0.06 inches; Copiapo receives only 0.6 inches per year.

Moisture comes only from the Chilean *camanchancas,* or winter fogs, similar to the *garuas* in Peru. One of the most arid regions in the world, the Atacama Desert was for centuries dreaded by travelers who had to cross it. It is only in some of the lower areas that subterranean waters sustain a stunted vegetation mainly of the family Mimosaceae, such as the *Prosopis* and the *Tamarugo.* The more favored zones have a scattering of oases which permit Indian communities to eke out a scanty existence, but only by constructing underground water-supply mains similar to those in the Sahara.

This barren region was coveted by Chile's two neighbors, Peru and Bolivia, and was the subject of a long battle—the War of the Pacific—which began in 1878. The fact is that this seemingly worthless desert hides a great treasure in the form of deposits rich in nitrates or saltpeter. Flanked by the coastal plateaus and by the foothills of the cordilleras, lies a low plain, which, between 19° and 25° Lat. S. contains deposits containing not only sodium nitrate but sodium chloride and iodized salts. These gray, rocklike deposits, called *caliche* in Chile, vary anywhere from ten to fifty miles in breadth and from several inches to several feet in thickness. The origin of these beds is still uncertain; some say they result from the chemical decomposition of algae or guano piles deposited during ancient geological times.

The importance of these salts was not realized until the beginning of the nineteenth century when it was discovered that nitrates make a valuable fertilizer. As soon as they were exploited on an industrial scale, the question of boundaries, which had thitherto been mere traces across deserts, became crucial. As a result of the War of the Pacific, the lands were declared Chilean territory.

With boundaries established, the industry made still further strides—to the great benefit of the Chilean economy; taxes on this industry alone covered 60 per cent of the national budget. The market dropped, however, when the techniques for producing synthetic nitrates were perfected; by 1932 the value of natural nitrates had fallen to 40 per cent of the 1920 value. Later, with more modern refining methods the market made a recovery, especially since these salts contain not only nitrates but iodines as well. Thanks to its reserves, Chile is capable of supplying 75 per cent of the world's demand for this valuable substance. Silver has also been found in great quantities in this arid region, and the nearby cordilleras furnish a considerable amount of copper ores. Thus a harsh, dry climate has here been counterbalanced by underground riches.

BALANCE BETWEEN LAND AND SEA

The zone from Chile to northern Peru displays, as we have noted, almost unique biological and climatic features. The only comparable area is along the Atlantic coast of southern Africa where the cold Benguella Current, bathing the shores of South-West Africa, gives rise to an analogous situation; aridity and desert on land, abundance of life in the sea.

Despite the desolation of the Peruvian deserts, this area witnessed the development of mighty empires and was the cradle of brilliant civilizations, notably in the north and middle south. The beginnings of agriculture, about 3000 B.C., gave birth around the fourth century B.C. to civilizations that reached their zenith in the Paracas, Mochica and Nazca cultures. The Chimu empire then had its turn in history and lasted until about the fifteenth century when the Incas poured down from the cordilleras to make their conquest. During that period the coastal region was highly populated. Chanchan, the largest city of pre-Colombian America, located midway between Lima and Chiclayo, had an area of no less than six square miles.

Thus history once again reveals that a great civilization may flourish in the midst of desert. In this case a set of favorable conditions were all supplied. The climate is good, and in certain areas water is not totally lacking. This is particularly true when torrents from the Andes are put to wide use. Of course the rich silts found along the Nile are lacking, and the violent rivers cannot be depended upon for sediments. Yet their waters permit widespread and profitable irrigation, and the deserts become fertile once they have the necessary moisture. In the past, the coastal oases and the lower river basins were cultivated to the utmost. Evidence of the highly perfected and well-organized irrigation systems reveals that nothing was left to chance. In fact, vestiges of water supply projects in what are now desert zones indicate that cultivation in the past was more widespread than it is today.

As we have observed, the sea also yielded its abundance to past civilizations, the Indians making good use of the wealth of fish and the accumulations of guano on the islands. De la Vega goes so far as to conclude that without guano agriculture would not have been possible along the Peruvian coast. Today modern man, combining ancient Indian methods of irrigation with powerful mechanical devices, continues to make use of guano—the most valuable fertilizer in today's market.

Thus, in the course of many centuries, the arid coast of Peru continues to be a zone of seeming desolation, but one where the surrounding seas bring great riches to the land.

Guanay cormorants congregate in colonies of as many as a hundred million birds. Here they keep at a safe distance from a sea lion in a sheltered inlet. (Rolf Blomberg: Full Hand)

Evolution's Showcase

The Galapagos Islands

14

On the 23rd of February 1535, winds being favorable, a ship sailed out of Panama harbor. On board was Tomas de Berlenga, the city's bishop, sent to Peru by the King of Spain to settle the differences between the conquistadors Francisco Pizarro and Diego de Almagro. The ship was heading south, keeping to the coast, when suddenly, on the eighth day, a dead calm set in. Crew and passengers bore as best they could the implacable tropical sun reflected by a sea without a ripple. Then the shore began to blur as if a current was carrying the ship out to open sea. This is precisely what was happening. We now know that in this area a current runs westward toward the then mysterious South Seas.

Right: Bartholomew, one of the Galapagos Islands, is located in the Pacific Ocean off the coast of Ecuador. (Tad Nichols) Below: The marine iguana, looking like a prehistoric monster, is peculiar to the shores of the Galapagos Islands, a habitat it shares with the sea-lions. (Bernard Villaret)

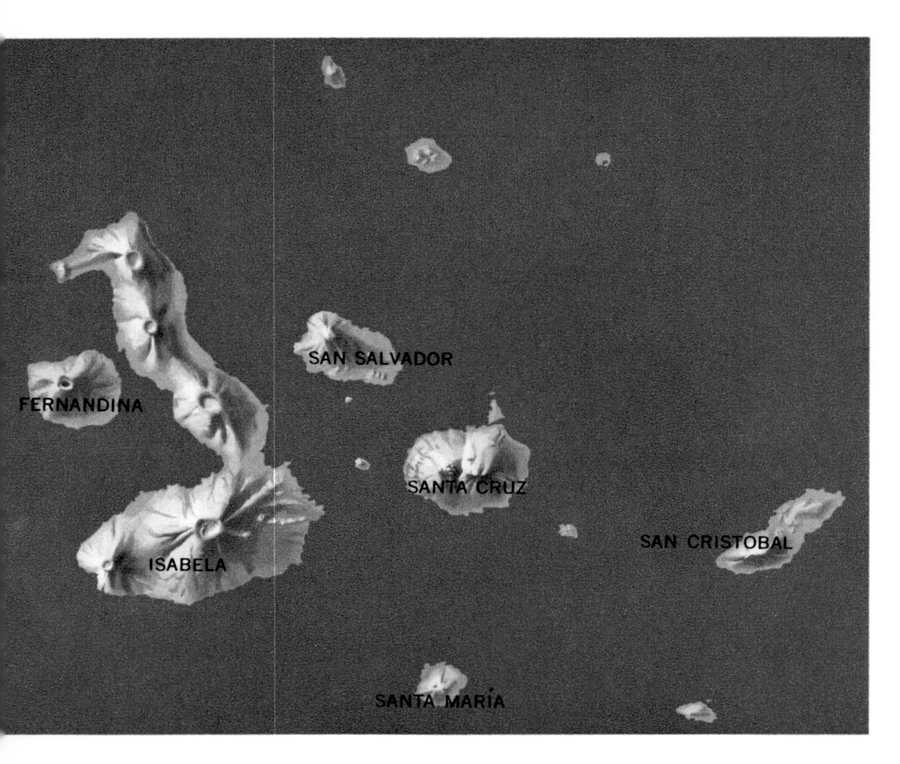

The Galapagos, an archipelago of the peaks of a volcanic complex that long ago emerged from the depths of the Pacific Ocean. Isolation from the mainland has preserved on it a fascinating and often archaic fauna.

Food and especially water began to run short and the situation seemed hopeless. But on the 10th of March, land became visible on the horizon. Soon the thirsty navigators were on shore, only to be confronted by a sort of prehistoric monster—dragons over three feet in length. Inland there was nothing but black rocks covered with cacti as far as the eye could see. There was not the smallest rivulet; the only water the sailors could discover lay in crevices among the rocks. And it proved even more bitter than sea water.

Tomas de Berlenga had discovered the Galapagos Islands, later named Archipélago de Colón, their official Ecuadorian name. The Bishop of Panama gave an accurate description of the place and calculated its location with noteworthy precision. He remarked that the landscape looked as if "God had showered stones on it."

Today's traveler gets the same impression. As he approaches, a black line of dark cliffs and rocky beaches, brightened here and there by sandy places, stands out against an ink-blue sea. In the distance are mountains enveloped in constantly shifting mist. *Las islas encantadas,* as the Spanish navigators called them, appear and disappear at the whim of these veil-like mists.

The approach to the islands is not easy. Landing points are scarce and anchoring insecure. In many places, the coast is a kind of cracked lava boulevard, hard, black and bristling with spikes of scoriae, built up by volcanic streams that flowed from the interior down into the sea, ending in huge submarine plateaus. In various places erosion has cut the rock into steep cliffs as much as thirty feet high, edged with white foam by the waves. Sometimes the sea, having worked its way between two bands of lava, forms a narrow, luminous, almost phosphorescent blue-green canal between two steep walls. The black lava blocks washed by waves are dotted with red spots in perpetual motion, each spot a hand-size scarlet crab with a red shell and sky-blue mouth parts. As you approach they rush into holes, then pop out again like little devils. Sea gulls also flutter about, the strangest being the fuliginous gull whose feathers are so close to lava color that he would be invisible if it were not for a small spot near the eye.

In other places, the coast slopes down into sandy beaches constantly swept by the surf. The sand is made up of particles of coral shell, which are actively sought by the settlers for building purposes, since they are the only calcareous sediments in the island. On the horizon, the fringelike coast is edged with dark green. Here grow mangroves whose roots hold the ground in a kind of black mud rich with marine organisms. They give shelter to numerous birds, including passerines, but mainly white egrets and bluish-feathered herons, attracted by abundant food. Brown pelicans, large and heavy, perch on the trees. When they take flight, they lose their awkward appearance and become graceful.

As soon as the visitor has disembarked, he must pick his way through the coastal plains. The barren ground is often a mere crust of cracked rocks, broken by many fissures and crevices. Flat expanses end abruptly against steep, wall-like cliffs, for the most part impassable. Elsewhere, gigantic cacti and thick bushes make it almost impossible to walk. Every plant seems edged with thorns and prickles. The liquid element seems to have disappeared from these Dantesque expanses; this is the land that Darwin compared to the tilled parts of Hell.

The visitor is surprised by the animals that occur here. Dragon-like reptiles, the very species that astonished Tomas de Berlenga, await him on shore and stare at him calmly before disappearing clumsily behind a rock. Inland, giant tortoises, whose Spanish name, *galapagos,* has been given to these islands, move with surpassing ease, considering their size. We feel as though we have stepped back into another age of the world, when reptiles reigned over the earth.

VOLCANO OUT OF THE SEA

The form of the Galapagos can be explained geologically. These are purely igneous islands, part of a large volcano complex that rose from the depths of the Pacific Ocean about six hundred miles off the South American coast and just below the Equator. Lava gushing from innumerable craters—there are still some two thousand numbered ones—has continually altered the topography of this region. In some places it has formed islands, in others it creates submarine rocks, extremely dangerous for navigation. Sinkings and upheavals have united crater cones with long bands of lava. The largest island, Isabela (or Albemarle, most islands having an official Spanish name taken from the history of Columbus, and an older English one given to it by British corsairs), has no less than five large volcanos, the lava of which has joined to form a strangely shaped island about eighty miles long. Others, for

The rocks of the Galapagos Islands, even when sculptured by the sea, as here on Kicker Rock, bear witness to their volcanic origin. (Rolf Blomberg: Full Hand)

instance Fernandina (Narborough) Island, consist simply of a single cone rising straight out of the ocean. The entire archipelago is composed of thirteen main islands, five of which are comparatively large, nineteen islets and forty-seven massive rocks. Their total area is about 4,500 square miles, with Isabela Island accounting for about half of this. Some of these islands are rather high, the highest points, over five thousand feet, being in northern and southwestern Isabela.

While the last big eruption, that of the Fernandina volcano, dates back to 1825, volcanic activity of varying intensity has been noted since, notably in the northern and southeastern parts of Isabela, where an eruption took place in October 1957. These seismic movements are not infrequently accompanied by landslides. They probably account for the strange history of the lake in the crater of the Fernandina volcano. This expanse of water seems to be drained periodically, probably following the formation of a fissure through which water flows out. This repeated drying out has not prevented colonization of the lake by fish whose origin is a mystery.

The relationship of the Galapagos with the South American continent was once the subject of long and lively controversy. According to one theory, these islands were in remote times united to America by a continental bridge that is now under the sea. According to the supporters of another theory, including such illustrious scientists as Darwin, Wallace and Agassiz, the islands are all of typically oceanic origin, that is, risen straight from the ocean bottom, and have never been linked to any continental mass. The rocks, progressively changed by erosion and with the surface transformed into soil, were colonized first by plants and then by animals. All living things are supposed to have reached the Galapagos by chance and not on foot over some kind of bridge. Some may have come by flight; some, such as seeds and small animals, especially insects, may have been driven by the winds; others, including even big tortoises, may have come by swimming. Still others may have drifted on natural rafts, tree trunks or floating clumps of soil and plants washed to sea from large tropical

Right: The lower levels of Plaza Island in the Galapagos are almost desert and only cactus grows on the expanses of lava that make up the coastline. (Tad Nichols) Below: The swallow-tailed gull (Creargus furcatus), *peculiar to the Galapagos, nests among the volcanic blocks on the shores. (D. Cavagnaro)*

rivers. These rivers uproot veritable floating islands from their banks. They accumulate in a solid mass in certain places, are carried out to sea when a flood occurs, and drift over great distances. Many terrestrial animals can travel aboard such natural rafts. And the ocean currents around the Galapagos come from the east, that is, from the American continent, as Tomas de Berlenga learned to his sorrow. Captain Colnett reported this in 1798, having found on the southeastern coast of San Cristobal (Chatham) trunks larger than any tree in the Galapagos, as well as bamboo and sugar cane unknown in the archipelago. Even now all sort of material drifts up on the beaches. There are no doubt great losses among the involuntary passengers on the rafts, but it is enough that a few do survive the journey and that the species has a chance to start a new colony.

It is probable that in some geological eras the passage from one island to another was easier than it is nowadays. The distance between the American continent and the Galapagos may have been less because of a projection of Central America; various submarine crests off the coast of Central America may be remnants of this land. There can be little doubt that these islands are of an oceanic nature for that alone can account for the extreme scarcity of animal life on them.

A LABORATORY OF EVOLUTION

These are the Galapagos: barren lands, often no more than mineral deserts; flora and fauna so sparse that they are almost nonexistent as compared to the life that swarms on the continent nearby. Why then are naturalists so interested in these islands? The answer is that they derive their importance from this very sparsity. They form a world in themselves, preserved from the evolution that has swept over the great continental masses. Isolation has made possible the preservation of archaic animals, long vanished from other parts of the world or playing only a tiny role as compared with creatures more evolved and better fitted for survival.

Besides, the very small number of species found in the Galapagos has permitted them to evolve in a special way. The proportion of endemic kinds is very high, because of their differentiation in a sealed area. Certain zoological groups exist only in the Galapagos, as, for instance, the Darwin finches or Geospizidae. Here, the biologist finds himself in the position of a chemist who has mixed only a few elements in his test tubes and can therefore easily study the reaction of each. On these islands, the thread of evolutionary history and the differentiation of forms become manifest.

No wonder then that Charles Darwin experienced such a thrill when he visited the islands in 1835 during the cruise of the *Beagle*. He was the first to realize the extreme interest of these islands for the comprehension of the evolution of life. As early as 1837, he wrote in his *Evolutionary Notebook:* "In July opened first notebook on 'Transmutation of Species.' Had been greatly struck from about month of previous March on character of South American fossils and species of Galapagos Archipelago. These facts origin (especially latter) all my views." This makes it easy to understand why biologists look upon the Galapagos as one of the key regions of science, containing the answers to some of the great enigmas of life.

The green heron (Butorides sundevalli), *a common bird in the Galapagos, lives on beaches near mangroves and feeds mainly on crabs. (Rolf Blomberg: Full Hand)*

CROSSROADS OF OCEAN CURRENTS

Even as the traveler enters the neighborhood of the Galapagos, he is amazed by the many colors of the water, the sea appearing to be divided into zones, as in a large mosaic. Dupetit-Thouars, who was in command of the French frigate *La Vénus* during its trip around the world in 1836–1839, mentioned that "the water was divided into long parallel stripes, dark blue choppy water alternating with smooth whitish waters. The latter gave the same impression as the foam one sees around and below bridge abutments, with the only difference that here it seems limitless." Oceanographers have since noted that these zones, some comparatively constant, others fluctuating, are very different in saline content but even more in temperature, the difference running from 10° to 18° F. Differences have been noticed even between neighboring areas.

These facts are related to a very peculiar oceanographic situation. The Galapagos are located at a crossroads where cold and warm currents meet without mixing. The equatorial countercurrent coming from the west along the Equator, between the 3° Lat. N. and 5° Lat. S., brings clear warm water. It meets another warm current running north-northwest, but also with a strong cold current, the Humboldt Current. This ocean stream, first flowing northward along the coasts of South America, suddenly inclines northwest and west at the latitude of the Peru–Ecuador border. It then washes the Galapagos before disappearing into the Pacific Ocean under warmer waters. During nine months of the year, when the strong southeast winds are blowing, the Humboldt Current carries huge quantities of waters at such a speed that a floating object can drift from the shore of the continent to the Galapagos in two weeks.

The influence of this cold current, which accounts for the desert aspects of the Chilean and Peruvian coasts, is predominant in the Galapagos and has determined most of its characteristics, and above all its oceanographic conditions. The sea water here is abnormally cold, considering that it is near the Equator, and except in a few favored places, prevents the formation of coral reefs. Even mangroves cannot grow on the shores unless sheltered from cold currents. On the other hand, the presence of both cold and warm water creates conditions particularly favorable to marine life. There is a rich plankton on which countless fish live, which in turn allow the proliferation of birds and sea-lions. The Galapagos Islands are famous for an abundance of cetaceans, such as whales and porpoises, which were hunted with great profit in the past and are still sought after. Crustaceans are also plentiful and in some bays it is only necessary to dive a few feet down to bring up armfuls of lobsters. At times they are so numerous that one settler is said to have fed them to his hens.

PENGUINS AND FRIGATE BIRDS

This juxtaposition of cold and warm waters and their occasional mixing is of never-ending interest to oceanographers

Marine iguanas on the Galapagos Islands never stray from the rocky, volcanic shore areas. (Rolf Blomberg: Full Hand)

because it has resulted in a strange meeting of cold-water and warm-water animals, both enjoying the conditions they prefer or even absolutely need. Thus, one finds many brightly colored coral fish living among the submerged coral cliffs, along with colonies of sponges, starfish and mollusks—all similar to those found in the vicinity of the Polynesian islands. On the other hand, the neighboring areas are inhabited by typical cold-water fish.

The contrast is still more striking among birds. The traveler nearing the Galapagos is greeted, long before he sees the coast, by frigates and three species of boobies, all pertaining to warm seas. The red-footed booby *(Sula sula)* and the masked booby *(S. dactylatra)* may be seen far off the coast, where they feed on deep-sea fish. The third, the blue-footed booby *(S. nebouxii),* definitely more of a shore bird, fishes along the coasts and in shallow bays. The colonies of these birds are an unforgettable sight. They are particularly strongly established in the extreme north of the archipelago, especially on the island of Genovesa (Tower). This island is made up of a volcano risen from the bottom of the sea; its crater, open in the south, has been invaded by the sea and now forms a circular bay. As the traveler approaches the island, he sees an intricate ballet of boobies in the air. On shore, especially at nest-building time, the lower bushes and the sand are so full of birds as to seem alive.

The most fascinating birds are the large frigates, which have a wingspan of up to seven and one half feet. The adult males have completely black feathers, glinting with green or purple; females and young birds have white bellies. In the mating season, the males develop a large bright scarlet pouch under the throat, which they puff up like a balloon during their mating parades. The male begins to make a rough nest in a low bush or occasionally on the ground. He then shows off his pouch to the females, spreading out his wings and shaking them spasmodically, and uttering a series of "kew, kew, kew" sounds. The call ends in a booming note, with the bird shaking his head violently. All the while the females are flying above where the males have settled, alighting here or there, then flying off again. Finally, they choose their mate and help him finish the nest platform. A single egg is laid and is then hatched by both parents. After that the male's pouch shrinks, hanging down like a burst balloon, and disappears until the next breeding season.

The red-footed boobies nest in much the same way. They like to perch, but their relatives, the blue-footed boobies, prefer to nest on the ground; there is a large colony of them on small Daphne Island, north of Santa Cruz (Indefatigable). From the rim of the crater, covered with cactus and thorny shrubs, the traveler enjoys a splendid view. On one side of the rim, the island plunges steeply down to deep blue waters. On the other side, hundreds of feet below, is the vast bottom of the crater—flat and entirely white, the whole surface occupied by a colony of several hundred blue-footed boobies. These birds do not build nests but simply lay their eggs in little hollows on the ground. There is no distinct breeding season; the island is just below the Equator and so there are practically no seasons, especially for sea birds. There, one can see some pairs marching toward each other, their big, sky-blue webbed feet showing clearly, while others hatch their eggs or feed their young.

Although red-footed boobies and frigates often nest next to each other in shrubs, they "coexist peacefully" only near their nests. Frigates cannot dive, but they can catch fish and other marine animals swimming on the surface. Yet they much prefer to steal them away from the boobies. As soon as the boobies have captured a prey, the frigates chase them and terrify them until they drop the fish. The frigate immediately dives and catches the fish before it falls back into the water. Christopher Columbus had noted these intimidating tactics in the logbook of his first trip, when he encountered frigates in the Caribbean. If the booby does not give in, the frigate will really attack and with its long curved bill can wound the booby seriously.

These two birds are typical of the kind found wherever there is warm water in the intertropical zone. But in the same archipelago there is also a sea bird that is typical of the coldest water: the penguin.

Penguins are known to live and congregate in the coldest area of the Antarctic. Some have come north along the Pacific coast of South America by following the Humboldt Current. The one member of the family that reached the Galapagos is the only equatorial representative of the group. This anomaly can be explained by the oceanographic conditions which made it possible.

The Galapagos penguin is peculiar to this archipelago, and is smaller and weaker than the South American penguins, as if it had degenerated under unfavorable conditions. It is found along the coasts of Fernandina and Isabela, the most likely place being where the Bolivar Strait separates the two islands. For a long time it was believed that this penguin was very rare and that only a few dozen had survived. According to a recent census, however, there are about 1,500 left. But the species is particularly threatened because it trusts too much its principal enemy: man.

These penguins are found on the lava shores projecting over the sea; from these they can drop feet first into the water. The sea in that part of the Galapagos is particularly rich in fish, so that these penguins need not regret that their ancestors emigrated long ago from the Antarctic. From May to August, during the cool season, they make a nest in a natural cavity or under a heap of rocks, sometimes partly in the dark. They are very gregarious, retaining the sociable character of their Antarctic relatives.

The penguin's presence in the Galapagos is a true paradox. Along with the frigates and the marine iguanas, it makes one of the strangest spectacles in the whole world—all the result of an unusual juxtaposition of marine currents.

THE FLIGHTLESS CORMORANT

On the coasts of Fernandina and Isabela we are able to observe another marine bird peculiar to the Galapagos, the flightless cormorant *(Nannopterum harrisi)*. It belongs to a group of birds found all over the world, especially near the sea, but also where there is fresh water with food enough to satisfy their robust appetites. Heavy-bodied, long-headed, with a long, almost serpentine neck and a straight bill hooked at the end, they are easy to identify. Unlike their relatives, the Galapagos cormorants have completely lost the ability to fly. In spite of their large size, these birds have only tiny wings, with atrophied quill-feathers not suitable for flight. They do not even walk very well, however they excel at swimming.

Today, the flightless cormorant, like the penguin, can be found only along the coasts of Fernandina and Isabela. There are only about a thousand of them left. They present an evolution similar to that of the great auk *(Alca impennis)* that used to live in the northern Atlantic before it was exterminated by man. Both are degenerated types in their lack of capacity to fly, but the lack is greater in the cormorant.

This regression in evolution is difficult to explain. A tempting explanation would be that the Galapagos cormorant, having no need of wings to protect itself from carnivores on the ground, has gradually stopped using them over the generations. It is an attractive theory, but there is no evidence to sustain it. However, it is interesting to note that gigantism and loss of flying ability is seen principally on islands. Isolation and lack of enemies have doubtless influenced evolution by increasing the survival possibilities of a species with reduced flying ability.

Nowadays, most such birds have disappeared because of man's destructive activities; the flightless cormorant remains the last example of a strange fauna.

SEA-LIONS AND ALBATROSSES

The cold Galapagos waters have also made possible the colonization of its shores by two kinds of sea-lions. The rarest is the fur seal, *Arctocephalus australis galapagoensis,* closely related to species living in the cold waters of the remotest part of South America; these also travel up to the Equator along with the cold currents. Their coat, a true fur like that of the Pribiloff Islands fur seals, is responsible for their destruction, hunters having killed them to secure their precious skins. While it is likely there were a great many in the archipelago in the nineteenth century, they can now be found in only a few places, mainly on Santiago (James), Isabela, and Fernandina islands; even in these places there are certainly no more than four thousand left. Through his thirst for immediate profit, man has deprived himself of an important source of wealth in a part of the world where such sources are scarce. A rational exploitation could have prevented this depletion.

On the other hand, the California sea-lions (which are represented in the archipelago by a separate race, *Zalophus californianus wollebaeki)* were never hunted because their

A close-up of the land iguana (Conolophus subcristatus) *of the Galapagos. (Bernard Villaret)*

skin is covered with long hard hair and has no commercial value. This species is still abundant—too abundant according to fishermen whose nets they damage. The males with their harems of females and young can be seen on many beaches. Prosperous colonies have settled on the shores of Española Island (Hood), which is further famous as the only known nesting place of the Galapagos albatross *(Diomedea irrorata)*. About two thousand nesting pairs visit the flat expanses of this island at reproduction time and engage in elaborate mating parades, including ritual dances, bows, and vocal performances resembling trumpet calls. The female lays a single egg directly on the ground. Hatching occurs in about sixty days and the young stay with the parents for a long period. Thus the birds remain in the islands for at least eight months. Adults move out over the Pacific in November or December, flying southeast to the coasts of Ecuador and Chile. Later, they fly back to their native island, attracted by the abundance of small cuttlefish and other fish.

SEAWEED-EATING DRAGONS

The most interesting animal on the coast of the Galapagos is the marine iguana *(Amblyrhynchus cristatus)*. Some of the smaller ones are found even around the primitive jetties at landing places, and adults can be seen not far from inhabited areas. These gigantic reptiles, as much as four feet long, look like dragons. A crest running down the middle of the back from the head to the end of the tail increases their resemblance to some prehistoric monster. They are black, but in the mating season the scales on the fore part of the body turn dark yellow or red. They have long limbs, and paws with sharp-clawed toes. The marine iguana swims with great ease, letting his paws float alongside his body and moving by means of sidewise undulations of his tail. He can thus escape his only true enemies, sharks, which abound in the coastal waters. He uses his claws to climb the rocky shores and to stay on the rocks and not be carried out to sea.

This iguana is the only "modern" saurian that restricts itself entirely to the sea. His whole life is spent in a tidal zone a few dozen feet wide on either side of the line where water and land meet. Except for a few hermits, marine iguanas are gregarious and sometimes form large colonies, especially on Fernandina where the coastal cliffs shelter hundreds of animals. Seeing one of these colonies is like getting a glimpse into the prehistoric past.

The rhythm of the iguana's activity is strictly regulated. An entirely diurnal animal, he spends his nights in crevices in the rocks, coming out in the morning to warm himself in the sun while waiting for low tide. As soon as the fields of seaweeds on which he feeds have been uncovered by the retreating tide, he goes down and starts eating the extremities of the plants. But a Santa Cruz settler has apparently succeeded in changing the eating habits of the animals. The iguanas on the cliffs near his house have literally been conditioned to come running when he whistles; they enter his house and wait impatiently to be fed, even taking bread and macaroni.

Like all marine vertebrates, these iguanas have physiological problems to solve. They have nothing at their disposal but sea water and salty seaweeds. The salt concentration in what they eat is such that their kidneys alone could not eliminate it all and an accumulation would rapidly cause serious complications. To prevent this, marine animals must possess a special physical mechanism. Recent experiments conducted on birds as well as the iguana have shown comparatively large glands opening into the nasal fossae. The glandular secretion flows through the ducts and is blown out by the nostrils in little drops loaded with excreted salts.

In spite of their dragon-like aspect, most iguanas are very peaceful. They are content to make threatening or belligerent gestures when a neighbor infringes on their rights. Only in the mating season do the threats lead to anything more serious. A menacing stance, raising the crest, and opening the jaws frighteningly are followed by a clash in which one animal tries to repel the intruder by striking him with his head and tail. The fight resembles a sparring exhibition more than a true battle. Marine iguanas are quite harmless to man; in fact, like many of Galapagos animals, they are not easily frightened and retreat only at the last minute.

Females ready to lay their eggs favor sandy beaches. There they dig a hole with their hind legs, throwing back a great deal of sand. Meanwhile they keep watch to prevent the approach of any other iguana, thus preserving a kind of territory for their offspring. When the hole is big enough, they bury their eggs, which are almost three inches long. The eggs are warmed by the sun in a sort of incubator, and the young are kept humid by water that filters through the sand by means of capillarity.

LAVA DESERTS

When the traveler penetrates into the coastal plains and climbs the first slopes of the mountainous masses, he comes upon a landscape that is stern and dreary but nevertheless gives an impression of wild grandeur: nothing but expanses of cracked lava strewn with cacti and other thorny plants. Probably the traveler has been expecting a luxurious tropical flora; he finds only thick low brushwood and even deserts.

This again can be explained by oceanographic conditions. Just as on the coast of Chile and Peru, where a complex mechanism prevents the condensation of atmospheric humidity, cold marine currents have a great influence on the climate, which is extremely dry. In the lowlands, rain is scarce, although it falls suddenly and abundantly during brief storms, occurring mainly during the period from January through March.

The temperature is comparatively low for equatorial latitudes, the average temperature being about 70° to 80° F. Indeed, the climate is very pleasant and not any hotter than on most of our temperate-zone beaches; nights are cool and as soon as the sun sets one feels the need to put on a light coat. Over the lowlands the sky remains a bright blue for a long time. But several hundred feet up the side of the mountains the sun is hidden by thick fog.

The coastal deserts are characterized above all by gigantic cacti, often growing on completely bare lava expanses. Their roots insinuate themselves into cracks with enough soil and

Land iguanas, which live in the interior areas and are much more aggressive than the marine iguanas, are vegetarians and feed chiefly on cactus. (Tad Nichols)

minerals to maintain a plant. These gigantic cacti, often thirty feet or more in height, belong to two distinct types. One of them, the prickly pear or opuntia, is particularly abundant. Prickly pears have a true trunk, red-brown in color, about eighteen inches in diameter; they thrust out racket-like pads thick with thorns as sharp as needles. These cacti sometimes form veritable forests. But torch cacti are even more abundant. Some are twenty feet high with numerous torch-like branches, each about a dozen inches thick and stretching vertically upward. Other less spectacular plants include low bushes, and occasional shrubby trees whose sparse, dull foliage give the landscape a greenish gray aspect. These concentrations of plants, squeezed beetween the black line of the coast and the dark basalt mountains with their tormented contours, are very characteristic of the Galapagos.

LAND IGUANAS

The thorny brush is the domain of some very strange reptiles. First there is the land iguana *(Conolophus subcristatus),* a distant cousin of the marine iguana, but more massively built and with a shorter tail. Its skin is, moreover, usually brighter, ranging from intense yellow to a slightly reddish brown. The land iguana never comes near the shore and hides at night in a crevice in the rock or a shallow hole that it digs for itself. It lives alone or with a mate, and does not appear to be as peaceful as the marine iguana. In the mating season, males fight ferocious battles. Unlike the other iguanas, whose tails serve as powerful whips, its main weapon is well-developed teeth capable of inflicting a severe bite.

These iguanas are vegetarians, feeding on leaves and twigs, with a predilection for juicy cactus fruit. They do not hesitate to eat large quantities of opuntia leaves, including the sharp thorns, which apparently cause them no discomfort and which pass out unbroken.

They have suffered much at the hands of man and have already disappeared from a great many places where they originally lived.

PEACEFUL GIANTS: LAND TORTOISES

William Dampier, the famous English navigator, relates that when he put in at the Galapagos Islands in 1684, he was impressed by the giant tortoises *(Testudo)* he saw there. "The Spaniards when they first discovered these islands," he writes, "found multitudes of Guanoes (sea birds), and land turtle or tortoise . . . are here so numerous that five or six hundred men might subsist on them for several months without any other sort of provision: they are extraordinarily large and fat, and so sweet that no pullet eats more pleasantly." The unhappy history of these giants, whose shells reach up to five feet and whose weight may exceed five hundred pounds, is made clear in those few lines.

Similar land tortoises—which must not be confused with marine turtles—have been found in fossil form in many places, mainly in Wyoming and Nebraska in the United States, in Europe and in the Siwalik Hills of India. They must have been numerous in the Tertiary era and particularly in the Miocene and Pliocene periods, some six million years ago. During subsequent geological periods, they gradually disappeared, probably because of climatic changes, but also, perhaps, because of competition from certain animals, especially mammals, that were further evolved and better fitted for survival. In our time, these giants can be found only in the Mascarene Islands in the Indian Ocean and in the Galapagos, which thus appear once again as a refuge for animals that have disappeared from every other part of the earth.

Although all the tortoises in the Galapagos have a family resemblance, scientists classify them in about fifteen species. There probably was a time when the Galapagos were a single continental mass, the various islands being united by lands similar to those that still link the Isabela volcanos. The initial stock of giant tortoises that swam across or drifted with ocean currents from the South American continent, spread

Left: A sea-lion keeps vigilant watch high on a rocky ledge. Right: Female sea-lions carefully tend their young. (Both by Rolf Blomberg: Full Hand)

out over the emerged lands. A series of sinkings divided these lands into distinct islands, and the tortoises were separated into isolated groups, each evolving according to its genetic potentialities. Mutations appeared among them, probably varying with the environment. Different species developed that even the older tortoise hunters, whose scientific knowledge was quite primitive, could tell apart. This very interesting evolutionary phenomenon did not escape Charles Darwin's attention, and he derived from it his conclusion concerning specific differentiation from a common stock.

Scientists still do not understand why land tortoises suddenly became sedentary and did not attempt to swim across the channels that separate the islands, when they had succeeded in a longer and much more hazardous crossing from the continent.

These carapace-covered reptiles live in the most varied environments. They are found in the dryest places, especially among cactus and other thorny plants, where they feed on leaves and shoots. But they prefer settling in richer regions, particularly on the slopes exposed to the damp winds of certain islands, Santa Cruz among others. There, amidst a denser vegetation, in the vicinity of temporary ponds or miniature marshes, they find grassy pastures which, according to the most recent observations, are their favorite food. They also find there the water they absolutely require, and they have been seen literally throwing themselves into ponds to drink gluttonously.

Their way of life imposes on them genuine migrations all around the year. Indeed, one cannot but be amazed to see such heavy, clumsy animals engage periodically in long journeys. But they are reputed to travel up to ten miles in two or three days, allowing for repeated stops for grazing. They climb like tanks up slopes covered with fallen rocks, or even up smaller cliffs, making sure with every step that the ground is secure enough. These seasonal moves are conditioned by food requirements, the tortoises looking for places that have remained green in the heart of the long dry season. Their journeys are also determined by the distribution of ponds which seem to have been visited for centuries, as evidenced by the tracks worn into the grounds by generations of tortoises. These regular tracks often offer the only path through a land covered with thorny bushes.

These periodical migrations are also a result of sexual forces. At reproduction time, the tortoises scatter all over the lowlands. The females prefer soft, sandy soil in the warmer, and hence lower, regions in which to lay their eggs, which they then cover with a thin layer of sand. When the ground is rocky, they are content to use fissures in the lava. Each nest usually holds from six to eleven eggs, often in two or three layers isolated by sand or fine gravel. When the reproduction period is over, the tortoises again go back to damper areas.

No sooner are the young out of their shells than they are able to leave their shelter and start on an independent life. In the beginning they grow very fast, their weight increasing almost three times in the first two years. After that, the increase slows down considerably. These tortoises probably reach a very old age, perhaps as much as three hundred or four hundred years. Thus there may be a few that were there in the days of such adventurers as Pizarro and Drake.

Such was the happy life these tortoises lived in the Galapagos, filling the niches that herbivorous mammals occupy elsewhere in the world. They had no natural enemies; diseases, accidents, and old age were most probably the only causes that put an end to their days. Then man appeared! The first visitors were corsairs. They found the tortoise flesh delectable. Dampier testified that no chicken could compete with these reptiles. Captain Colnett tells us that "the fat of these animals when melted down was like fresh butter." In 1813, Captain Porter added that "the meat of this animal is the easiest of digestion and a quantity of it, exceeding that of any other food, can be eaten without experiencing the slightest inconvenience." This accounts for the slaughter of the animals that followed. The crews of the ships would go ashore, feast, and leave only after they had filled the ship's storerooms with tortoises; they found the animals easy to keep, since they can survive for a long time without food.

The fame of the animals became so great that they began to be exploited commercially. Expeditions specially equipped to collect tortoises arrived in the Galapagos. The hunters would disperse over the country, kill the animals and split open the shells with an axe. All that remained was to take out the fat which, when melted, yielded a choice oil. A good-size tortoise gave from one to three gallons, younger adults yielding the most. Their flesh, too, was very much appreciated.

According to logbooks discovered in archives, 105 American ships made away with fifteen thousand tortoises between 1811 and 1844, but this is only a small part of the total killed. It is estimated that the United States alone sent out seven hundred expeditions to the islands during this period; ships from other countries also took part in the hunt.

Another kind of destruction resulted from the expeditions. As in many other areas, the navigators brought with them goats, which can survive in arid areas and live on scrawny vegetation. Multiplying in the wilderness without man's help, they were supposed to provide the ships stopping in the Galapagos with fresh meat. This acclimatization proved so successful that the goats became an evil, devastating the vegetation, devouring every young shoot in sight. They thus compete with the tortoises, who, not being able to move about so quickly, are literally famished. This development gives us a glimpse of what probably happened when, in the course of evolution, reptiles receded with the advent of mammals.

At about the same time, man brought along rats, dogs, cats, pigs, and oxen, each one adding to the damage done by goats and slowly building up a community tending to displace the indigenous species. Pigs and dogs proved particularly harmful, digging up tortoise nests, eating the eggs, and killing the young ones. It is estimated that only one egg in ten thousand produces a tortoise that reaches a length of one foot, that is, large enough to fend off assailants. Then the tortoise must begin competing with goats and, even worse, becomes of interest to man. For all these reasons, land tortoises are among the most threatened animals in the Galapagos.

Several species have been entirely exterminated on Floreana (Charles), Santa Fé (Barrington) and Rabida (Jervis). Elsewhere they have become very rare and they are still plentiful only on Santa Cruz and Isabela.

Giant tortoises are so characteristic of the Galapagos that their Spanish name was bestowed on the islands themselves. (Rolf Blomberg: Full Hand)

The waved albatross (Diomedea irrorata) *is native to the Galapagos, with the only known colony located on Hood Island. It nests amid stunted bushes. (J. Bryan Nelson)*

There is still much to be discovered concerning the habits of these giant reptiles, if only to protect them efficiently from man's direct and indirect impact. With this object, the Charles Darwin Research Station was established a few years ago on the coast of Santa Cruz under the control of an international foundation, to study the tortoises. First they had to be counted, then marked, so that their movements could be followed. After unsuccessfully trying to use numbers painted on the shells of the animals, biologists now cut marks into the edge of the carapace. If the animal is over a foot in length, this is absolutely harmless. Thanks to this marking, much information has been gathered; in one or two centuries scientists working in the Galapagos laboratory will be able to determine, for example, whether the giant tortoise really live as long as has been believed.

LIVING PROOF OF EVOLUTION: DARWIN'S FINCHES

Should the visitor land on any one of the islands of the archipelago, he would soon come upon an array of tiny passerines darting about on the ground or in the branches and uttering shrill cries. They are comparable in size and color to sparrows although in some the gray of the plumage is more accentuated, while others are completely black. With these modest characteristics, they could easily pass unnoticed if there were any more colorful birds on the islands. But let us not make the error that Captain Colnett made when in the 1790's he declared: "This island contains no great number or variety of land birds, and those I saw were not remarkable for their novelty or beauty." This observer simply overlooked a discovery that was to shed the greatest light on the theories of evolution.

It was not until 1835 that Charles Darwin landed in the Galapagos. He returned to Europe with a variety of specimens, and an extensive study of these was made by the great British ornithologist, John Gould. This study revealed types of birds of a group thitherto unknown, enabling Darwin to deduce valuable arguments in favor of his theories on the origin of species. Significant is a statement found in the second edition of his *Journal,* published in 1845: "Seeing this gradation and diversity of structure in one small, intimately related group of birds, one might really fancy that from an original paucity of birds in that archipelago one species had been taken and modified for different ends." Indeed, the fifteen species of Darwin's finches, differing mainly in the form and strength of the beak, are so similar that the distinctions made between them seem almost arbitrary. They are more like a continuous series, each having adapted to a slightly different mode of life, simulating, as it were, the whole range of songbirds throughout the world.

Let us imagine a virgin land, covered with vegetation and sheltering different kinds of insects, and that pure chance brings a single stock of birds; they begin to proliferate and soon penetrate the entire territory. Suppose that the birds in question are grain-eating; in a short while their population will have attained a point at which grain becomes scarce. Far from being a stable entity, however, a species may vary within certain limits; mutations may occur that reveal new characteristics or emphasize certain traits already present. As a result, the birds may be able to exploit a new range of food resources: they may develop a thick beak and begin to eat fruit, or a sharp-pointed beak suitable for eating insects, or a more powerful beak that enables them to crack larger and tougher grains. After many generations, a variety of species will arise from the one stock. The bird population will function as a community in which each element exploits one particular portion of the total food resources. Differentiation of the species would thus have been achieved through population pressure as well as natural selection.

A hypothesis of this nature, however, must be supported by objective proof. Needless to say, it would be extremely difficult to establish any evidence amidst the birdlife on the vast continental landmasses: evolution there is far too ancient and the first ancestors too numerous. For this reason, Darwin's finches furnish a model of diversification and permit the study of various species almost in their "native" state. As Charles Darwin pointed out: "In that little world within itself, or rather that satellite attached to America, both in space and time, we seem to be brought somewhat near to that great feat—that mystery of mysteries—the first appearance of new beings on this earth."

Right above: During the breeding period, male frigate birds display an immense, brightly-colored sac that hangs from the throat and plays a part in the courting. (Rolf Blomberg: Full Hand) Right: The Galapagos dove, still abundant on some of the isles, is the most familiar bird in the entire archipelago. Far right: The blue-footed booby, one of three species of boobies found on the Galapagos, displays its bright blue feet to the female during courting. (Both by Tad Nichols)

Simply by making a tour through the bush of the Galapagos we are thus able to reconstruct the way Darwin's finches must have evolved. In the lowlands, we find the small ground finch *(Geospiza fuliginosa)* with a beak only slightly developed, like that of a sparrow. He feeds almost exclusively on tiny grains found on the ground or in the vegetation, avoiding, because of his relatively weak beak, larger grains. On the other hand, the medium ground finch *(G. fortis)* and especially the large ground finch *(G. magnirostris)*, with a large beak recalling that of a grosbeak, can choose and husk grains of much greater size. There is thus little or no competition between these birds.

Although the plumage of the cactus ground finch *(G. scandens)* is similar to that of the species mentioned above, the bird is in other ways even further differentiated from the others. Nature has provided it with a robust beak, but elongated and rather downcurved at the tip so that it is well equipped to feed on pollen and nectar found chiefly in the blossoms of the opuntia. Even more, he is equipped with a tongue that is split at the tip, like that of such other nectar-drinking birds as certain honey-eaters of Australia or the flowerpeckers of the Far East. He is as much at home in tearing the tender fleshy leaves of the opuntia as in pillaging the fruit of such introduced trees as the orange and the plum.

The tree finch *(Camarhynchus crassirostris)* with a greenish plumage, hooded with black in the male and striated in the female, is equipped with a short, thick beak—a miniature version of that of a parrot. Since he makes his home in trees, he feeds principally on tender leaf buds, flowers, and fruit. He disdains insects, except on rare occasions, as well as grains, for which his beak would hardly be adapted.

The so-called insectivorous tree finches *(C. psittacula, pauper, parvulus)*, on the other hand, have a similar beak and yet feed exclusively upon insects. Their habits are similar to those of our titmouse—flitting about trees and bushes in quest of insects hidden in the foliage. In this case the differentiation is not in form but in habits.

Thus Darwin's finches constitute a community of terrestrial birds such as one might find in an entire country. Within the family can be found the equivalent of sparrows and other grain-eating birds, as well as fruit-eating birds, the titmouse and the grosbeak. This astonishing bird community even includes a type that one might name "woodpecker finch" *(Camarhynchus pallidus)*. In the course of its evolution it developed a strong, straight beak, somewhat elongated and resembling that of a woodpecker or a nuthatch. Such a beak is still too short to enable it to feed, like a woodpecker, on insects beneath bark, or grubs sheltering in wood. But it compensates by going to a cactus and plucking off a thorn, which it then trims down to size. With this miniature fork it explores all the crannies in bark or wood. When it finally makes a find it uses the thorn to dig it out, just as the Frenchman uses a tiny fork on a dish of snails. As soon as its prey appears, it puts down the thorn and quickly swallows the morsel. It then picks up the thorn and resumes its patient exploration. This astonishing behavior is one of the most elaborate known among animals. No other birds make use of any kind of tool and we would have to go up the phyletic tree of the animal kingdom as far as the chimpanzee to find an example of the regular use of a tool.

One of the most impressive examples of evolution among these birds is the warbler finch *(Certhidea olivacea)*. This bird is strikingly similar to the true warbler; in fact, ornithologists first classified it as a warbler, refusing to believe that a bird could be so like a warbler in size, proportions, color and shape of beak without belonging to the same family. Yet there is no doubt that it is a highly evolved Darwin's finch. Like the flycatcher, it feeds exclusively on insects in the foliage, branches or even on the ground, and pounces on them in flight.

Such then is the curious world of the Darwin's finches. This small family of birds, peculiar to the Galapagos and evolving there in total isolation, has by itself given rise to various passerines belonging to separate families and only remotely related to each other. It is thus easy to understand the importance of these creatures as evidence for Darwin's theories. The fact that birds springing from the same initial stock could become so diversified is due to the effects of population pressure; in other words, the struggle for life forced them to adapt to new ways of life, and especially to modify their diet. An additional factor in their success was the lack of competition from other birds already adapted to the modes of existence hit upon by Darwin's finches. In this sense the Galapagos are like a controlled experiment where differentiation has taken place under such clear-cut conditions that biologists are able to trace the process of evolution without too much of a leap from fact to hypothesis.

FERTILE HEIGHTS

Although intense aridity prevails in the more low-lying islands of the Galapagos, the higher islands, particularly San Cristobal and Santa Cruz, lie athwart southeasterly winds and consequently enjoy a moister climate. During the rainy season the rainfall is greater there, and for the rest of the year mists similar to the *garuas* of the Peruvian coast counteract the dryness. There is thus a striking contrast between the meager vegation of the dry coastal zones and the dense growth on the heights.

Such a contrast can be noted at Santa Cruz by taking the route leading from Academy Bay to the summit at an altitude of 2,665 feet. The traveler first passes through stretches of bare lava and then comes upon growths of cactus and thorny plants sprouting either among the rocks or from the poor soil. With altitude, the vegetation becomes denser and the expanse of dry brush is broken by occasional spots of deep green. This soon gives way to lush forest. Here the trees are mainly endemic with a characteristic umbrella or bouquet shape, some of them reaching a height of sixty feet. The thick underbrush is laden with shrubs and a host of ferns. Clinging to the trunks and branches are epiphytes: enormous lichens, ferns, and orchids trailing like beards in the misty breeze. Creeping plants entwine everywhere. This mass of drenched vegetation creates a true rain forest—only several miles from the barren coasts and in some places only five hundred feet above sea level. The explanation is simply that the moisture carried by the prevailing winds does not condense at the lower levels but is reserved for these higher slopes.

The highest areas in the Galapagos Islands, such as those on Santa Cruz, shown here, are covered with a dense forest maintained by the fogs and abundant rainfall. (Tad Nichols)

The mockingbird (Nesomimus melanotis) *frequents the lower parts of the Galapagos, particularly around cactus stands. Variant forms of this bird from one island to the next have given zoologists insights into the evolution of species. (Jean Dorst)*

The humidity has at the same time broken down the rocky masses and transformed them into a quite fertile soil. Soil experts have found that the dark soil originating in the basalt can be as much as six feet in depth. These elevated zones are thus the only areas where cultivation is possible and in several places the land has been cleared for plantations, often very successfully. There is a wide range of cultivated plants and it is not unusual to find potatoes, a crop characteristic of more temperate countries, growing beneath banana trees and not far from thriving coffee shrubs. Such cultivated areas, however, are extremely limited, and the islands can scarcely be thought of as agriculturally attractive.

At higher points the forest gives way to prairies of grasses where trees and even bushes are rare, perhaps because of the strong winds. Once the traveler passes the ridge and begins to descend toward the north and northwest, he finds himself again in arid territory since these slopes are not exposed to wind and moisture.

THE FUTURE OF THE GALAPAGOS

On the whole the Galapagos Islands are quite desolate and barren. Except for a few verdant zones, the terrain bears the imprint of its volcanic origins—a great uprush of smoldering lava from the depths of the Pacific. At a time when it was perhaps easier to cross the seas from the continental land-mass, a scattering of plants and animals gradually came to inhabit the rocky masses through the ages. Sheltered from the rest of the world, strange biological communities were able to develop, with archaic creatures able to persist and thrive to the present day. Other species were engendered according to the immutable laws of evolution and in isolation from the complexities of the outside world. The Galapagos are thus unique, furnishing a kind of condensed version of phenomena that normally occur on a much vaster scale. The geologist can observe all the stages, from rocks as they are when they first emerge from the depths of the earth's crust, to arable soil. At the same time the biologist can witness the genesis of species, some even at that point where they have not yet evolved into distinctly different forms.

Much remains to be learned from the Galapagos. We are still living on the legacy left by Charles Darwin. However, men on the islands have committed a long series of depredations. When the British ornithologist David Lack called human history in the Galapagos "a tale of disaster, tempered by squalid crime," he was not too far from the truth. During the eighteenth century, pirates took over the role of the earlier privateers. Later on, efforts at land improvement were made. But they were initiated by overly idealistic men who too often recruited the settlers from prisoners or mutineers. At about this time expeditions arrived to exploit and massacre the tortoises and fur seals. Vandalism accomplished the rest. The settlers of today are honest and hard-working but unfortunately unsophisticated in conservation and enlightened methods of cultivation. The prolonged impact of unscrupulous visitors has cruelly affected the wildlife, and it continues to be menaced by introduced species.

Man's influence on the fauna is all the more tragic here because most of the creatures exhibit a remarkable confidence in human beings, either ignoring their presence or regarding them as neutral. The notion of predator just doesn't seem to exist in the Galapagos. Paradoxically, the only "wild" animals on the islands are the descendants of introduced domestic species, particularly goats. But it is not rare to see an indigenous dove come to perch upon a resting traveler, and buzzards, the only indigenous birds of prey, can practically be petted. The same is true of the sea birds. Unfortunately, this exaggerated confidence has only led to the destruction of many of them.

The woodpecker finch, most remarkable of all Darwin's finches, feeds on insect larvae in wood, but since its beak is short and it lacks a protractile tongue, it uses a cactus thorn skillfully manipulated with the beak, the only known use of a tool by a bird. (I. Eibl-Eibesfeldt)

Man has fortunately realized how much could be lost in the realm of scientific discovery should the natural populations of the Galapagos disappear. Responsible officials of the Republic of Equador, to which the islands belong, have taken effective conservation measures. Some day, biologists visiting these rocky islands may discover among its creatures a key to some of the secrets of the history of life. They will still be watched over by giant, submissive reptiles—the last representatives of a world that flourished long before man appeared on earth.

Glaciers, Lakes and Dismal Straits

Patagonia and Tierra del Fuego

15

The air traveler flying south from northern Chile passes over miles and miles of great deserts. Then at about 30° Lat. S., the landscape gradually changes. From the valley of Coquimbo to the valley of the Rio Aconcagua there is a long transitional zone where the annual rainfall increases progressively. Bordered on the east by the Andes, this zone is crossed by a series of mountain torrents that dry up in summer and expose river beds that give the countryside a tormented look.

The first coastal forests appear between 30° an 31° Lat. S., on the banks of the Rio Limari, where they cluster at the bottom of the valleys, while the plateaus are covered with a brush in which thorny plants and cactus predominate. This transition zone heralds central Chile, particularly its plain, the true cradle of the Chilean nation. Chile is indeed a strange country, geographically speaking. The upthrust of the Andes down the whole of South America has isolated a narrow strip of land between the mountains and the Pacific. Chile achieved its unity as a nation by staying within the cordillera to the east, but extending itself to the north and south. With an average width of one hundred miles, this country stretches over about forty degrees of latitude and has a coastline 2,900 miles long. This explains the great variety of its natural habitats, one extremity having hot deserts while the other has a polar climate.

The heart of Chile, its central plain, is a north-south depression between the Andes and a low coastal range extending from Santiago to the Ancud Gulf. These coastal hills, with their rounded forms and wide valleys are very different from the Andes with its steep slopes and deep valleys.

At its northern end the plain is bounded on the east by some of the highest peaks in all South America. For example, the Argentine peak of Aconcagua, near the Chilean border, attains a height of 22,835 feet making it the highest mountain in the Western Hemisphere. The level of eternal snows lowers rapidly and the altitude of the entire range decreases as one goes south. In addition, as one travels south from Santiago, volcanos appear again atop the cordillera—Manipo, Overo, Tinguiririca among others. Farther south, the volcanos are markedly toward the west—for example, the famous Osorno—almost forming a second chain of snowy cones overlooking the plain and overshadowing the cordillera.

Between these two mountain systems extends the central plain, irregular and narrow toward the north and in the south but with a width of from thirty to forty miles in its medial portion. The climate of this part of Chile is remarkably temperate. Toward the south the average rainfall increases and the average temperature is lower. Moderate temperatures are notably constant on the coast.

Humidity due to rainfall has allowed a dense vegetation of a Mediterranean type to flourish in central Chile. Where the plain has not been transformed by agriculture and is not too fertile, it is covered with acacias and other shrubs. The western slopes of the Andes have a poor growth of bush, more or less drought-resistant xerophytes extending as far north as Santiago and up to an altitude of about 6,500 feet. At 34° S. we come upon the first false beech trees *(Nothofagus obliqua),* with deciduous leaves somewhat resembling those of oaks, and a little farther south, toward the Rio Maule, the evergreen *Nothofagus dombeyi* and the *Libocedrus chilensis.* These forests become more extensive as one goes south, heralding the magnificent forests of the Valdivian region and Patagonia.

Because of central Chile's delightful temperate climate, much of the population is concentrated there, mainly between the Rio Aconcagua and the Rio Bío Bío, and not only in the central plain but in the mountains to the west.

We must not forget the role played by vineyards in the Chilean economy. Grapevines imported from France and North America cover a vast area north of Rio Bío Bío, where the climate is favorable in spite of the dry summer and the frequent fogs caused by the *terral,* the cold wind that blows down the Andean valleys at night.

JUAN FERNANDEZ—CRUSOE'S ISLANDS

There are two reasons why we take space to describe the Juan Fernandez Islands of the coast of central Chile: they are of special interest biologically and they were the locale of the events which inspired Daniel Defoe's immortal *Robinson Crusoe.*

". . . There was a hill not above a mile from me which rose up very steep and high . . . I travelled to the top of that hill and saw . . . that I was in an island environed on every side by the sea: no land to be seen except some rocks . . . and two small islands . . . which lay about three leagues to the west . . ."

Thus Robinson Crusoe described the desert island where he spent so many years. It is well known that Defoe took his inspiration from the journal of a Scottish sailor, Alexander Selkirk, who quarreled with the captain of his ship, was put ashore on the Juan Fernandez Islands in September, 1704, and lived there for four years and four months before being rescued. The event would surely have sunk into oblivion had not Defoe immortalized it in *Robinson Crusoe.* Both the true and fictional heroes are commemorated in the names of several plants, such as the Borraginaceae known as *Selkirkia* or the Compositae called *Robinsonia.*

Large stretches of the coast of central Chile consist of rocky cliffs. (Samuel Rojas Garrau)

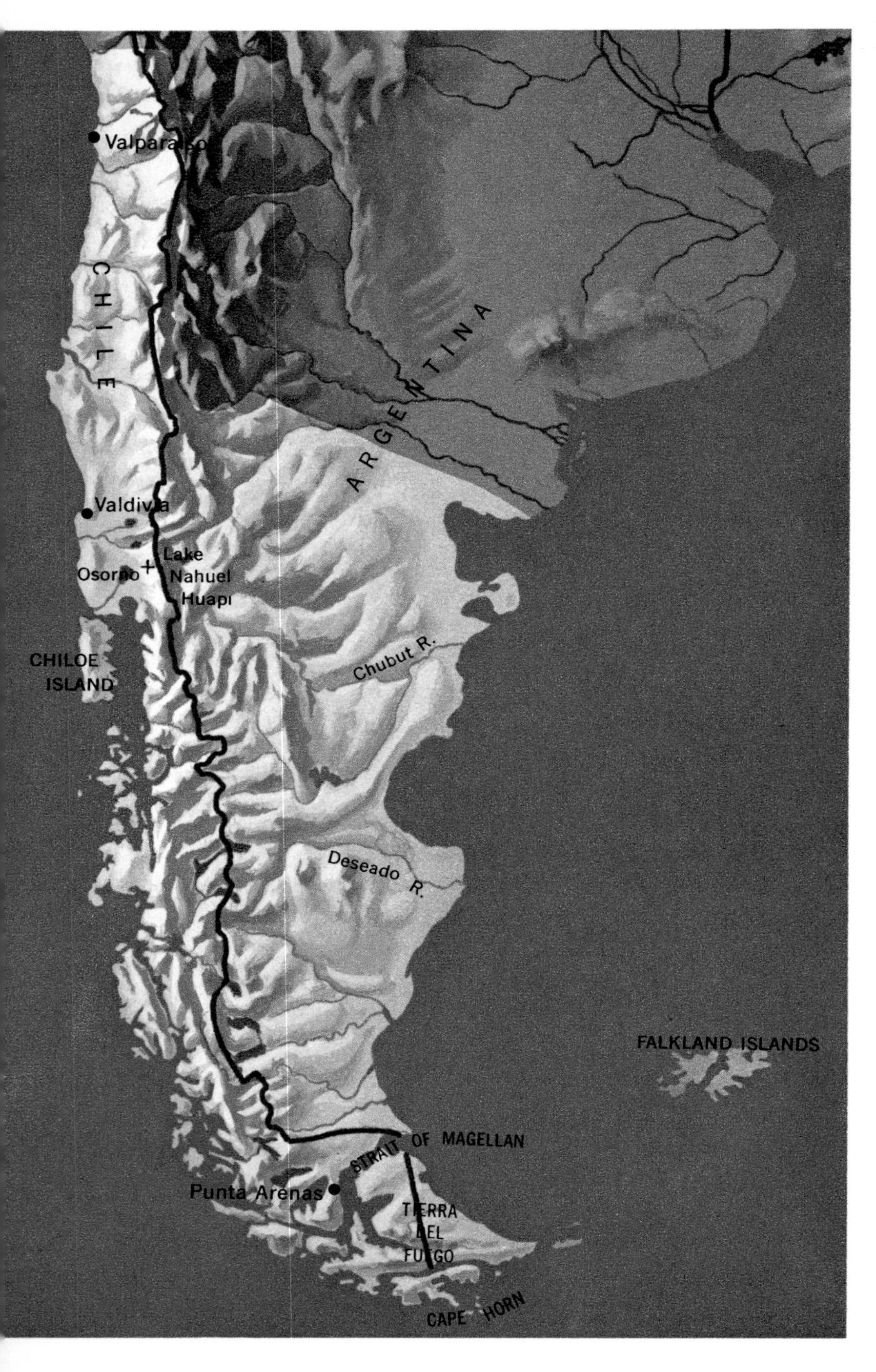

Patagonia is a land of contrasts—with a jagged, mountainous coastline penetrated by innumerable arms of the sea in the west and vast tablelands in the east.

The Juan Fernandez Islands, a dependency of Chile, are in the Pacific Ocean to the west and slightly to the south of Valparaiso. The more easterly island, Más Atierra, is 417 miles west of the continent while Más Afuera is one hundred miles farther west. The first island is thirty-six square miles and its highest point is 3,002 feet above sea level. The second is smaller but higher, rising to 6,024 feet. Both islands are volcanic in origin but show no signs of activity. Like the Galapagos, they have never been attached to the continent.

Más Atierra forms a jagged mass, the crest of a suboceanic mountain of great height. The parts not covered by forest consist of hundreds of layers of lava flows. While Más Afuera is also made up of lava flows, streams flowing mainly northeastward have hollowed out canyons, and the summits of the island form more or less level tableland.

The climate of the Juan Fernandez Islands is milder and more humid than that of the Chilean coast and is fundamentally a subtropical oceanic climate with winter rains. Instead of being subjected to the cold currents of the continental coast, the islands are bathed by the warm waters of the Mentor current. Properly speaking, there is no dry season, and frost is unknown here.

The flora of these islands is relatively poor but is nonetheless of great interest because of its many endemic species and its diversity. There are only 143 plants here but 98 of them are native. Botanists have been struck by certain isolated types, some of them having no precise relation to others elsewhere, while some are related to plants of New Zealand, the South Sea islands, and Hawaii. As might be expected, the most evident affinities are with Chilean flora, although the species are often different. Many species are rare and some are known only from specimens in a herbarium.

The most interesting vegetation on Más Atierra is an evergreen subtropical-temperate forest made up mainly of *Myrceugenia fernandeziana* along with *Faqara mayu,* the tallest tree of the islands, growing to a height of over sixty feet, the canelo or cinnamon tree *(Drimys winteri),* and a few other species. Woody lianas are absent, but the many ferns—including tree ferns—the mosses and liverwort, and epiphytes give this vegetation a tropical aspect. The undergrowth is dense and the ground is littered with rotting tree trunks and branches. Once there were many sandalwood trees *(Santalum fernandezianum),* a precious endemic tree long ago ruthlessly exploited by man. Elsewhere a grassy heath intermingled with bushes extends over the unwooded portions of western Más Atierra and all the lower portions of Más Afuera. This formation now prevails in deforested areas.

The vegetation of the Juan Fernandez Islands thus has a double interest for botanists: The high proportion of local plants is that of a refuge zone protected from the evolution that has taken place on the continent. And the juxtaposition of a subtropical flora and an antarctic flora, depending on altitude, makes this a meeting place of elements from everywhere.

Because they are isolated islands, their animal life is scarce and includes a large proportion of local elements. Most of the species are of course related to South American fauna. The Juan Fernandez Islands have no reptiles, a very important difference from the Galapagos, where these vertebrates are predominant. Mammals are likewise absent; a fur seal, Philippi's seal *(Arctocephalus ph. philippii),* is now extinct. The British explorer, William Dampier, who visited these islands in 1683, said of these seals that "there is not a bay or rock that one can get ashore on that is not full of them." The seal population was at that time estimated at two or three millions, but man, urged by avarice, massacred them without restraint. In a period of seven years, toward the end of the

The southernmost representative of the palm family, Jubaea spectabilis, *is found in the temperate climate of central Chile. (E. Aubert de la Rüe)*

eighteenth century, no less than three million skins were collected, and by 1807 "the business was scarcely worth following." In 1891 it was estimated that there remained about four hundred seals. Only a related subspecies, the Guadalupe fur seal *(A. ph. townsendi)*, still maintains itself in small numbers on Guadalupe Island, off Baja California.

Among the birds there are only eight land species. One of them, *Thaumaste fernandensis*, is endemic and is found especially in the forests, where it builds its nest among the ferns. The other birds are all sea birds, and are a singular mixture of subantarctic and subtropical forms, reflecting the dual climate of the islands. However, none of the species characteristic of the cold Humboldt Current of the South American coast is present, another example of the difference between the islands and the continent.

RAPE OF RESOURCES

About 1624, it was discovered that precious sandalwood abounded on the islands, and an intensive exploitation of this tree was soon under way. By the middle of the eighteenth century the industry had exhausted its resources, and by 1800 the tree was virtually extinct. The Spaniards who fortified Más Atierra in the eighteenth century, and the American whalers who replenished their ships with wood and water there in the nineteenth century both contributed to the destruction of the forests. The goats did the rest, along with the colonists and the convicts who tried to put the islands under agriculture. The resources of the sea did not escape. We have already described the slaughter of the fur seals. Besides this, there was an intensive exploitation of lobsters *(Jasius lalandei)* and fish, especially the codfish *(Polyprion prognatus)*. Formerly the waters swarmed with lobsters and a fisherman could catch as many as he liked in one or two feet of water. Now it is necessary to go out to water more than one hundred feet deep.

In 1935 the Juan Fernandez Islands were decreed a national park. Unfortunately, this decree has never been adequately carried out.

GRANDEUR AND DESOLATION

To the south of the transitional region of central Chile lies the cold and humid region of Patagonia. In his famous journal of the voyage of the *Beagle*, Charles Darwin declared that this country in no way resembled any he had ever seen before. This impression is fully justified; in no other place is there such a combination of grandeur and desolation. The names given to places here by the first voyagers—Island of Desolation, Anxious Point, East and West Furies, Deceit Island, Useless Bay, Port Famine—suggest "the end of the world." Here land and water are fantastically mingled in thousands of islands of every size. Gigantic glaciers fall into the sea, dense fogs obscure the sky, thick black clouds discharge rain, snow, and storms. From time to time the clouds move away from mountain peaks of unsuspected height, revealing them covered with sparkling ice or with cascades falling in silvery streaks.

Patagonia thus resembles the upper Pacific coast of North America. The humid, wooded districts of the north are like the coasts of Oregon and Washington, and some travelers have compared Chiloe Island to Vancouver Island. As for southern Patagonia, the parallels between it and Alaska are striking: it is as though nature has repeated itself slightly at each end of the Americas.

This region is still not well known in spite of the many scientific expeditions that have covered it. Moreover, except for a few small coastal settlements, Patagonia was peopled only with wild Indians until about 1850. Yet one of the busiest sea routes in the world once passed nearby. The oldtime sailing ships, rounding the Horn on the western wind, used the passage discovered by Magellan and named Cape Horn in 1616 by a Dutch navigator after his native town, Hoorn. This cape is considered the southern tip of the continent although the Diego Ramirez Islands, sixty miles to the southwest, are slightly farther south. Nowadays motorized ships use the Strait of Magellan, a route sheltered from the gigantic waves of the Pacific.

The complex topography of this region of wild grandeur has still not been completely mapped, and even today we must depend for descriptions upon early voyagers. Toward the middle of the eighteenth century, John ("Mad Jack") Byron, British admiral and grandfather of the poet, was shipwrecked on the coast of the Guayaneco Islands south of the Gulf de Penas. Describing his adventures in *Narrative* (1768), he wrote: "The country hereabout wears the most uncouth, desolate and rugged aspect imaginable; it is so circumstanced as to discourage the most sanguine adventurers from attempts to settle it; were it for no other reason than the constant heavy rains, or rather torrents which pour down here, and the vast sea and surf which the prevailing westerly winds impel upon this coast, it must be rendered inhospitable. All entrance into the woods is not only extremely difficult, but hazardous; not from any assaults you are likely to meet with from wild beasts; for even these could hardly find convenient harbour here; but from the deep swamp, which is the reigning soil of this country and in which the woods may be said rather to float than grow; so that except upon a range of deformed broken rocks which form the sea-coast, the traveller cannot find sound footing anywhere." The description is just as valid today.

Despite its desolate character, Patagonia is of great interest to naturalists. A glance at a world map shows that the area thrusts farther south than any other in the South Temperate Zone, including even New Zealand. Besides this, Patagonia shows some striking peculiarities and some strange affinities with other southerly regions of the Southern Hemisphere. This is particularly true of its forests of *Nothofagus*, a timber tree of the birch type, which is as common in this region as it is in far-off New Zealand. This coincidence is best explained by the theory that there was an antarctic continent that sank ages ago beneath the Pacific. From the beginning of the Tertiary to the Eocene and Oligocene, Patagonia, Antarctica and New Zealand were all part of this vast landmass. This allowed the distribution of certain vegetation as far apart as the Patagonian Andes and the New Zealand Alps.

The southern portion of South America consists in reality of two distinct environments: the one Pacific, the other Atlantic.

Lake Todos los Santos, Chile, is rimmed with austral, or southern, forest. (Peter Krauer)

The western sector, Andean in type, is mountainous, broken and very humid; the mountain chain splits into steep-sided islands between which flow narrow arms of the sea. Here is the realm of the forest. The eastern sector, a continuation of the Argentine pampas, comprises vast plateaus covered with herbaceous steppe vegetation, corresponding to the dry and sometimes arid climate. The contrast between the two sides of the continent is often visible within short distances—a juxtaposition of two worlds that have only a few points in common.

WHERE THE ANDES SINK INTO THE SEA

Extending 1,150 miles from north to south, the western or Chilean portion of Patagonia is of a complexity unequaled on the rest of the continent. In fact, this sector is comprised of two parts—the one insular, formed by a string of islands beginning with Chiloe Island in the north and ending at Tierra del Fuego. The other part, occupied by the Andes, is continental. These two parts overlap in a most bewildering way, for the coast of the continent is itself extraordinarily indented and embraces an infinity of islands separated by a maze of channels.

On the continent the Andean Cordillera is divided by several depressions into a series of mountains. Farther south, between 52° and 54° Lat. S., the height drops, then rises again at Tierra del Fuego. Active volcanos—Hornopiren, Corcovado, Maca—line the coast, overlooking the entrance to the fjords. Here fire has a tryst with both sea and ice, making this one of the most astounding landscapes in the world.

The Andes of Patagonia have also been profoundly carved by glaciers. In the wake of these glaciers, lakes have formed, the largest of which (such as Buenos Aires and Argentino) are five or even ten times the size of the great Alpine lakes. In form they are long, like similar lakes in the Italian Alps, and extend eastward, following large valleys.

On the whole, the topography of this region is exceedingly complex. A part of the cordillera has sunk beneath the sea and the waters have penetrated everywhere and formed innumerable islands outlined by cliffs and steep slopes. Frank Chapman declared that a voyage through the Smyth, Sarmiento, and Darwin channels was in reality "a voyage through the Andes." It would be hard to find a more vivid and accurate discription.

GLACIERS AND RAINS

The profusion of glaciers in this region surprises every traveler. Darwin describes his amazement when, at a latitude in the Southern Hemisphere corresponding in the Northern Hemisphere to that of Cumberland in the British Isles, he saw that every valley in a chain of mountains with summits no higher than 4,000 or 5,000 feet was filled with rivers of ice flowing down to the coast.

The climate, on the whole, is colder but varies less than

At high altitudes, the Andes of Chile and Argentina are barren mountains stripped of all vegetation. (Weldon King)

An unusual feature of Darwin's frog is the long nasal appendage. The male shelters the young tadpoles in its cheek pouches until they are fully developed. (A.Y. Owen: Life Magazine © Time Inc.)

that of comparable latitudes in the Northern Hemisphere. It is never warm here, but the winters are much less severe than, for example, in Labrador, which is in a similar latitude north of the Equator. There is less snow, and freezing is never intense or of long duration. Thus the presence of major glaciers must be less the result of severe winters than of cold and cloudy summers during which snow and ice do not melt.

Surprisingly, there are greater thermal differences from west to east than from north to south, in spite of the great north-south extent of Patagonia. The zone of the islands and canals has a relatively uniform climate throughout the year. The eastern part, notably the Andean range, has a climate of much greater contrasts, the summers being rather warm, the winters much more severe.

The differences in rainfall between the coast and the continental range are still more marked, and it is in fact this that determines the differences in climate. The coast is one of the most heavily watered regions in the world. The meteorological station at Guarella, on the Madre de Dios islands off the

Chilean coast at 50° Lat. S., registers rainfall ranging from 240 to 360 inches annually, while at 53° S. Punta Arena, sheltered from the influence of the ocean, has an average of 24 inches of rain per year.

Heavy precipitation, low temperatures, little evaporation and feeble sunlight explain the abundance of ice. Although the Andean glaciers, like all glaciers, are receding sharply, they still occupy about 1,900 square miles. Some constitute the ice-cap, which has long terminal tongues submerged in the lakes along the frontier between Chile and Argentina. This ice-cap is in places twenty miles wide and extends more than 750 miles between Rio Aysen and the Darwin Cordillera south of Tierra del Fuego.

CHILOE ISLAND

In spite of a fundamental uniformity in the region, we cannot expect to find the same flora and fauna in areas separated by twelve degrees of latitude.

Chiloe Island, with an area of 3,230 square miles and extending 110 miles in the vicinity of 42° Lat. S., is characteristic of what biogeographers call the Valdivian province. It is relatively flat, although actually an insularized segment of the coastal mountains. The straits that isolate it from the mainland are shallow, the coasts dropping gently to the sea. Since the tides reach a height of twenty feet or more, they uncover immense mudbanks at low tide, creating conditions very favorable to the marine life that flourishes on the mud and in the beds of seaweed. Among the birds that find this a paradise, the waders are particularly abundant, especially those that come here during the North American winter. Travelers have described, for example, a horde of sanderlings made up of five thousand individuals. No less than twenty-nine species of water fowl native to North America have been seen along the coasts of Chiloe, a fact all the more interesting since few North American migrants frequent South America.

Inland on Chiloe we are in the realm of the Chilean rain forest, which, thanks to heavy rains, is one of the densest in the world. The false beech is the characteristic tree of these woods, which include species typical of the South Temperate Zone, some evergreen, others deciduous. The leafy trees are mingled with various conifers, notably the larch, *Fitzroya patagonica,* some specimens of which are more than two thousand years old and attain a height of 180 feet and a diameter of more then fifteen feet. There is a dense understory of shrubs, lianas, ferns and mosses, and the trees themselves are covered with epiphytes and parasitic plants. Dense stands of bamboo *(Chusquea)* occur at intervals.

In places the ground is covered to a depth of several yards with rotting tree trunks and detritus, so that one can walk long distances without, properly speaking, setting foot on the ground. The ground beneath this mould is so muddy that several of the early explorers sank in it and were suffocated.

The forests of northern Patagonia thus constitute an environment almost tropical in the richness of vegetation and the abundance of ferns, bamboos and epiphytes. Yet overlooking this vegetation are the snowy summits of the nearby cordillera, and through the trees one can catch glimpses of a cold and turbulent sea.

On the northernmost frontier of Patagonia, Chiloe Island has long been populated by man. The eastern coast, sheltered from the wind, has been cleared and farms have been established. This area, including its villages, reminds one of parts of New England. Although wheat must be harvested before it ripens because the summer temperatures are too low for this grain, snow and sharp freezes are exceptional, and the overall climate is favorable for agriculture. Stock-raising and market gardening, along with the exploitation of marine resources, could make this island a rich source of central Chile's increasing food needs.

DIMINISHING FORESTS

The forest we described on the island of Chiloe is of a type called Valdivian and is found, with variations, as far as 43° Lat. S. There the climate is drier and the forest is dominated by that unique conifer, araucaria. As we go farther south, the forest area diminishes, and slopes exposed to the western winds have no forest cover whatever. The *Nothofagus* forest takes shelter in nooks and crannies. In the southern part of Magellanes province, it consists of twisted, creeping trees merging with a kind of heath. The pampas intrudes on the Chilean portion of Patagonia and takes over almost entirely from the Cordillera de Paine to Punta Arenas.

The species of trees likewise change as one goes from north to south. The coihue *(Nothofagus dombeyi),* with evergreen leaves, gives way to species that are deciduous, for example the nirre *(N. pumilio)* and the rauli *(N. procera)*. The underbrush disappears, especially the bamboos, toward 49° Lat. S. Omitting the thickets of stunted and twisted trees and considering mainly the true forest, that of the *Nothofagus,* woodland doubtless covers no more than 22,800 to 30,400 square miles or less than one third of Chilean Patagonia. Man has, moreover, cut into the forest areas. Burning of forests to convert them into pastures increases from year to year. Immense forest fires occur throughout Patagonia every summer, even in the most humid districts, as on the island of Chiloe. Aubert de la Rüe estimates at 600,000,000 Chilean pesos the loss in timber and cattle caused by fire in 1958 in Magellanes province alone. Such lands are thereafter subject to serious erosion, and the rains cause continual landslides. In addition the materials carried off will cause huge sand banks downstream, obstructing the rivers and preventing large vessels from entering Puerto Aisen. A strict forestry program should be set up to save the natural wealth of the region, for valuable timber is being wasted without assurance that the cleared land will be put to satisfactory agricultural use. And with the disappearance of the forest will vanish a very unusual fauna.

PARAKEETS AND THE RARE RINCOLESTA

The *Nothofagus* forests of Patagonia provide a habitat for a large number of local species. Indeed, whole groups of animals, notably among the insects, are indigenous. For example,

The 23,835-foot summit of Mount Aconcagua in Argentina is the highest peak in South America. (E. Aubert de la Rüe)

the ground beetles group *(Ceroglossus)* includes a wealth of species entirely Patagonian although closely related to the *Carabus* of the Northern Hemisphere.

There is also a variety of birds in these forests, although they are not so gorgeous as those in the tropics. However, quite a few species of birds originally tropical have penetrated the Patagonian region. Such is the Chilean fire-crown *(Sephanoides sephanoides),* a hummingbird found as far south as Tierra del Fuego and as high as six thousand feet in the Patagonian Andes. Thus the hummingbird family is distributed from Alaska to the southern extremity of the New World.

The presence of parakeets in Patagonia seems equally surprising. Although the slender-billed parakeet, the Chilean *choroy (Enicognatus leptorhynchus),* is not found south of Chiloe, the Tierra del Fuego parakeet *(Microcitace ferruginea)* occurs in large flocks and is thus the most southern representative of all the Psittacidae.

The Patagonian forests have attracted several species of woodpeckers. The most remarkable of these is the Magellanic woodpecker *(Ipocrantor magellanicus),* which is seventeen inches long, and, in the male, black with a red head; it is called *gallo del monte,* "cock of the mountain," by the Chileans. Related to the ivory-billed woodpecker and to the black woodpecker of Europe, these birds nest in the holes of dead trees at a height rarely less than fifty to sixty feet from the ground.

The song birds are relatively numerous and include some very characteristic species of the Pteroptochidae called by the Chileans *tapaculos*—"hide your hind end"—because they lift up their tail so that it stands above their head. These chunky little birds, from four and a half to ten inches long, with sturdy legs, have rather short and weak wings. They fly only a few yards at a time and live on the ground, where they run about like mice. With their strong feet they scratch the ground like chickens, finding their food, either grain or insects, among the leaves and the humus.

There are also some interesting mammals in the Patagonian forests. Among these are several opossums, wild cats and many rodents. But the most interesting is a marsupial, *Rhyncholestes raphanurus,* the rincolesta of Chiloe, known only to this island, where it inhabits the forests. This animal has a very long head, short tail, and uniformly dark brown pelage; it is virtually a living fossil and of great interest to the student of primitive mammals.

ARGENTINE PATAGONIA

In strong contrast with Chilean and western Argentine Patagonia are the vast and dreary plains of eastern Argentine Patagonia, the Atlantic slope of the southernmost part of South America. Although these plateaus are a continuation of the pampas, the traveler crossing the pampas from the north sees a great change taking place in the landscape after the Rio Negro and the Rio Limay. On the approaches to the Rio Colorado the alluvium of the pampas is replaced by sheets of rounded pebbles and crumbling sandstones. These formations become predominant at the Rio Negro.

The eastern part of Argentine Patagonia is a series of gigantic plateaus or tablelands covered with steppe vegetation and sloping eastward to end on the eastern coast in steep and often high cliffs. Volcanic eruptions have spread layers of basalt on the plateaus. These lava flows cover enormous areas near the Chico and Santa Cruz rivers. Here and there the sedimentary plateaus are dotted with eruptive cones. In the cliffs overlooking the sea the waves have carved ledges between the levels of high and low tide. On these ledges are many small depressions where water remains at low tide. Sea birds, mainly gulls, congregate here in enormous flocks.

This part of Argentine Patagonia is also very different from the Chilean portion in its climate. The southern sectors of South America are in the zone of the violent western winds. Since the rains come from the Pacific and must cross the cordillera, humidity decreases rapidly from west to east, and this affects the vegetation: the forests on the Andean slopes give way to a steppe that becomes so impoverished that in the east it is almost a desert. The Atlantic coast therefore is very arid and has clear skies. San Antonio, on the gulf of San Matias, has an average annual rainfall of only seventy inches, a singular contrast to the Pacific coast. As with the deserts of Peru and Chile, the combined effect of the Andes and the cold Falkland current running along the coast from the south, is a subdesert climate. The clouds coming from the Pacific cannot cross the Andes, and the cold waters bathing the Atlantic coast cause fogs that prevent rain from falling.

Because of the lessening of humidity, the climate is much more severe. There are hard freezes here—as low as -4° F—that can occur throughout the year.

The variations of climate in Argentine Patagonia are reflected in the vegetation. The environment rapidly becomes more humid as one enters the zone subjected to the western winds. Cactuses and drought-resistant plants common in the north disappear and are replaced by thickets of "molle" *(Schinus),* grasses become abundant, then broken ribbons of forest. Between the latitudes 38° and 39° S., true forest begins along the cordilleras, narrow bands scarcely sixty miles wide but extending as far as Tierra del Fuego. The same divisions can be observed as in Chile—Valdivian forest in the north, Magellanic forest in the south.

Toward the east, we find a kind of steppe formed of bushes rarely more than three feet tall, occasionally tufted plants, mingled with grasses *(Poa, Agrostis)* and sedges. This bush country diminishes toward the south. Only the well-irrigated spots preserve a dense verdure, which contrasts with the dusty yellow brush of the plateau.

The great diversity between the vegetation of the extreme south of Argentina and that of Chile is of course mainly the result of the very different climates on either side of the Andes. It is also due to the age-old separation of the two slopes following the uplift of the Andes. If we take, for example, the cactus in the Temperate Zone of South America, we see that of the 150 species in Argentina only four or five are also found in Chile.

THE GUANACO

Ever since the colonization of the plateau after 1880, Patagonia has been—except for a few old Spanish settlements—a zone of sheep-raising, thanks to colonists from the British

The 8,730-foot Osorno volcano, as seen from lake Todos los Santos, Chile. (Emil Muench)

Forests of false beech (shown here is Nothofagus betuloides), *widespread in western Patagonia, grow in dense stands in the more sheltered districts. (E. Aubert de la Rüe)*

Isles. Sheep-runs on great estates now cover most of the land. Because of this, the number of wild animals, already few by comparison with more clement regions, has dwindled. The animals that remain are similar to those of the pampas and thus contrast sharply with the woodland animals of Chilean Patagonia. The species are often related to those of the temperate Argentine plains to the north, but here too the approaches to the Rio Negro mark a frontier. Thus, the common nandu of the north does not cross this river, but a smaller, darker brown species, Darwin's nandu *(Pterocnemia pennata),* is found to the south of the river.

Similarly, the condor never frequents the low regions to the north of the Rio Negro, while in Patagonia it is often seen along the Pacific shores which are bathed by the Humboldt Current. Also, many sea birds stay south of the Rio Negro during the mating season, as for example the Magellanic penguin *(Spheniscus magellanicus),* which does not breed beyond San Matias Bay, but goes north as far as Brazil during the austral winter.

The most typical animal of the Patagonian steppe, the guanaco *(Lama guanicoe),* a small member of the camel family, is found from the high plateaus of southern Bolivia and the Argentine pampas to southern Patagonia.

The guanaco is essentially a diurnal animal and lives in family groups consisting of an adult male accompanied by from four to ten females. At certain periods of the year the herds may include a hundred or so individuals. The young males live in separate herds until they attain sexual maturity. The leading male of the herd acts as sentinel and warns the females of the approach of danger, whereupon the herd flees in a gallop so rapid that a horseman cannot catch them. Guanacos are often found together with flocks of nandus, apparently depending upon the keen senses of the latter to warn of impending danger—exactly as the zebras and antelopes of the grasslands of Africa keep company with the ostriches.

Guanacos were very common on the Argentine pampas at the time of colonization. Certain Indian tribes hunted them and the animal had for them the same multiple significance the bison had for the North American Indians. It provided them with meat and with hides, wool and bones from which they fabricated a thousand articles. It continues to be hunted today, professional hunters especially prizing the young guanaco. This hunt with modern arms and the transforming of the pampas into cattle ranges have considerably reduced the number of guanacos, to the great concern of the wildlife conservationists.

The guanaco's relative, the vicuña, is characteristic of the steppes, where it is found as far as Navarin Island. Standing nearly four feet high at the shoulder, its relatively short wool is soft, very silky, and a faun color becoming whitish on the undersides.

Among the birds, many show interesting adaptations. Noteworthy is a group of Anseriformes, the South American sheldgeese, which are all, except for a species of the High Andes, native to Patagonia and the pampas. One species is exclusively marine and does not leave the seashore, but the others are land birds, although they are good swimmers. These sheldgeese resemble geese, having a short and narrow bill.

The ashy-headed goose *(Chloephaga poliocephala)* is native to the herbaceous vegetation of western Patagonia, where it nests from Chiloe Island to the islands off Cape Horn, but in winter migrates north to a limited extent. Both sexes of this species have the same coloring.

The smallest of all sheldgeese, the ruddy-headed goose *(Chl. rubidiceps),* is native to Tierra del Fuego and the Falkland Islands. In the Magellan goose *(Chl. picta),* the male is white with a tail partly black and with black lines on its back and sides, while the smaller female is reddish but with black streaks on both back and undersides.

The sheldgeese hide their eggs in the tall grass, or among the rocks and bushes. The female alone sits on the eggs, the male taking no active part in the defense or raising of the young. They feed mainly upon weeds and grasses, eating an enormous amount; for this reason they are hunted by stockbreeders, who assert that six of them can eat as much as a

The Villarrica volcano, near Pucon, is one of the many volcanic peaks that stud the Chilean Andes. (J. Allan Cash)

sheep and that their huge flocks are consequently competitors of the domestic animals. The first explorers described how these birds swarmed in early times; and the birds are still incredibly numerous despite a systematic effort to eliminate them, especially the Magellan goose. In a single year, 75,000 eggs were destroyed on a ranch in Tierra del Fuego and 250,000 on another in Patagonia, and yet their number does not seem to have suffered. In clearing land for pasture and in destroying the foxes that fed on both the eggs and the young, man has in a way been responsible for this almost uncontrollable proliferation of the birds. In the balance of nature in primeval Patagonia, doubtless these sheldgeese were, along with the guanacos, the principal animals that made use of the grassy ground cover.

NAHUEL HUAPÍ NATIONAL PARK

The beauty of the Patagonian landscapes is bound to attract travelers to this part of the world. Despite their remoteness, many parts of Patagonia are easily accessible by air and one could suggest no more interesting trip than the Lago Nahuel Huapí region, now an Argentine national park. If the traveler takes the comfortable train to San Carlos de Bariloche on the eastern shores of the lake, the journey of almost 1,100 miles carries him through all the natural habitats of Argentina, as if through a gigantic living atlas. From Buenos Aires to Bahia Blanca the railway crosses one of the most populated sections of the pampas; it then goes to the Rio Negro, where it turns west to the Patagonian plateau. The landscape here becomes very monotonous, with not a tree to be seen for 450 miles. The vegetation is all low shrubs, reminding a French traveler of the *garrigue* of Provence. The land then gradually rises to an altitude of 3,000 feet, entering the Patagonian steppe, where waves of tufted grasses stretch to the horizon. Finally the mountains loom up and the first tree conifers *(Libocedrus chilensis)* and false beech appear, especially in the deep valley of the Rio Limay, called *Valle Encantado* (Enchanted Valley) because of its picturesque rocks. Then, beyond the edge of the Andean forest the train reaches Nahuel Huapí, forty-four miles long and at least six miles wide. The eastern part, which stretches to the end of the Patagonian plateau, has gently sloping banks bordered by low mountains. The western part, by contrast, has a series of long and narrow arms, like fjords, with steep slopes. Thus, side by side with landscapes that recall those of Switzerland are fjords that recall Norway. Overlooking the winding sheets of water is the ice-cap of the extinct volcano Tronador, its peak at 11,188 feet. Several small lakes amidst dense forests add to the beauty of the landscape. False beech trees are numerous here, with an undergrowth of bamboos shooting up like fireworks, and bushes with bright flowers overlooked by tall conifers, especially the alerce *(Fitzroya patagonica)*.

These forests are inhabited by countless birds, and also some big mammals, among which are the huemal *(Hippocamelus bisulcus)* and the pudu *(Pudua pudu)*, the smallest of the deer family. These aboriginal deer have become rather rare as a result of excessive hunting. The Argentinians have therefore introduced European deer *(Cervus elaphus)* and even fallow deer *(Dama dama)*. These have multiplied in a disastrous way: as a result of competition from these robust rivals, the aboriginal species have diminished in number.

Interestingly enough, the introduced European deer has considerably increased in size, the antlers becoming so gigantic that the trophies of a stag-hunt here would make European hunters green with envy. Nonetheless, the introduction of exotic species, especially in a national park, must be condemned. Wild boars and hares that were also introduced from Europe ravage the plantations. The introduction of the North American salmon and the European trout *(Trutta fario)* has made possible the development of game fishing, but has seriously upset the natural balance of the rivers. These magnificent regions had no need of all these added attractions in order to lure travelers.

Among the other national parks of this region are Lanin, which adjoins Nahuel Huapí, Los Alerces, in the western part of Chubut province, Perito Francisco P. Moreno, which is hidden between lakes Buenos Aires and San Martin, and Los Glaciares, famous for its majestic glaciers. All are rich in wildlife and beautiful landscapes.

TIERRA DEL FUEGO

The Andes of Patagonia are divided by transverse valleys, and a bygone continental subsidence has allowed sea water to enter these trans-Andean valleys. Some of the fjords thrust east of the Andes, where they are prolonged by vast gulfs; such, for example, are the Seno Skyring and the Seno Otway. One of these depressions has even gone so far as to detach a part of the continent—the Strait of Magellan, which is no more than a sea-level pass through the Andes. Its western end is a channel similar to other channels of western Patagonia, while its eastern end, from Punta Arenas on, is a valley submerged in the sea. The large island that is thus cut off from the continent is Tierra del Fuego.

Tierra del Fuego, meaning "land of fire," does not derive its name from volcanic activity but from the fires that the Indians light in their encampments and that illuminate the austral fogs; it is formed of two distinct parts, as is the southern tip of the continent itself. The west is mountainous and is a continuation of the Andean Cordillera, with summits higher than 6,000 feet above sea level. In contrast, the eastern part is level and is a continuation of the Argentine pampas. Nothing better illustrates this contrast than a sail through the Strait of Magellan from the Atlantic. The eastern end seems to flow through the pampas, the banks consisting of gently sloping sandy beaches. But from Cape Froward, the southern point of Brunswick peninsula, the strait turns northwest between a line of mountain peaks and glaciers. The contrast in climate is equally striking. The western part of Tierra del Fuego is well watered by rains from the Pacific and is thus enveloped in perpetual fog. The eastern part is much drier; the sky is often clear and a gentle light illuminates vast stretches of water and plains. Similar conditions prevail around Beagle Channel in southern Tierra del Fuego. Navarin Island, where the farms are the farthest south of any in the world, is a pleasant expanse of alluvial plains. The land to the west of the channel is shut in, however, by

View of the amphitheatre and the Limay River near Bariloche, Argentina. (J. Barnell: Image International)

cliffs. Here the slopes are covered with beech and laurel. Countless waterfalls cascade over the cliffs while glaciers crown one of the most beautiful mountain chains in the world. Many of the glaciers flow down to the sea, where they break off in icebergs that glitter against the dark vegetation. Perhaps the most majestic of these is Italia Glacier, coming down from Mount Darwin, its sea-front almost a mile wide.

The eastern part of Tierra del Fuego has been exploited by man for a very long time. Aside from recent oil discoveries, stock-raising constitutes the sole natural wealth of the island. Immense flocks of sheep flourish there in spite of a high mortality rate in winter, when the snow deprives the animals of pasturage for too long a time. The pastures of Tierra del Fuego are far richer than those of the Patagonian mainland, a sheep needing only a little over two acres of pasture there but requiring five to ten acres on the mainland. But here, too, thoughtless deforesting has stripped the land bare. Notably near Beagle Channel, two or three times more forest was burned off than was necessary.

To the south of Tierra del Fuego are some islets forming a tight little archipelago. Some of these islands are relatively flat and are covered with a kind of peat bog. Others are completely carpeted with tussock grass and are colonized by some Magellan penguins that dig their burrows in the ground. Still others stand high above the sea, Wollaston and Mount Hyde islands attaining an altitude of 2,020 feet, their coastal cliffs resting on great pillars of basalt. These islands, the austral sentinels of the continent, are inhabited by a great number of birds. In addition to thirty species of sea birds there are the Magellan thrush *(Turdus magellanicus),* which imitates the calls of petrels, oyster-catchers, and sheldrakes; two species of wrens, four of finches, one member of the genus *Cinclodes* and no less than fourteen other species of land birds, a surprising fact on such desolate islands. The only land mammals are a few species of bats and one of rodents.

The Antarctic begins to the south of Cape Horn, which the old sailing ships used to round before racing toward Valparaiso or the islands of the South Pacific.

THE FALKLAND ISLANDS

From the end of the Tertiary to the Pliocene, the entire continental plateau rose up from the Atlantic and then, in the Quaternary, subsided again, leaving in the east only a cluster of islands—the Falkland Islands. This archipelago, about 375 miles to the east of southern Patagonia, is comprised of two main islands, West and East Falkland, and about a hundred islets. These islands are on the whole flat (except for a few lines of hills in northern East Falkland), the southern portion being so low that they are not visible from a distance of ten miles as one approaches by boat.

The Falklands have been modelled by glaciations, which have carved out innumerable fjords. One of their geological peculiarities is "stone-runs" or rivers of quartzite blocks that seem to flow down the slopes, as if a sorcerer had transformed water into stone. The climate, subantarctic in character, is strongly marked by oceanic influences. The summers are cool and the winters mild. Although it either rains or snows on close to 250 days of the year, the annual precipitation is only about twenty-four inches. Snow melts rather quickly, but gales are very frequent and calm sunny days very rare. It is, in short, a climate that closely resembles that of the Orkneys, the Shetlands, and other islands north of the British Isles.

The vegetation closely reflects the climate: the most striking feature is the total absence of trees. Even the attempts made to acclimatize the false beech and certain pines have failed, the shoots dying as soon as they emerged from the protection of the ground. Only two species of bushes rise above ground level. The most widespread vegetation is that of tussock grass *(Poa flabellata),* which consist of tufts of several hundred shoots and look from a distance like dwarf palms. This grassy carpet is of great ecological importance, for in it the penguins and many other sea birds make their nests. Since the introduction of cattle and then of sheep, the tussock grass is found only in steep sectors beyond the reach of sheep, or on a few islets where stock-raising has never been attempted. This grass has here been replaced by a group of heath plants.

Bogs and swamps also occur in the central portions: because of the large-scale exploitation of the peat in these bogs the plants that grow in these environments are also in danger. It is to be hoped that some of these zones will be set aside as reservations, so that the Falkland Islands may remain the richest refuge of subantarctic flora in the world.

VANISHED GIANTS

South America has acquired the reputation of being the land of miniature mammals. But it has also produced some giants. Among the rodents, the capybaras, a kind of guinea pig, reach a length of thirty-nine inches and a weight of 150 pounds. Other forms even more gigantic have disappeared only in recent times. The *Megamys* of the Pliocene and the Quaternary were rodents related to the viscachas and chinchillas of today, but they were as large as a rhinoceros, making them the largest rodents known.

Gigantism was even more evident among the edentata, a group that remains well represented in South America. The *Megatherium,* identified in 1789 and described by Cuvier, was an enormous sloth, more than sixteen feet long, its hind parts well developed, its paws armed with strong claws, and a cranium with grotesquely large mandibles. The *Glyptodon* was a huge armadillo, the body encased in a bony armor, the head protected by a kind of helmet, and the tail covered with projecting points—all in all like a medieval conception of a monster.

These animals disappeared only in very recent times. Remnants of horny epidermis and muscle of an animal, *Neomylodon,* related to the *Megatherium* have been found in caves, and other vestiges indicate that the enormous carapaces of the glyptodonts were used as roofing material by early man in Patagonia. Certain legends and beliefs of the Argentine Indians, the Tehuelche and Tobas among others, support this evidence, as do the observations of a few nineteenth-century travelers. All this has led some writers to theorize that survivors of this strange fauna have retreated to the north and still linger in some wilder areas.

The rock ledges of Laja Falls in Chile have been polished for ages by the rushing waters. (Weldon King)

TURBULENT SEAS

The oceans that bathe Patagonia are considered among the most turbulent in the world. Atmospheric pressure is often low, for this is the zone of the great western winds. These winds sometimes stir up waves over fifty feet high. The lighthouse keepers on the island of Los Evangelistas at the western entrance to the Strait of Magellan have had to construct walls to protect a cistern of drinking water from the salt mists produced by the waves breaking on the rocky shores; yet the cistern is more than 165 feet above the sea. The islands are notoriously difficult to approach. According to tradition one ship waited forty days near the island of Pacheco before being able to approach it, and the anchorage still bears the name of *Cuarenta Dias* (forty days).

The extreme south of South America is a meeting place of many very strong ocean currents. One of the strongest comes from the Pacific, strikes Patagonia and splits up into two branches, one sweeping toward the north. These waters spread out into the channels that wind among the network of islands. The movement of the tides here is so complex that Darwin compared it to the movement of water in a boiling cauldron. In amplitude, the tides here are the highest in the world, reaching 45.6 feet at Puerto Gallegos.

The hulks of vessels that have been shipwrecked in these boiling waters attest the dangers of navigation here. The only water route between the Atlantic and the Pacific before the construction of the Panama canal, it was, despite the dangers, the most frequented in the world. The Cape Horners created their legend before steam enabled ships to take the calmer route of the Strait of Magellan.

GIANT SEAWEED

From the Valdez peninsula in Argentina to the southern islands of Patagonia and then along the Pacific coast washed by the Humboldt Current, the shore is surrounded by a belt of giant kelp *(Macrocystis pyrifera)*, seaweed often as much as six hundred feet long. This algae, very characteristic of the cold Antarctic oceans, grows in waters from six to twenty fathoms deep and is of very great ecological importance. From a basal trunk fronds branch out bearing growths and long streamers that thrust to the surface and there divide into a multitude of jagged fronds. These fronds are from six inches to two feet long, and each one has at its base a vesicle filled with air. These fronds form such a mass on the surface of the water that ships navigate among them with difficulty.

A rich fauna shelters in this seaweed. Practically every type of marine invertebrate may on occasion hide in the folds and creases of these interlaced stems. And hydroids and moss animals of every kind cling to the surface of the fronds, entirely covering them. Never did woods on land shelter as many animals as do these suboceanic forests.

THE WEALTH OF THE SEA

The coldness of the waters along the shores of Patagonia scarcely discourages animal life. And the mud holes uncovered at low tide are very favorable to the development of life. Although no systematic study of this marine fauna has yet been made we know that mollusks, sea urchins and crustaceans abound here and are caught in considerable numbers by fishermen. This shellfish industry, more productive on the whole than that of fishes, keeps the small local canning factories busy. In one year, more than six thousand tons of *mariscos* (the Spanish term that embraces all of these invertebrates) are taken on the average in Chilean Patagonia. This production could be greatly augmented, for the mariscos are abundant and the demand for sea food is increasing in central Chile. At present, however, this wealth is being destroyed. As a result of the depletion of the oyster beds, the oyster production of Chiloe has fallen from 12,000 baskets in 1955 to no more than 3,000 in 1958.

Much the same is true of the fishes that abound along the coasts of Patagonia. There is a profusion of fish everywhere in the region that oceanographers call "the subtropical convergence," that is, where the relatively tepid waters from farther north meet the cold subantarctic waters. This contact zone is greatest in the vicinity of Chiloe and has helped to make that island one of the great fishing centers of Chile. In 1957 Chiloe provided 1,860 of the 2,230 tons of fish produced in Patagonia.

Because of the wealth of fish (only a moderate number of them are truly Patagonian) a great many sea birds have established themselves here. Among the cormorants there are several species that are native but show a relationship to other subantarctic species, particularly the New Zealand cormorants. An unusual species is the rock shag *(Phalacrocorax magellanicus)*, distributed along the South American coasts from Rio Santa Cruz in Argentina, around to Corral, in Chile. Its favorite environment is the island channels, and notably the Strait of Magellan. The shag's rounded wings evidently do not encourage it to struggle against the violent winds of the high seas; it therefore flies on a level with the water, taking advantage of the calm air just above the waves. This has led local inhabitants to declare that the rock shag cannot fly until it has wet its tail! It nests in the chinks of rocky cliffs, or sometimes in caves, and it fishes a short distance from shore, among the seaweed "forests" that abound in these latitudes. Other cormorants of this region are the bigua *(P. olivaceus)*, so plentiful throughout Latin America, the red-footed shag *(P. gaimardi)*, and especially a relative of the rock shag, the Magellanic blue-eyed shag *(P. atriceps)*, which is the most abundant of all, some of its colonies being incredibly dense. The king shag *(P. albiventer)* also frequents Patagonia, nesting from Puerto San Julian, in Argentina, to Cape Horn. Each species of this considerable variety of cormorants appears to occupy a particular ecological niche.

During the winter, the channels of southern Patagonia and Tierra del Fuego are invaded by large flocks of oceanic birds, notably cape pigeons, fulmars and other petrels of the Antarctic. All these birds lend the scene a "polar" look that is accentuated by the presence of numerous penguins. The Magellanic penguin *(Spheniscus magellanicus)* is native to this zone, nesting in every part and as far as Concepción in the north, their colonies sometimes including as many as fifty

In summer the Patagonian countryside is covered with flowers like those on an Alpine prairie. Shown here are some thickets of Grindellia chilensis, *near Zapala in the province of Neuquen. (Jose M. Cei)*

thousand individuals. The rockhopper penguin *(Eudyptes crestatus)* is found in Tierra del Fuego, on the islands near Cape Horn and on many Antarctic islands; so is the king penguin *(Aptenodytes patagonicus)* which is also found all around the Antarctic world.

Found on the seashore here is a species of highly specialized South American sheldgeese, the kelp goose *(Chloephaga hybrida);* it is exclusively marine, in contrast to its inland relatives. It is distributed all along the coasts of Patagonia, from Corral in Chile to the islands south of Tierra del Fuego. Its webbed feet do not prevent it from jumping from rock to rock, behaving in some ways more like a gull than a goose. It does not feed on mollusks and other shallow water animals—as has been occasionally suggested—but uniquely on seaweed, particularly a certain green algae known as *Porphyra umbilicalis,* pasturing on it at low tide. This diet saves it from persecution by the sheep breeders while giving it the reputation of not being edible.

Another group of water birds characteristic of Patagonia are the steamer ducks or *Tachyeres,* mysterious birds as far as their affinities go. They are large, heavy ducks and two of the three species have completely lost the use of their wings. Their name results from their curious way of flying over the water, vigorously using their wings like oars. Darwin describes them thus: "These great logger-headed ducks, which sometimes weigh as much as twenty-two pounds, were called by the old navigators, from their extraordinary manner of paddling and splashing over the water, race-horses, but now much more properly steamers. Their wings are too small and weak to allow of flight, but by their aid, partly swimming and partly flapping the surface of the water, they move quickly." Darwin overestimated the weight of these ducks, for we know that they do not much exceed fourteen pounds, but his description of their flight is nonethelss good. They can fly at a speed of fifteen miles an hour over a distance of several miles and they dive with great agility.

Another duck of this region, the Magellanic flightless steamer duck *(T. pteneres),* like its congeners on the Falkland Islands *(T. brachypterus),* is completely unable to fly although its very small wings are constituted normally. Perhaps this is why it avoids coasts where the tides are of great amplitude, as on the western side of the Strait of Magellan. However, it is abundant and very widely distributed along channels where the tides are weaker. The flying steamer duck *(T. patachonicus)* is better able to fly—although heavily—and at a well-sustained speed. It also frequents fresh water, going up estuaries and even inhabiting certain lakes of eastern Patagonia.

The steamer ducks feed mainly on mollusks, both gasteropods and bivalves, and also on crustaceans, both shrimps and crabs.

PATAGONIA AND MAN

Before the arrival of Europeans, Patagonia was inhabited by some of the most primitive Indians in the world. In spite of the cold and humidity they wore only a kind of cloak made of guanaco hide or sealskin and they led a nomadic life, eating shellfish, seals, and the meager wild fruits of the forest. They did not hold out very long against the diseases transmitted to them by the Europeans and what sometimes amounted to systematic massacre. By the beginning of the twentieth century, the three principal tribes were almost extinct. The Alakalufs, some ten thousand of whom were distributed along the western channels in Darwin's time, are now only a hundred or so in number. The Onas, who lived inland, are at this writing represented by only seven individuals. The Yahgans, the most southerly of the tribes, who inhabited the offshore islands of Cape Horn, and whose resistance to the cold was so much admired by Darwin, are now represented by only nine pure-bred individuals. In some ways these Indians lived like our Paleolithic ancestors. No wonder they disappeared so rapidly on contact with modern

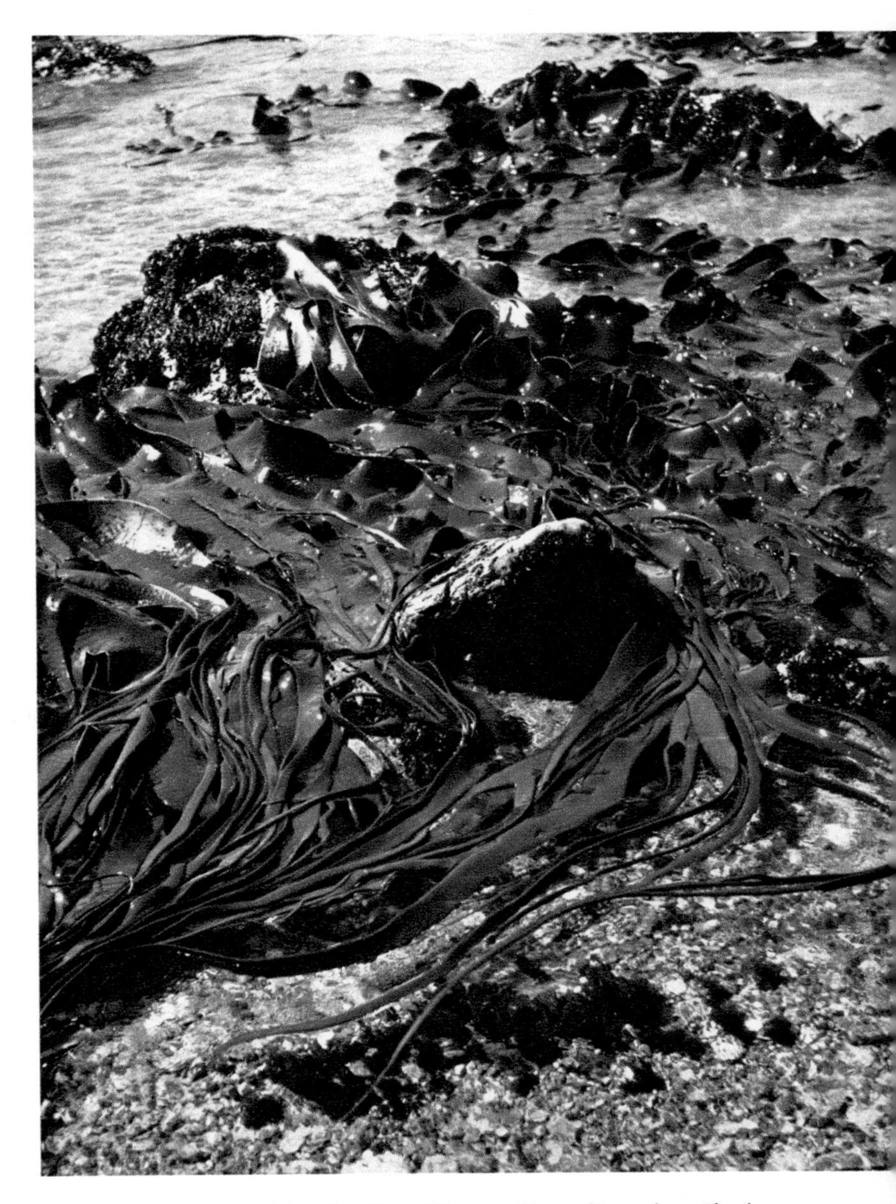

Strange algae, notably the Durvillea utilis, *often described as suboceanic forests, grow in dense tangles along the coasts of Patagonia. (E. Aubert de la Rüe)*

The Ramuncho Cliffs, near Concepción, Chile. (J. Allan Cash)

Overleaf: The deep seas of the Strait of Magellan burdened with floating ice torn from the glaciers. (Tony La Tona)

man! The other Indians who were established in some number to the north have also declined dramatically.

The population of Patagonia is still small. In 1958 Chilean Patagonia was estimated to have a population of 220,000, almost half living in Chiloe and 50,000 at Punta Arenas, the town farthest south in the world. There are vast areas here without a single inhabitant.

Yet there is no lack of resources. Aside from the fish, there is forest wealth that can be exploited intelligently instead of being ravaged. Unfortunately, the fur-bearing animals, such as seals, otters and skunks, have declined so in number that this resource is now negligible. The idea of introducing animals from elsewhere is very dangerous, as in the case of the rabbit, which multiplied uncontrollably in Tierra del Fuego and Patagonia before myxomatosis cut short the increase. Agriculture has only a very limited future in Patagonia because of the climate and various soil factors, but stock-raising flourishes, especially the breeding of sheep, in both the natural and man-made pampas of the southern sections; this area has, in fact, the highest proportion of sheep per inhabitant in the world. Cattle are raised in great numbers in the provinces of Aisen and Chiloe in Chile. The subsoil resources are many, ranging from oil (especially in Tierra del Fuego) to lignite (there are thought to exist reserves of three and a half billion tons around Punta Arenas) and minerals such as copper, lead and zinc. Patagonia produces gold washed down from the Andes. A large nugget weighing twenty-nine ounces was discovered in 1906 in a placer on the Rio del Oro, in Tierra del Fuego, and even primitive methods of exploitation produced an average of four to five pounds of gold every week up to 1923. The annual production of gold in Magellanes province is at the present time about thirty-five pounds.

Thus Patagonia is far from lacking attractions and since many districts can now be reached by plane the tourist trade may be expected to develop substantially. The region of the channels and Tierra del Fuego present landscapes that are among the most beautiful in South America. The juxtaposition of arms of the sea, precipitous coast, glaciers plunging into the ocean, often against a background of tropical-looking forests or of trees twisted by the wind, provide spectacles that will draw those who love wild places, in spite of cold, wind and rain. For these reasons Patagonia also constitutes a resource of natural grandeur that should be preserved.

Albatrosses (Diomedea chrysostoma) *nest in foot-high mounds composed of plant debris amid tufts of tussock grass* (Poa flabellata). *(E. Aubert de la Rüe)*

Magellanic penguins (Spheniscus magellanicus), *common in southern Patagonia, congregate in very large colonies on level islands. (Annemarie Heinrich)*

Wandering Albatrosses and Elephant Seals

South American Antarctica

A sickle-shaped arc of islands prolongs the southern tip of South America all the way into the Antarctic Circle. These are mountainous island outposts, as though the Andean range continued on into the ocean. This region, called the Scotia Arc, extends from Tierra del Fuego to Isla de los Estados, Shag Rocks, South Georgia, Clerke Rocks, the South

Right: *Around Iris Bay, on the southeast coast of South Georgia, the mountains plunge abruptly down to the sea.* Below: *The gray-headed albatross* (Diomedea chrysostoma) *nests among tussock grass, using the tufts to build its platform nest. (Both by R. W. Vaughan)*

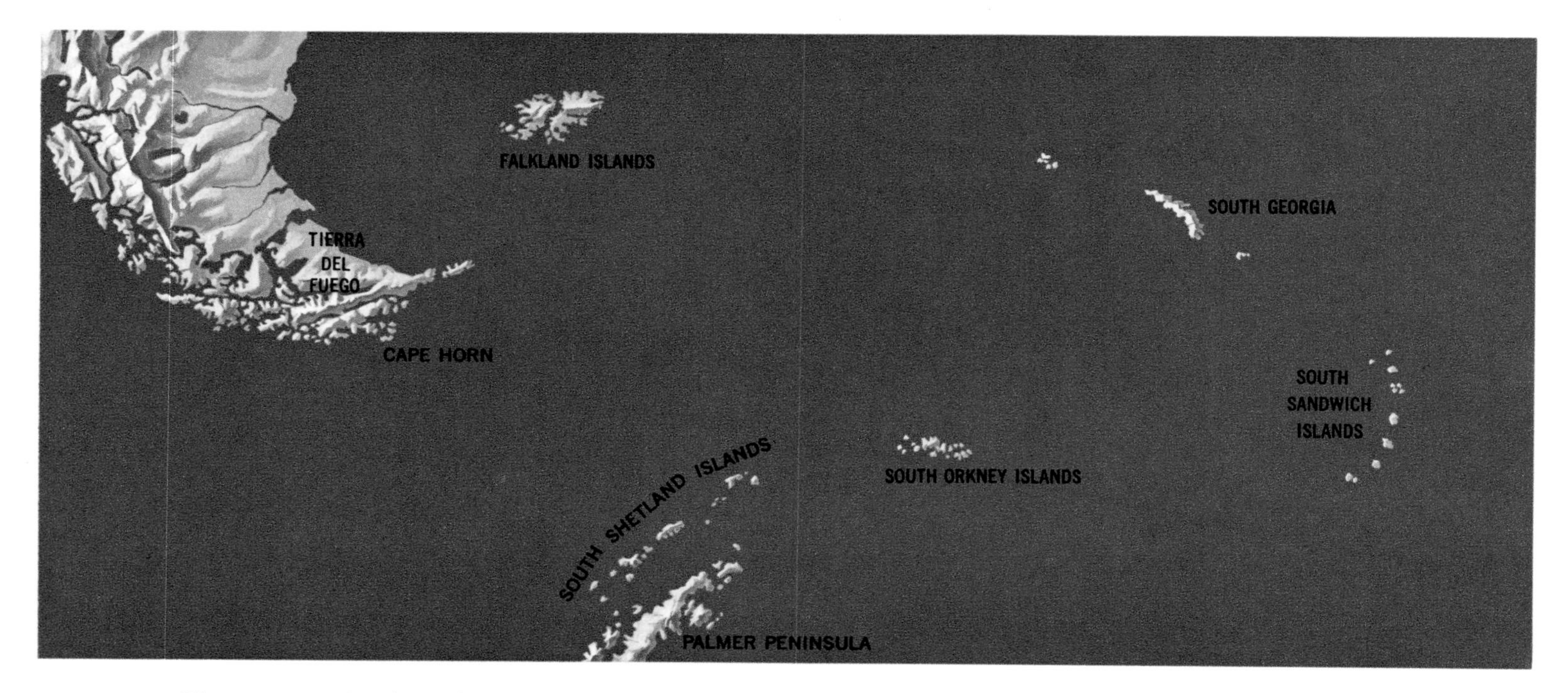

The extreme tip of South America is linked with Antarctica by a sickle-shaped arc of islands, the summits of an emerged cordillera. These islands are a meeting ground of Patagonian fauna and the polar world.

Sandwich Islands, the South Orkneys, and the South Shetlands, to Graham Land or Palmer Peninsula. All of these islands rest on the same bedrock, and in this respect resemble the Caribbean islands.

The climate of this region is very harsh, with rigorous winters and cold, cloudy summers that maintain an ice-cap on the islands. Nevertheless, considering the latitude, even the most southerly islands have a relatively temperate climate. Hence, the more favorable localities are covered with vegetation, and animals from more clement regions find this the only part of the Antarctic in which they can survive.

With an appreciable portion of its land free of ice and snow during a part of the year, South Georgia sustains a small community of land animals. But farther south, the islands are only accidentally free of ice as a result either of latent volcanic activity or of slopes too steep to allow snow to collect on them. The only animals found there are those that live off the sea. Except for seals, the fauna is comprised of sea birds.

Thus, beyond a certain latitude in the Antarctic—as in the Arctic—only sea animals survive.

SOUTH GEORGIA

The farthest north of these islands, South Georgia, is crossed by mountains that reach a height of 9,200 feet and are covered with glaciers that descend toward the sea. In good weather the spectacle of these mountains and their accumulations of snow and ice is one of the most majestic imaginable. As voyagers have said, it is like seeing the Alps rise from the sea. The average land temperature is low, and the sea averages 35° F, the water freezing over in winter. The precipitation is relatively abundant.

The vegetation of South Georgia reflects the climate. The vascular plants include only nineteen species, of which none is arborescent. Prairies of tussock grass cover the lower regions and the slopes up to about one thousand feet. Acaena *(Acaena adscendens)* is also characteristic. Other vegetation, for instance ferns and mosses, is much more rare.

The animal life is equally meager: about a dozen insects and a few land vertebrates but no indigenous mammal. Attempts to introduce sheep and rabbits have failed; however, reindeer have adapted and herds of them have returned to the wild state. Among the birds, the upland goose *(Chloephaga picta)*, introduced from the continent into the Falklands in 1910, has multiplied but is not plentiful. South Georgia has a duck, *Anas georgica*, and it also has one passerine that is endemic, a pipit, *Anthus antarcticus*, which finds refuge in a grassy expanse. No other perching bird is found this far south. These are the only inroads made by species from the South American mainland.

All the other birds are of Antarctic origin. Of penguins, no less than four species breed in South Georgia. The large king penguins establish their rookeries in the low regions or denuded moraines exposed to the wind from the mountains. This penguin was very numerous, according to the early explorers, but it was decimated during the nineteenth century, being hunted for its fat which, like whale blubber, yields oil. Since the passing of laws protecting the rookeries, the species is once more multiplying. The gentoo penguin *(Pygoscelis papua)*, distributed throughout the Antarctic, prefers to breed inland, where it builds a kind of nest of humus and tussock grass or stones. The ringed penguin *(P. antarctica)*, found only in the American sector of the Antarctic, likes high terrains and some have called it "the alpinist of penguins." Its nest is a simple depression in the ground, bordered by a few pebbles to keep the eggs from rolling. The macaroni penguin *(Eudyptes chrysolophus)*, with tufts of yellow feathers on either side of the head, is very abundant. It establishes its rookeries on the top of cliffs of the island in the midst of the tussock grass meadows. Each of these four penguins thus exhibits very definite ecological preferences, preventing too much competition in the choice of territories.

Among the sea birds there is a cormorant, *Phalacrocorax atriceps georgianus,* that nests in small colonies on the grassy ledges of cliffs. There are, besides, various kinds of gulls, terns and Antarctic skuas that live by devouring the eggs and the nestlings of other birds.

THE ALBATROSS—GIANT OF THE SOUTHERN SEAS

No island in the seas bordering the Antarctic would be really complete without some representatives of the procellariiformes, particularly petrels and albatrosses. No less than eight species of petrels nest in South Georgia, among them Wilson's petrel *(Oceanites oceanicus),* which migrates toward the North Atlantic during the winter of the Southern Hemisphere. All the seas of the south polar region and indeed a part of the tropical seas are inhabited by the albatross.

Native to the Southern Hemisphere is the largest flying bird in the world, the wandering albatross *(Diomedea exulans),* which attains a length of four feet, a weight of twenty-five pounds, and a wing-spread of eleven and one half feet. (The condor is heavier, but its wings are shorter.) This albatross nests on the southern islands, such as Crozet and Kerguelen in the Indian Ocean, New Zealand and the Antipodes in the South Pacific, and South Georgia.

Although this albatross is found along the continent as far north as the Rio de la Plata on the Atlantic side and Valparaiso on the Pacific side, and occasionally even farther, its only South American nesting place is in South Georgia, where it begins to arrive in November. Here as elsewhere it establishes its colonies in the windiest and most exposed spots: the wind no doubt assists this heavy bird in its take-off and landing.

The males arrive first. When the females arrive, each is immediately courted by five or six males. The nuptial parades of these great birds have been described many times for they always amaze travelers. The males assemble round the female and bow very low to her, uttering a harsh groaning sound. The female responds with a bow, then the males spread their wings and sidestep around her. After this they face her, open their wings wide and high, raise their necks vertically upward and utter a long loud braying cry. Then the entire maneuver is repeated.

After the mating, the pair begins to build the nest. The female settles on the vestiges of the nest of a former year while the male goes to and fro, bringing tufts of tussock grass and moss, all this time indulging in complex dance steps and bowing low to the female. The building of the nest is often interrupted by even more "affectionate" demonstrations, with the two partners standing face to face, raising their beaks perpendicularly to the sky, and trumpeting like old-fashioned automobile horns. Then they lower their beaks and bring the tips together. The female lays only one egg, which measures about five and a half inches long with a weight averaging just over a pound. These eggs were eaten by the whalers although in flavor they are rather disappointing. As Robert Cushman Murphy, the American ornithologist who has told us so much about sea birds, remarks: "Delicious to start but by the time you have progressed halfway to the bottom, you begin to wish that the bird had laid a somewhat smaller egg."

After it hatches in January or February, the nestling must be protected from the skuas, which are all too fond of eggs and nestlings. By the beginning of August the young achieves adult size and is then abandoned by the parents. For three months it remains in or near the nest, living on its reserves of fat. It is not until the young albatross is ten or twelve months old that it really launches forth to roam the seas of the world.

The wandering albatross flies incredible distances in search of its favorite food—squids, cuttlefish, and other cephalopods. It is believed that these birds fly around the globe above the Antarctic oceans, borne irresistibly by the great western winds. Birds that were banded on Kerguelen Island, in the southern part of the Indian Ocean, have been captured near Cape Horn and in Chile, having flown more than eight thousand miles sometimes in less than ten months. Three other species of albatrosses are found, among which are the black-browed mollimawk *(Diomedea melanophrys)* and the light-mantled sooty albatross *(Phoebetria palpebrata)* of dusky plumage.

ELEPHANT SEALS

At certain periods the beaches of South Georgia are visited by elephant seals *(Mirounga leonina),* the largest of all the pinnipeds, an adult male attaining a length of twenty feet and a weight of more than three tons. It does not cut a very graceful figure, for it has a distressing amount of fat, its muscles buried in a thick layer of blubber. It gets its name from a proboscis that the male acquires when about three years old. When aroused to anger, the animal can swell this appendage, which is really an inflation of the nostrils, so that it looks like two small footballs at the end of its nose.

The year of the elephant seal can be divided into four periods: a winter period spent at sea, followed by the breeding season in the spring, then a short period again at sea, after which the animals return to land in the autumn to moult. Toward the end of August, the females arrive on land, first in small groups, then in larger herds. After ten or so days, the cow gives birth to a pup about three feet long. It grows rapidly, the mother's milk being particularly rich in fat, and is soon like a hairy ball. The beach at this time is animated and noisy, with the pups calling their mothers.

At the age of three or four weeks, the pups begin to play together, bathing and swimming in streams or in the shallow waters at the edge of the beach. Toward Christmas, they have grown large enough to swim at a distance from the shore. As soon as the males arrive on the beach, the first preoccupation of each bull is to establish a harem, ranging from ten to as many as thirty females, and then, if need be, fight off rivals. From the time they come ashore the male elephant seals do not eat. After two months of fasting, they return to sea and take an enormous amount of nourishment, feeding especially on cephalopods.

Around February, after two months at sea, they return to land to moult. This time they make their way as much as half a mile inland to expanses covered with tussock grass and interspersed with small pools of water—a journey that takes considerable effort. Two or three animals plunge into each

Gentoo penguins (Pygoscelis papua) *often establish their colonies far from the coast and must make long journeys to reach the sea and food. Left above: A king shag* (Phalacrocorax albiventer), *a characteristic sea bird of southern Patagonia. Left: Macaroni penguins* (Eudyptes chrysolophus), *which owe their name to the yellow plumes that adorn their head, build a nest of tussock grass. (All by Ian J. Strange)*

The male sea-lion (Otaria byconia) *gathers his small harem on a rocky beach. He keeps constant watch over his females, one of whom is suckling her young. (Ian J. Strange)*

pool, soon making the water muddy and filthy. This activity probably reduces skin irritation caused by the shedding of the old hair and the growth of new hair and caused also, perhaps, by a "fever" resulting from several physiological changes. Toward April, the seals return to sea, where they lead a pelagic existence until the next breeding season.

These large seals have only one natural enemy, the killer whale, which, with its enormous jaws, is capable of cutting a seal in two at a single bite. But its worst enemy is man. The elephant seals have been hunted for their blubber and oil; at the time of the seal's return to land as much as eighty gallons can be extracted from a single individual. Sealing expeditions from North America and Great Britain were responsible for a destruction of these seals that caused them almost to disappear from South Georgia by 1885. Efficient measures of protection have saved the species and allowed the revival of the rookeries. At present some six thousand male elephant seals are slaughtered each year, with a small number preserved for reproduction purposes. This reasonable exploitation conserves the herds, which have increased enormously and spread to the South Orkneys.

BLEAK ARCHIPELAGOS

As early as 1819, a Russian admiral, von Bellingshausen, described how penguins established themselves in those parts of the South Sandwich Islands where volcanic vapors had melted the snow. The penguins inhabit the slopes, avoiding only the vicinity of the active cones or the immediate area of the smoke-holes. The ringed penguin is the most numerous but the gentoo and the king penguin are also represented. Among the other land birds that frequent these bleak lands are the Cape pigeon, very abundant on most of the islands, the silver-gray fulmar, and the giant petrel.

The list is small. But it demonstrates that birds can live on the most desolate lands by taking advantage of the fire beneath the earth's crust.

Situated seven hundred miles to the southeast of the Falklands, the South Orkneys are the summits of a submerged mountain range, some of them reaching a height of more than 6,500 feet. These islands are constantly swept by strong west and northwest winds that darken the sky with clouds during four fifths of the year. The average annual temperature is 23° to 39° F and the average for the warmest month, January, is just above freezing.

With their deeply indented coasts forming rocky peninsulas advancing like tentacles into the sea, the South Orkneys are almost completely covered with ice. During the brief summer, a few small areas are freed from snow and covered with patches of moss and lichens. These unfavorable conditions have not, however, discouraged seventeen species of nesting birds, including several species of petrels, a cormorant, a tern, a gull, and the Antarctic skua; these migrate to the north in winter. Four species of penguins are known on these islands, the Adelie and antarctic being remarkably abundant.

The South Shetland Islands are mountainous and have summits more than three thousand feet high. They are of volcanic origin and the best known among them, Deception Island, is a volcano that erupted from the sea. Its crater, almost six hundred feet deep, was a mooring ground for sealers of the nineteenth century and is now used by whalers. Although surrounded by less floating ice than the South Orkneys and the South Sandwich group, these islands have only a very meager carpet of moss and lichens. A latent vulcanism melts the snow in patches rather early in the spring, allowing the kelp gull to nest here one month earlier than in the Falklands.

The birds are mainly of the same kind as in the South Orkneys, but they seem to be extraordinarily abundant, perhaps attracted by the debris of the whaling industry. The penguins are numerous and petrels of all species darken the sky at certain periods of the year. Sir Hubert Wilkins, the polar explorer who used Deception Island as a base during his reconnaissance flights over the Antarctic Continent, reports that he had to send an advance boat through the waters of the crater to clear a channel among the dense flocks of birds on the surface.

The northern part of the Antarctic Continent, called Graham Land, or Palmer Peninsula, has a steep western coast while the eastern slope is gentler and has expanses of tablelands. Naturally, this region is completely covered with snow and ice. The vegetation is very much reduced, and the land fauna consists of only a few insects, some rotifers (animals often called wheel animalcules for the movement of their ciliated bands) and some tardigrades—those tiny mitelike creatures sometimes found in damp moss. These creatures can survive only in the penguin rookeries.

Birds are relatively numerous and nest to the south on the western coast rather than on Weddell Sea. From observations made by the Second French Antarctic Expedition under the command of Dr. Jean Charcot, no less than twenty-five species of birds can be observed south of 60° Lat. S. Most of them are, however, only strays from more northern and more clement latitudes. The emperor penguin, whose rookeries are farther south, appears along the coasts at the time of its migrations, thus accentuating the polar character of this part of the globe, a link between the Antarctic and South America.

Such then is the region extending from the continent of South America to the Antarctic. At the end of a period of glaciation, the glaciers here are now retreating—as elsewhere in the world. But some of these lands still give us a glimpse of what conditions were probably like in Scandinavia or North America during the great Quaternary glaciations.

It was not always so. A rich fossil flora is known to exist in this part of the Antarctic, dating from the Jurassic to the Cretaceous and the beginning of the Tertiary. Trees like the great sequoias, the araucarias, the austral beeches, flourished in this part of the world when it was a part of a vast continent embracing Patagonia and New Zealand. Then the continent subsided and extreme climatic fluctuations buried these lands beneath a thick mantle of ice. Perhaps one day in the distant future forests will again extend over land now covered with ice and whipped by the great western winds.

Index

Asterisks indicate pages containing illustrations

THE AUTHOR

Dr. Dorst, internationally known ornithologist and zoologist, is head of the Department of Mammals and Birds in the Muséum National d'Histoire Naturelle in Paris. He has studied the flora and fauna of South America, and especially the Andes and the Amazon region, during four visits there, including two sojourns of almost a year. Dr. Dorst is the author of many books, articles, and scientific papers on birds, particularly of South America, including authoritative works on the birds of the world and on bird migration.

ENGRAVED AND PRINTED BY CONZETT AND HUBER OF ZURICH – DESIGNED BY ULRICH RUCHTI

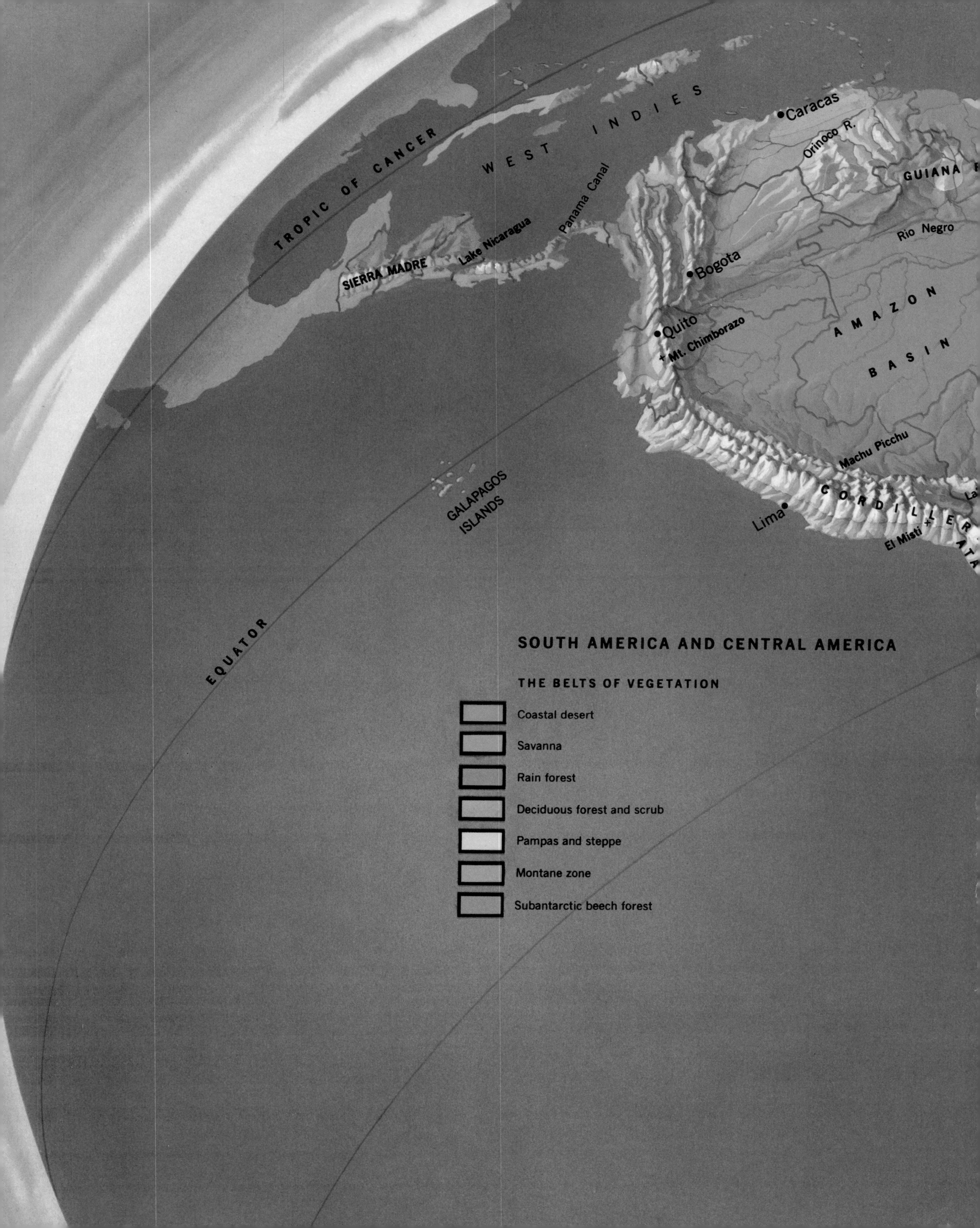
TROPIC OF CANCER
WEST INDIES
Caracas
Orinoco R.
GUIANA
Panama Canal
Lake Nicaragua
SIERRA MADRE
Rio Negro
Bogota
AMAZON
BASIN
Quito
Mt. Chimborazo
Machu Picchu
GALAPAGOS
ISLANDS
CORDILLERA
Lima
El Misti
EQUATOR
SOUTH AMERICA AND CENTRAL AMERICA
THE BELTS OF VEGETATION
Coastal desert
Savanna
Rain forest
Deciduous forest and scrub
Pampas and steppe
Montane zone
Subantarctic beech forest